MAN'S MOST DANGEROUS MYTH

By *Ashley Montagu*

Editor

MAN'S MOST DANGEROUS MYTH:

THE FALLACY OF RACE

FOURTH EDITION
REVISED AND ENLARGED

by

ASHLEY MONTAGU

THE WORLD PUBLISHING COMPANY
CLEVELAND AND NEW YORK

Published by The World Publishing Company
2231 West 110th Street, Cleveland 2, Ohio

Published simultaneously in Canada by
Nelson, Foster & Scott Ltd.

Library of Congress Catalog Card Number: 64–12067

FOURTH REVISED EDITION

25629

TO THE MEMORY
OF
JOHN FITZGERALD KENNEDY
(1917–1963)
THIRTY-FIFTH PRESIDENT
OF THE UNITED STATES

Contents

List of Tables

Preface

IN OUR TIME the problem of *race* has assumed an alarmingly exaggerated importance. Alarming, because racial dogmas have been made the basis for an inhumanly brutal political philosophy which has resulted in the death or social disfranchisement of millions of innocent human beings; exaggerated, because when the nature of contemporary "race" theory is scientifically analyzed and understood it ceases to be of any significance for social or any other kind of action. It has been well said that there is no domain where the sciences, philosophy, and politics blend to so great an extent and in their contact have so much importance to the man of the present day and of the future as in modern "race" theory. Few problems in our time more pressingly require solution than this. It is highly desirable, therefore, that the facts about "race," as science has come to know them, should be widely disseminated and clearly understood. To this end the present volume has been written.

This book is not, however, a textbook or a treatise on "race." It purports to be an examination of a contemporary aspect of "race" theory, and seeks only to clarify the reader's thinking upon an important subject about which clear thinking is generally avoided. It would be quite beyond the powers of a single person to say all that there is to be said upon the subject. As Aldous Huxley has put it, "The problem of race is as much a problem for historians and psychologists as for geneticists. Anything like a definite and authoritative solution of it must be cooperative. Also, to carry conviction, it should be official and international. The race theory claims to be scientific. It is, surely then, the business of science, as organized in the universities and learned societies of the civilized world, to investigate this claim."

It is as a contribution towards such an end from a scientist, who is a student both of human culture and human biology, that the present volume is offered.

It may appear to some that I have been a little hard on the physical anthropologists. I can only plead that as a physical anthropologist myself I believe it is high time that the traditional conception of "race" held by my professional brethren be dealt with frankly. Friends can afford to be frank, let enemies be cautious.

This book then is designed to expose the most dangerous myth of our age, the myth of "race," by demonstrating the falsities of which it is compounded. In the pursuit of this design it is difficult to avoid the appearance of "special pleading." By showing that the many differences which are alleged to exist between "races" do not in fact exist or that those which do exist are of no significance from the standpoint of social action, the cumulative effect upon some readers may be that the author's thesis is that there are no genuine differences between the various groups of mankind.

The fact is that there are numerous differences between ethnic groups, and even regional segments of such groups, in many bodily traits. These differences are real enough, and they are of the greatest interest to the student of variation. Their classification and analysis belong in a treatise of a nature more technical than this. Suffice it here to say that such variations prove that man is an extremely variable creature, constantly in process of undergoing change, and that these changes can be studied in the minutest detail in every living population. I have, in my own small way, demonstrated such variations in the teeth, in insignificant muscles, and in various structures of the skull, and I have shown how in the same nation local differences in the frequencies of such characters have appeared. All these are very real differences, and their meaning is of the greatest significance to the student of the evolution of man. To discuss these matters in this book would have been of some interest to the reader, and would certainly have served to give our discussion a better balanced appearance. And although to do so might have resulted in a more convincing demonstration of the truth that such variations are of moment alone to the theoretical biologist but are of no significance whatever in the practical universe of human relations, contemplation of the consequent increase in the size of this book acted as a sufficient deterrent.

Differences are not denied where they exist. What is denied is that they are biologically either great or significant enough to justify men in making them the pretext for social discrimination of any kind. If this is "special pleading," then this viewpoint is what the evidence set out in the following pages specially pleads with the reader to examine critically.

In the past the tendency has been strong to overstress the differences, as if stressing the differences were an argument against the likenesses. Looking back now upon the history of the nineteenth century it seems fairly clear that this drive to find differences in the "races" of mankind grew out of the general social climate of the day. A natural stratification of the races mirrored the social stratification of the classes, and in the light of the doctrine of "the survival of the fittest" justified the exploitation and oppression of both. Differences were therefore maximized and exaggerated. They still are in the service of much the same motives.

But the facts make it abundantly clear that these differences constitute the proof of the fundamental unity of all mankind. The very nature of the variations provides the completest evidence of that truth, of the basic likeness in difference. It is therefore as unnecessary to minimize as it is falsely to maximize the significance of these differences. All that should be required is to state the case against those who have endeavored to magnify the differences. This I have done, and somehow the decline in size of the differences seems automatically to have followed, while many other differences alleged to exist completely disappear in the light of the facts. If we can learn to understand the nature of the insignificant differences which remain, we shall then be happier in their presence, and find them in every way as acceptable as we do those which exist within our own immediate group.

Since this book first left the press the world has been horrified by the calculated murder of millions of Jews and Poles by the Nazis. This represented the practical realization of the doctrine of "racism" which had been so viciously enthroned as a political doctrine in the Nazi *Weltanschauung*. That doctrine, from beginning to end, was an absurdity; but absurdities have never wanted for believers, and, as Voltaire remarked, "as long as people believe in absurdities they will continue to commit atrocities."

We, in the United States, have every hope of eradicating the contagion of "racism" from our own body politic; but hope alone will not suffice. We must act, and in order to do so intelligently we must know what this disease is and how it may best be dealt with. At a time when "race" riots and the Negro revolt have awakened many Americans to the seriousness of the problem of "race" on their own hearths, when discrimination against colored and "minority" groups in the armed forces and in industry has shocked many Americans into an awareness of their own guilt, it is incumbent upon every decent American to acquaint himself with the facts relating to the "race" problem, so that he may be prepared to deal with it in an intelligent, efficient, and humane manner.

It is even yet not widely enough realized that from its earliest beginnings the doctrine of the racists has had as its object the overthrow of democracy. This should become clear to anyone who reads the account which is given in the following pages of the rise and development of that doctrine.

This is the fourth edition of a book that was first published in 1942. The first edition was critically read by Professors Franz Boas and Ruth Benedict of the Department of Anthropology, Columbia University; by Professor Robert K. Merton of the Department of Sociology of the same university, by Professor E. G. Conklin of Princeton University, and Professor Conway Zirkle of the Department of Botany of the University of Pennsylvania. The manuscript of the second edition, published in 1944, was read by Professor Theodosius Dobzhansky of the Department of Zoology of Columbia University and Professor and Mrs. William C. Boyd of the Department of Biochemistry of Boston University. Professor A. A. Neuman, Principal of Dropsie College, Philadelphia, kindly read Chapter 14. My daughter, Audrey, read part of the manuscript to me while I typed it, and my wife read the galleys. Mrs. Nancy Brattle Palmer of Philadelphia and Mr. Cedric Dover of London read the manuscript of the third edition. It was Mr. Jake Zeitlin, bookseller, of Los Angeles, who originally persuaded me to write this book. To all these kind friends I am much indebted.

The present edition, like the preceding ones, has been extensively revised. I am grateful to Dr. Andrew D. Weinberger for his helpfulness in contributing the authoritative section on state laws relating to intermarriage. This has been especially revised and brought up to date, by Dr. Weinberger, for this book. To Mrs. Janet Rosenberg of The World Publishing Company, I am particularly grateful for the fine editorial work she did on the manuscript.

Princeton, New Jersey   ASHLEY MONTAGU

As man advances in civilization, and small tribes are united into larger communities, the simplest reason would tell each individual that he ought to extend his social instincts and sympathies to all members of the same nation, though personally unknown to him. This point being once reached, there is only an artificial barrier to prevent his sympathies extending to the men of all nations and races.

CHARLES DARWIN

Ethnic facts, though they constitute the main problem in the early stages of history, gradually lose momentum in proportion to the progress of civilization.

ERNEST RENAN

On the reality or unreality of this principle, which dominates at the present hour the secret or avowed aspirations of the peoples, depends the whole of their future. Peace among peoples and the crown of such a peace—that is, the vast solidarity of mankind, the dream of the future—can in any case only triumph when founded on the conviction of the organic and mental equality of peoples and races.

JEAN FINOT

Human unity is rooted as truly in the physical as in the spiritual nature of man, and is revealed to his reason no less certainly than to his emotions. This idea lies at the root of the great moral conception of human brotherhood. The kindred by descent of all mankind, known directly through sense experience and emotional response, and indirectly through rational inference, is the substance out of which has been woven the entire fabric of civilized life.

WILLIAM EMERSON RITTER

MAN'S MOST DANGEROUS MYTH

I

The Origin of the Concept of "Race"

THE IDEA OF "race" represents one of the most dangerous myths of our time, and one of the most tragic. Myths are most effective and dangerous when they remain unrecognized for what they are. Many of us are happy in the complacent belief that myths are what primitive people believe in, but of which we ourselves are completely free. We may realize that a myth is a faulty explanation leading to social delusion and error, but we do not usually realize that we ourselves share in the mythmaking faculty with all men of all times and places, that each of us has his own store of myths which have been derived from the traditional stock of the society in which we live. In earlier days we believed in magic, possession, and exorcism, in good and evil supernatural powers, and until recently we believed in witchcraft. Today many of us believe in "race." "Race" is the witchcraft of our time. The means by which we exorcise demons. It is the contemporary myth. Man's most dangerous myth.[1]

In our own time we have lived to see the myth of "race" openly adopted as an expedient fiction.

What "race" is everyone seems to know, and is only too eager to

---

[1] For excellent discussions of contemporary mythmaking and myths, see Dunham, *Man against Myth;* Evans, *The Natural History of Nonsense;* Calas, "Myth and Initiation," *Chimera,* IV (1946), 21–24; Bain, "Man, the Myth-Maker," *Scientific Monthly,* LXV (1947), 61–69; Bidney, "The Concept of Myth and the Problem of Psychocultural Evolution," *American Anthropologist,* LXII (1950), 16–26; Monro, "The Concept of Myth," *Sociological Review,* XLII (1950), 115–32; Feuer, "Political Myths and Metaphysics," *Philosophy and Phenomenological Research,* XV (1955), 332–50.

tell. All but a few persons take it completely for granted that scientists have established the "facts" about "race" and that they have long ago recognized and classified the "races" of mankind. Scientists do little to discourage this view, and, indeed, many of them are quite as deluded as most laymen are concerning the subject. One man's fancy is another man's fact. It is not difficult to see, therefore, why most of us continue to believe that "race" really corresponds to something which exists. As Hogben has remarked: "Geneticists believe that anthropologists have decided what a race is. Ethnologists assume that their classifications embody principles which genetic science has proved to be correct. Politicians believe that their prejudices have the sanction of genetic laws and the findings of physical anthropology to sustain them." [2] In reality, none of them have any grounds, but those which spring from their prejudices, for such beliefs.

The myth of "race" refers not to the fact that physically distinguishable populations of man exist. Such populations are often called races. Distinctive populations of this kind are not myths, but neither are they races in the sense in which that term is usually employed. That sense is the myth, the myth of "race," the belief that physical and mental traits are linked, that the physical differences are associated with rather pronounced differences in mental capacities, and that these differences are measurable by IQ tests and the cultural achievements of these populations.

Writing in 1915 Lord Bryce put the matter clearly. "No branches of historical inquiry," he wrote, "have suffered more from fanciful speculation than those which relate to the origin and attributes of the races of mankind. The differentiation of these races began in prehistoric darkness, and the more obscure a subject is, so much the more fascinating. Hypotheses are tempting, because though it may be impossible to verify them, it is, in the paucity of data, almost equally impossible to refute them." [3]

It was as long ago as 1869 that Walter Bagehot wrote: "When a philosopher cannot account for anything in any other manner, he boldly ascribes it to an occult quality in some race." [4]

[2] Hogben, "The Concept of Race," in his Genetic Principles in Medicine and Social Science, pp. 122–44.
[3] Bryce, Race Sentiment as a Factor in History, p. 3
[4] Bagehot, Physics and Politics, p. 3.

Certainly it is true that many scientists have attempted to classify and fit the varieties of mankind into distinct groups, the so-called "races," but all such attempts have thus far met with complete failure, because they were too arbitrary and were based upon a misconception of the nature and variability of the characters to be classified. It is easy to see that an African Negro and a white Englishman must have had a somewhat different biological history, and that their obvious physical differences would justify the biologist in classifying them as belonging to two different races. In biology a race is usually defined as a subdivision of a species which inherits physical characteristics distinguishing it from other populations of the species. In this sense a number of human races have been arbitrarily recognized. But this is not the sense in which most of the older and some modern physical anthropologists, race classifiers, and racists use the term.

In the biological sense there do, of course, exist distinctive populations of mankind. That is to say, mankind may be regarded as being comprised of a number of groups which as such are often physically sufficiently distinguishable from one another, in the sense defined above, to justify their being classified as distinctive populations but not as separate races.[5] For example, Germans, taken as a whole, do not differ sufficiently from Englishmen or any other people of Western Europe to justify their separation into a physically distinct population or variety. All the peoples of Western Europe belong to the same major group, the Caucasoid, and the differences some of them exhibit simply represent small local differences arising from either circumscribed inbreeding or crossbreeding with members of a different population. In Eastern Europe, among the Russians, the influence of Mongoloid admixture is to this day discernible in a small proportion of Russians far removed from the geographic habitat of the Mongoloids. But this admixture does not make such Russians members of a distinct race. In Russia, as in

---

[5] See Montagu, *An Introduction to Physical Anthropology;* Montagu, "A Consideration of the Concept of Race," *Cold Spring Harbor Symposia on Quantitative Biology,* XV (1950), 315–36; Montagu, "The Concept of Race," *American Anthropologist,* LXIV (1962), 919–28; Hulse, "Race as an Evolutionary Episode," *American Anthropologist,* LXIV (1962), 929–45; Livingstone, "On the Non-Existence of Human Races," *Current Anthropology,* III (1962), 279–80.

America, there are many different local types of men, but the majority of these belong to the white or Caucasoid major group of mankind. In Russia some are obviously of Mongoloid origin, and in America some are clearly of Negroid origin, but in both countries it is often difficult to say whether a person belongs to the one major group or the other. It is frequently just such difficulties as these which render it impossible to make the sort of racial classifications which some anthropologists and others have attempted.[6] The fact is that all human beings are so much mixed with regard to origin that between different groups of individuals intergradation and "overlapping" of physical characters is the rule. It is for this reason that it is difficult to draw up more than a few hard and fast distinctions between even the most extreme types. As Huxley and Haddon have remarked, "The essential reality of the existing situation . . . is not the hypothetical sub-species or races, but the *mixed ethnic groups,* which can never be genetically purified into their original components, or purged of the variability which they owe to past crossing. Most anthropological writings of the past and many of the present fail to take account of this fundamental fact." [7]

The classifiers of the "races" of mankind who have devised the various classificatory schemes of mankind during the past hundred years have mostly agreed in one respect—they have unexceptionally taken for granted the one thing which they were attempting to prove, namely, the existence of human "races." Starting off with the fact that "extreme" types of mankind, such as Negro, white, and Mongol, could obviously be recognized as "races," they proceeded to refine these grosser classifications by attempting to fit local groups of mankind into similar racial schemes. Thus, to take a contemporary example, Coon has created a large number of new European "races" and "subraces" upon the basis, principally, of slight differences in the characters of the head exhibited by different groups of

---

[6] For an anthropological example of this fractionating method of race-making see Coon, *The Races of Europe;* also Garn, *Human Races.*

[7] Huxley and Haddon, *We Europeans,* p. 114. In order to avoid possible misunderstanding of this passage, it is desirable to point out that by the words "genetically purified into their original components" the authors are not referring to pre-existing "pure races," but to the earlier states of the ancestral groups entering into the formation of the mixed ethnic groups as we know them today.

Europeans, and this in spite of the fact that it has been repeatedly shown that the form of the head is not as constant a character as was at one time believed.[8] It is true that some biologists have seen fit to create new subraces among lower animals on the basis of such single slight characters as differences in pigmentation of the hair on a part of the tail. Such a procedure would be perfectly justifiable if it were taxonomically helpful. Nor would it be necessary to stipulate that animals in other groups shall not exhibit this character, but one would have to insist that almost all members of one or both sexes of the new subrace shall exhibit it. No such requirement is fulfilled by the "races" and "subraces" which Coon has created.[9]

Coon simply assumes that within any group a certain numerical preponderance of heads of specified diameters and, let us say, noses of a certain shape and individuals of a certain stature are sufficient to justify the creation of a new "race" or "subrace." Few biologists would consider such a procedure justifiable, and there are few anthropologists who would. Yet this kind of overzealous taxonomy, which has its origin principally in the desire to force facts to fit pre-existing theories of this kind, does not even require the sanction of facts to be put forward as such. In this sense the concept of "race" represents one of the worst examples we know of a viewpoint which from the outset begs the whole question.

Recently, Anderson[10] has offered a practical example, which is quite typical of the manner in which populations have in the past been classified by rule of thumb or authority in the most arbitrary manner. The Lapps, a Caucasoid people, have for almost two centuries been forced into the mythical status of Mongoloids, because in

---

[8] Boas, *Changes in Bodily Form of Descendants of Immigrants;* Shapiro, *Migration and Environment;* Dornfeldt, "Studien über Schädelform und Schädelveränderung von Berliner Ostjuden und ihren Kindern," *Zeitschrift für Morphologie und Anthropologie,* XXXIX (1941), 290–372; Goldstein, *Demographic and Bodily Changes in Descendants of Mexican Immigrants;* on the absurdity of classification by head shape, see Weidenreich, "The Brachycephalization of Recent Mankind," *Southwestern Journal of Anthropology,* I (1945), 1–54; Lasker, "Migration and Physical Differentiation," *American Journal of Physical Anthropology,* N. S., IV (1946), 273–300.

[9] Coon, *Races of Europe.*

[10] Anderson, "Lapp Racial Classifications As Scientific Myths," *Anthropological Papers of the University of Alaska,* XI (1962) 15–31.

1795, the father of physical anthropology, Johann Gottfried Blumenbach, said that they belonged to "the Mongolian variety." [11]

As Anderson remarks, "In this day when scientists are entering precipitously into world council chambers, the history of Lapp racial classification reminds us anew that even venerable conclusions or the opinions of experts may be no more than scientific myths, perhaps useful in the development of ideas, but irresponsible bases for policy or administration." [12]

The very failure of ambitious anthropological attempts at classification strongly suggests that human populations do not, in fact, exist in anything like the form that many of these classifiers would have us believe.

From the standpoint of a classificatory view of mankind which has due regard for the facts it is arbitrarily possible to recognize four distinctive major groups of mankind. These are the Negroid or black, the Archaic white or Australoid,[13] the Caucasoid or white, and the Mongoloid major groups of mankind. It is preferable to speak of these four large groups of mankind as *major groups* rather than as *races,* and to speak of the varieties of men which enter into the formation of these major groups as *ethnic groups.*[14] The use of the term "major group" is purely arbitrary and is merely calculated to indicate that the likenesses in certain characters exhibited by some populations appear to link them more closely than to other populations. Nothing more is implied in the term than that.

Within the four major groups of mankind there exist many local types, but most of these local types are much mixed, so that only in a relatively small number of cases is it possible to distinguish distinctive local types or ethnic groups among them. Every honest attempt to discuss such types or ethnic groups within the larger parent groups or major groups deserves the fullest encouragement. Truth will not be advanced by denying the existence of large groups of mankind characterized, more or less, by distinctive inherited

---

[11] Blumenbach, *De Generis Varietate Humani.*
[12] Anderson, *op. cit.,* 29–30.
[13] The Archaic white, or Australoid, is really a subdivision, larger than an ethnic group, of the Caucasoid major group. For a more detailed discussion and classification of the major and ethnic groups of mankind see Montagu, *An Introduction to Physical Anthropology;* Coon, Garn, and Birdsell, *Races.*
[14] For a definition of ethnic group see p. 80.

physical traits. Such physical differences are found in geographic and genetic populations of animals and plants in a state of nature, and in many varieties of domestic animals and cultivated plants. They are, to a certain extent, also found in the human species, but in a much more fluid condition, since the biological development and diversification of mankind has proceeded upon quite different lines from that which has characterized animals and plants. With the exception of the domesticated animals and plants, few if any other living forms have had a comparable history of migration and hybridization, and this is the fundamentally important fact to be remembered when comparisons are made between man and other living forms. Not one of the major groups of man is unmixed, nor is any one of its ethnic groups pure; all are, indeed, much mixed and of exceedingly complex descent. Nor is there any scientific justification for overzealous or emotional claims that any one of them is in any way superior to another.

As Darwin put it eighty years ago, "Although the existing races of man differ in many respects, as in colour, hair, shape of skull, proportions of the body, &c., yet if their whole structure be taken into consideration they are found to resemble each other closely in a multitude of points. Many of these are of so unimportant or of so singular a nature, that it is extremely improbable that they should have been independently acquired by aboriginally distinct species or races. The same remark holds good with equal or greater force with respect to the numerous points of mental similarity between the most distinct races of man." [15]

The differences between the four major groups of man and between the ethnic groups comprising them merely represent a distribution of variations which, for reasons that may be fairly clearly understood, occur more frequently in one group than they do in another. We shall deal with these reasons later.

It has already been pointed out that in biological usage a race has been conceived to be a subdivision of a species which inherits the *physical* characteristics serving to distinguish it from other populations of the species. In the genetic sense a race has been defined as a population which differs in the incidence of certain genes from other populations, with one or more of which it is exchanging or is

---

[15] Darwin, *The Descent of Man,* Chapter VII.

potentially capable of exchanging genes across whatever boundaries (usually geographical) may separate them.[16] If we are asked whether in this sense there exist a fair number of races in the human species, the answer is definitely that there do. It is, however, more than questionable whether such a narrow definition of a "race" can be profitably employed in relation to man. Furthermore, this is not the sense in which racists and many race classifiers employ the term. For them "race" represents a complex of physical, mental, personality, and cultural traits which determines the behavior of the individuals inheriting this alleged complex.

Let us see, as an example typical of this school, what a leading exponent of Nazi "race science," Dr. Lothar G. Tirala, has to say upon this subject.[17] He begins by asserting that it is "a well-grounded view that it is highly probable that different human races originated independently of one another and that they evolved out of different species of ape-men. The so-called main races of mankind are not races, but species." Far from being "well-grounded," this is a view which no biologist and no anthropologist with whom I am familiar would accept.[18] It is today generally agreed that all men belong to the same species, that all were probably derived from the same ancestral stock, and that all share in a common patrimony.

But Dr. Tirala's principal argument is that "the voice of blood and race operates down to the last refinements of thought and exercises a decisive influence on the direction of thought." Hence, "race

---

[16] Dobzhansky, "On Species and Races of Living and Fossil Man," *American Journal of Physical Anthropology*, N. S., II (1944), 251–65; For a criticism of this viewpoint, see Livingstone, "On the Non-Existence of Human Races," *Current Anthropology*, III (1962), 279–80.

[17] Tirala, *Rasse, Geist und Seele*.

[18] A contrary view has, indeed, been expressed by Dr. R. Ruggles Gates, who claims that many of the races of man must be regarded as belonging to different species. Such claims are rendered possible by the utter disregard and complete violation of the principles of zoological taxonomy and the accepted definition of a species, principles and definitions which represent the judgment of generations of scientists. For Gates's view see his "Phylogeny and Classification of Hominids and Anthropoids," *American Journal of Physical Anthropology*, N. S., II (1944), 279–92. As Weidenreich has said, "raising the differences between racial groups to the rank of specific differences by giving those groups specific names is nothing but an attempt to exaggerate the dissimilarities by the application of a taxonomic trick." *Apes, Giants, and Man*, p. 2.

science proves" that there exist irreconcilable differences in soul, mind, and blood between the numerous "races" which German "race scientists" have recognized. And, of course, that the German, or "Aryan," "race" is the "superior" and "master" "race." Precisely similar views are expounded by a contemporary German anthropologist in a work published in 1951.[19]

Lest it be thought that these mystical and mythical conceptions of "race" are a peculiarity of the Germans, let us turn to what a Greek professor of anthropology wrote about the Greek "race" in the year 1948. The Greek race, he wrote, "has almost uniform physical characteristics, physical and psychical, inherited in its descendants; it has all the characteristics of the basic elements, which are all Greek and indigenous in spite of the variety of types. If the British, for instance, with their various nuclei, form one race,[20] the Greeks have a greater right to be so considered. This race is distinguished today by a kind of 'fluid constancy,' with its own soul and especially with its own variety, dating from prehistoric times. Races exist and will continue to exist; and each one defends itself. Because every infusion of new 'blood' is something different and because children of mixed parents belong to no race, the Greek race, as all others, has to preserve its own 'fluid constancy' by avoiding mixture with foreign elements.

"The Greek race was formed under the Acropolis Rock, and it is impossible for any other to keep the keys of the sacred rock, to which the Greek Soul is indissolubly linked."[21]

Such views as those of Tirala and Koumaris, and the practices to

---

[19] Weinert, *Der Geistige Aufstieg der Menschheit vom Ursprung bis zur Gegenwart.* For an interesting account of the Nazi application of the "methods" of "race science" in which the writer himself repeats many of the favored Nazi doctrines, see Ellinger, "On the Breeding of Aryans," *Journal of Heredity,* XXXIII (1942), 141–43. For replies to this article see Goldschmidt, "Anthropological Determination of 'Aryanism,'" *Journal of Heredity,* XXXIII (1942), 215–16, and Montagu, "On the Breeding of 'Aryans'" *Psychiatry,* VI (1943), 254–55. The term "Aryan" is frequently misused to describe a physical stock or alleged member of that stock. In reality it refers to a stock of languages which are spoken by a wide variety of ethnic groups. It has nothing whatever to do with physical characters.

[20] Which, of course, they do not.

[21] Koumaris, "On the Morphological Variety of Modern Greeks," *Man,* XLVIII (1948), 126–27.

which they lead, are far from being limited to any one country. Actually they are to be found in many lands. In America discrimination against colored peoples is of long standing. No American needs to be told that racism is scarcely moribund in the United States. He may, however, be surprised to learn that at the present day there are in the United States over one thousand organizations, more than a hundred of them on a national basis, whose declared purpose is the suppression of "foreigners." Well might he exclaim that he would rather be a foreign-born American than an American-born foreigner. In March, 1950, Representative Hobbs of Alabama, stating that he spoke for Congress, declared before the United States Supreme Court that "God is the author of discrimination, and His creatures have proved they liked His handiwork." In March, 1951, and again in 1958, a former secretary of state, James F. Byrnes, of South Carolina, declared that education in South Carolina must remain segregated.[22]

American writers such as Lothrop Stoddard, Madison Grant, Henry Fairfield Osborn, Ruggles Gates, Henry Garrett, and Carleton Putnam have freely espoused racist views of the most reactionary kind. Osborn, in his preface to Madison Grant's book, writes, "race has played a far larger part than either language or nationality in moulding the destinies of men; race implies heredity, and heredity implies all the moral, social, and intellectual characteristics and traits which are the springs of politics and government." [23]

Endlessly shuffled and reshuffled, this is a typical statement of the

---

[22] The racist viewpoint was succinctly stated by another Southerner, the Alabama proslavery anthropologist, J. C. Nott, in 1854 when he wrote: "It is the primitive organization of races, their mental *instincts,* which determine their characters and destinies, and not blind hazard. All history, as well as anatomy and physiology, proves this." Nott and Gliddon, *Indigenous Races of the Earth,* p. 460. See Appendix G. In at least one state of the Union a book such as this is against the law. Mississippi, 1930, Code Ann., sec. 1103: "Any person, firm or corporation who shall be guilty of printing, publishing or circulating printed, typewritten or written matter urging or presenting for public acceptance or general arguments or suggestions in favor of social equality or of intermarriage between whites and negroes, shall be guilty of a misdemeanour and subject to a fine not exceeding five hundred dollars or imprisonment not exceeding six months or both fine and imprisonment in the discretion of the court."

[23] Osborn, in Grant, *The Passing of the Great Race,* p. vii.

racist position. It is alleged that something called "race" is the prime determiner of all the important traits of body and soul, of character and personality, of human beings and nations. And it is further alleged that this something called "race" is a fixed and unchangeable part of the germ plasm, which, transmitted from generation to generation, unfolds in each people as a typical expression of personality and culture.

In an article, published in 1939, entitled "Race: A Basic Concept in Education," Alfred Baeumler, a leading Nazi "philosopher," clearly presented the racist conception of the individual. "History," he wrote, "has shown, and daily shows anew, that man can be trained to be nothing that he is not genuinely, and from the beginning, in the depths of his being; against this law, neither precept, warning, punishment, nor any other environmental influence avails. Realism in the study of man does not lie in attributing evil tendencies to him, but in recognizing that all that man can do emerges in the last resort from himself, from his innate qualities." [24]

Herr Baeumler modestly describes this as thinking "Copernically" when most others so far as such matters are concerned are still thinking "Ptolemaically"—an unfortunate slip on the part of Herr Baeumler, in view of the fact that Copernicus belonged to an allegedly "subhuman" race, for Copernicus was a Pole.

The late Nazi professor of physical anthropology at the University of Freiburg defined "race" as "a definite psycho-physical type which is common to a larger national and tribal circle of men, and maintains itself by hereditary descent. . . . Race is the alpha and omega of the life of nations in its entirety." [25]

The ex-dictator of Argentina, Señor Perón, gave a new twist to the concept of "race." On October 12, 1947, in a speech on the "Day of Race," he put Argentina right on the side of Torquemada. On that occasion he said: "For us, race is not a biological concept. For us, it is something spiritual. It constitutes a sum of the imponderables that make us what we are and impel us to be what we should be, through our origin and through our destiny. It is that which dissuades us from falling into the imitation of other communities whose

---

[24] Baeumler, "Race: A Basic Concept in Education" (trans. from the original article in the *Internationale Zeitschrift für Erziehung,* Bd. VIII, 1939), *World Education,* IV (1939), 506–09.

[25] Schemann, *Die Rassenfrage im Schrifttum der Neuzeit.*

natures are foreign to us. For us, race constitutes our personal seal, indefinable and irrefutable."

The gallery of "race" concepts set out above has no basis in scientific fact or in any other kind of demonstrable fact. These conceptions of "race" are compounded of impure wishful thinking and represent naught but muddied myth—the tragic myth of our tragic era. Tragic, because it is believed and made the basis for action, in one way or another, by so many people in our time. It is this conception of "race" which will be principally examined in the following pages.

The modern conception of "race" owes its widespread diffusion to the white man. Wherever he has gone he has carried it with him. The growth of racism is associated with slavery and imperialism in its various forms, so that it is not until the second half of the eighteenth century that one begins to encounter its expression. This is not to say that discrimination against persons or groups on the basis of skin color or "race" did not exist in the ancient world. There is plenty of evidence that it did.[26] But it is to say that such views never became the officially established doctrine, upon any large scale, of any ancient society. Caste and class differences certainly were made the basis for discrimination in many societies, and in ancient Greece some attempt was even made to find a biological foundation for such discrimination, but this was of a limited nature and never gained general acceptance.

When, in the fourth century, the institution of slavery in Greece began increasingly to come under attack it fell to the lot of Aristotle to develop the necessary theoretical bases upon which to justify its existence. His justification consists of nothing but the most ill-founded rationalizations, and shows Aristotle—as it does every man, when he rationalizes—at his weakest. The slave, Aristotle argued in the *Politics,* was but a partial man, lacking the governing element of the soul and therefore needed to be ruled by those possessing this element. In short, that some men were more fitted by nature to be slaves than others.[27]

---

[26] Dover, "Antar for the Anthropologist," *The Eastern Anthropologist,* V (1952), 165–69. Dover shows that the famous Bedouin warrior-poet of the sixth century was very conscious of the social disability of being a mulatto.

[27] "By nature, too, some beings command, and others obey, for the sake of

Before Aristotle, Plato had deliberately proposed a piece of disingenuous fiction concerning the innate differences existing between men, calculated to convince the workers that there were people who by nature were better qualified to rule than they.[28] But this "Phoenician lie," as Plato called it, failed to germinate.[29] Most serious scholars are agreed that, with the exception of the lone Aristotle, while the Greeks affected to despise the barbarian, they did so on purely cultural grounds, never on biological ones.[30] The Greeks, indeed, as Isocrates (436–338 B.C.) put it, thought of Hellenism as a thing of the spirit rather than of "race." "So far," he wrote, "has Athens distanced the rest of mankind in thought and in speech that her pupils have become the teachers of the rest of the world; and she has brought it about that the name 'Hellenes' is applied rather

mutual safety; for a being endowed with discernment and forethought is by nature the superior and governor; whereas he who is merely able to execute by bodily labour is the inferior and natural slave." Aristotle, *Politics*, Book I, Chapter II. To this Rousseau made an excellent reply. "Aristotle said," he writes, "that men were not naturally equal, but that some were born for slavery, and others for domination. Aristotle was right, but he took the effect for the cause. Nothing can be more certain than that every man born in slavery is born for slavery. Slaves lose everything in their chains, even the desire to escape from them; they love servitude as the companions of Ulysses loved their brutish condition. If then, there are slaves by nature, it is because there have been slaves against nature. Force made the first slaves, and their cowardice perpetuated them." Rousseau, *The Social Contract*, Book I, Chapter II.

[28] Plato, *The Republic*, 547a.

[29] Eisler, "Metallurgical Anthropology in Hesiod and Plato and the Date of a 'Phoenician Lie,'" *Isis*, XL (1949), 108–12. For an excellent book on Plato see Popper, *The Open Society and Its Enemies*. It is not for nothing that during the nineteenth century Plato was considered an indispensable part of the education of a gentleman, that is to say, of a person who relied upon others to do the job of earning a living for him.

[30] For excellent discussions of this subject see Sikes, *The Anthropology of the Greeks*, pp. 69–89; Schlaifer, "Greek Theories of Slavery from Homer to Aristotle," *Harvard Studies in Classical Philology*, XLVII (1936), 165–204; Snowden, Jr., "The Negro in Ancient Greece," *American Anthropologist*, L (1948), 31–44; Westermann, "The Slave Systems of Greek and Roman Antiquity," *Memoirs of the American Philosophical Society*, XL (1955), xi–180; Westermann, "Slavery and the Elements of Freedom in Ancient Greece," *Quarterly Bulletin of the Polish Institute of Arts and Sciences in America*, I (1943), 332–47.

to those who share our culture than to those who share a common blood." [31]

The Greeks, as also the Romans, were singularly free of anything resembling race prejudice.[32] A study of the cultures and literatures of mankind, both ancient and recent, shows us that the conception that there are natural or biological races of mankind which differ from one another mentally as well as physically is an idea which was not developed until the latter part of the eighteenth century. In this connection, Lord Bryce, after surveying conditions in the ancient world, in the Middle Ages, and in modern times up to the French Revolution, arrives at the following conclusions, which he regards as broadly true. The survey of the facts, he says, "has shown us that down till the days of the French Revolution there had been very little in any country, or at any time, of self-conscious racial feeling ... however much men of different races may have striven with one another, it was seldom any sense of racial opposition that caused their strife. They fought for land. They plundered one another. ... But strong as patriotism and national feeling might be, they did not think of themselves in terms of ethnology, and in making war for every other sort of reason never made it for the sake of imposing their own type of civilization. . . . In none of such cases did the thought of racial distinctions come to the front." [33]

It is not to be thought that ethnocentrism did not exist before the eighteenth century. It did. As Katherine George has said, "To be born into a culture has generally implied being supported by it, being upheld, as it were, on a pedestal, from which one might look down with varying degrees of disinterest or antagonism upon other, alien cultures." [34] The observer of alien cultures has tended to be prejudiced in favor of his own culture, and to view the alien and

---

[31] Isocrates, *Panegyricus*, 4, 50. Trans. by George Norlin, pp. xxiv, 149.

[32] Diller, *Race Mixture among the Greeks before Alexander;* Hertz, *Race and Civilization,* pp. 137 ff.; Nilsson, "The Race Problem of the Roman Empire," *Hereditas,* II (1921), 370–90; Detweiler, "The Rise of Modern Race Antagonisms," *American Journal of Sociology,* XXXVIII (1932), 738–47; McClure, "Greek Genius and Race Mixture," In *Studies in the History of Ideas,* III (1935), pp. 25–33; Haarhoff, *The Stranger at the Gate;* Davis, *Race-Relations in Ancient Egypt.*

[33] Bryce, *Race Sentiment as a Factor in History,* pp. 25–26.

[34] George, "The Civilized West Looks at Primitive Africa," *Isis,* XLIX (1958), 62–72.

unfamiliar as barbaric and inferior. The Greeks divided the world into themselves and barbarians, and this has more or less been the pattern that most peoples have followed. Hence, from the earliest times ethnocentrism has been a concomitant of virtually every culture.

Within any society, in earlier times, men might be persecuted or made the object of discrimination on the grounds of differences in religion, culture, politics, or class, but never on any biological grounds such as are implied in the idea of "racial" differences. In Europe during the Middle Ages and also during the Renaissance the Jews, for example, were singled out for discrimination and persecution, but this was always done on social, cultural, or religious grounds. The Jews, it was urged, had killed Christ; they were accused of murdering Christian children and using their blood for ritual purposes; they were infidels, anti-Christians, usurers; they were almost everything under the sun;[35] but whatever was held against them was never attributed to clearly defined biological reasons. The "racial" interpretation is a modern "discovery." That is the important point to grasp. The objection to any people on "racial" or biological grounds is virtually a purely modern innovation. That is the basic sense in which modern group antagonism differs from that which prevailed in earlier periods.

It is perfectly true that in ancient Rome, as in ancient Greece and elsewhere, the suggestion was sometimes heard that other peoples were more stupid than they and that occasionally an attempt was made to link this difference with biological factors; but this idea, at no time clearly or forcibly expressed, seems, as we have already said, never to have taken root. On the other hand, in a stratified society based upon slavery, in which birth was operatively related to social status, it can easily be seen how the notion of the biological character of social classes, as of the persons comprising them, could have originated. Yet so far as the Western world is concerned anything remotely resembling such an idea was held by no more than a handful of Greek and Roman thinkers, and never for a moment extended beyond the boundaries of their own esoteric circles.

In the year 1455 by papal decree approval was given to the subju-

---

[35] For a fully documented, pitiless revelation of the history of Jew-hating from the idea stage to that of mass murder see Hay, *The Foot of Pride*. See also Trachtenberg, *The Devil and the Jews*.

gation of infidels by Christians. The net effect of this decree was the official sanction of the enslavement of Negroes, Indians, and other "infidels," for the salvation of their souls and their entrance into God's Kingdom.

It was only among peoples who had themselves for centuries been emancipated from serfdom and slavery, but who themselves kept slaves, that the hereditary or biological conception of race differences was developed. What is of the greatest interest and importance for an understanding of this matter is that the concept developed as a direct result of the trade in slaves by European merchants. It is of even greater interest and importance to note that as long as the trade was taken for granted and no one raised a voice against it, or at least a voice that was heard, the slaves, though treated as chattels, were nonetheless conceded to be human in every sense but that of social status. This may well be seen in the treatment accorded to slaves in Portugal and Spain, where many of them rose to high positions in church and state, as was the case in ancient Greece, Rome, and Arabia. Portugal, it should be remembered, initiated the African slave trade as early as the middle of the fifteenth century. A study of the documents of the English and American slave traders down to the eighteenth century also serves to show that these men held no other conception of their victims than that by virtue of their position as slaves, or potential slaves, they were socially their captors' caste inferiors. But that was not all, for many of these hardheaded, hardbitten men recorded their belief that their victims were often quite clearly their own mental equals and superior to many at home.[36]

Similarly, almost all seventeenth-century observers agree in their high judgment of the abilities and intelligence of the American Indians.[37] All that they lacked was education and instruction, wrote Father Le Jeune more than three hundred years ago. "I naturally compare our Savages with certain villagers, because both are usually without education; though our Peasants are superior in this regard;

---

[36] Donnan, *Documents Illustrative of the History of the Slave Trade to America;* Williams, *Capitalism and Slavery.*
[37] Hallowell, "Some Psychological Characteristics of the Northeastern Indians," in *Man in Northeastern North America,* 199–200. *Papers of the R. S. Peabody Foundation for Archaeology,* III (1946), 195–225; Hanke, *Aristotle and the American Indians.*

and yet I have not seen anyone thus far, of those who have come to this country, who does not confess and frankly admit that the Savages are more intelligent than our ordinary Peasants."[38] Indeed, it was no less a person than the discoverer of America himself, Christopher Columbus who, in his famous letter to Ferdinand and Isabella announcing his discoveries, wrote, in March, 1493, of the great friendliness of the Indians and of their "excellent and acute understanding." [39]

It was only when voices began to make themselves heard against the inhuman traffic in slaves, and when these voices assumed the shape of influential men and organizations, that, on the defensive, the supporters of slavery were forced to look about them for reasons of a new kind to controvert the dangerous arguments of their opponents. The abolitionists argued that those who were enslaved were as good human beings as those who had enslaved them. To this, by way of reply, the champions of slavery could only attempt to show that the slaves were most certainly not as good as their masters. And in this highly charged emotional atmosphere there began the doleful recitation of the catalogue of differences which were alleged to prove the inferiority of the slave to his master.[40] When they had quoted at them the clear injunction from Exodus 21:16, "And he that stealeth a man, and selleth him, or if he be found in his hand, he shall surely be put to death," the proslavers could make reply, as the South still does today, that the Negro was not a man, or by twisting meaning quote Scripture against Scripture, and the Bible as their authority for slavery.[41]

---

[38] Le Jeune, *Quebec and Hurons: 1640, Jesuit Relations*, XIX (1898), p. 39. Quoted from Hallowell, *op. cit.*, p. 200.

[39] Newhall, *The Columbus Letter*, p. 8.

[40] So far as I know, an historical study of this aspect of the subject has never been attempted. It would make a fascinating and highly desirable contribution to our better understanding of the period and of the antecedents of racism. For the early period see Moore, *Notes on the History of Slavery in Massachusetts*. For the later period immediately preceding the Civil War there is the attractive little volume by Dodd, *The Cotton Kingdom*. See also Williams, *Capitalism and Slavery;* Dumond, *Antislavery;* Fuller, *The Crusade Against Slavery;* McKitrick, *Slavery Defended: The Views of the Old South;* Ruchames, *The Abolitionists;* Genovese, "The Slave South: An Interpretation," *Science & Society*, XXV (1961), 320–37.

[41] See, for example, Cobb, *An Inquiry into the Law of Negro Slavery*.

I have thus far only had in mind the literature published in England during the latter half of the eighteenth century. Much of this literature found its way to the American colonies, and after the successful conclusion of the War of Independence a certain amount of controversial literature was published in this country. In France and in Holland similar works were making their appearance. It is also well to remember that it was during this period that the conception of the noble savage was born in France and that the romantics were not slow to capitalize upon the new-found theme in such novels as Bernardin de Saint-Pierre's *Paul et Virginie* (1788).[42] In Germany, during this period, we have such distinguished thinkers as Kant,[43] Hardenberg, Herder, Goethe, and Novalis, not to mention many others, emphasizing the unity of mankind. Herder, in particular, foresaw the danger of those loose and prejudiced utterances of the defenders of the institution of slavery, and in a memorable passage of his remarkable book *Ideen zur Philosophie der Geschichte der Menschheit,* he writes: "I could wish the distinctions between the human species, that have been made from a laudable zeal for discriminating science, not carried beyond due bounds. Some for instance have thought fit to employ the term *races* for four or five divisions, originally made in consequence of country or complexion: but I see no reason for this appellation. Race refers to a difference of origin, which in this case does not exist, or in each of these countries, and under each of these complexions, comprises the most different races. . . . In short, there are neither four or five races, nor exclusive varieties, on this Earth. Complexions run into each other: forms follow the genetic character: and upon the whole, all are at last but shades of the same great picture, extending through all ages, and over all parts of the Earth. They belong not, therefore, so properly to systematic natural history, as to the physico-geographical history of man."[44]

---

[42] For an account of the rise and development of the convention of the noble savage in French and, particularly, in English literature see Fairchild, *The Noble Savage;* see also Dykes, *The Negro in English Romantic Thought.*

[43] Whose categorical imperative is seldom spelled out in our time. Here it is: "So act as to treat humanity, whether in thine own person or in that of another, in every case as an end withal, never as means only."

[44] Herder, *Outlines of a Philosophy of the History of Man,* trans. by T.

This was written in 1784, and I have quoted from the English translation of 1803. That Herder was able to write so clearly and sensibly was, I suspect, principally due to the publication, in 1775, by a young countryman of his, of a work entitled *De generis humani varietate,* that is to say, *On the Natural Variety of Mankind.* In this work the author, Johann Friedrich Blumenbach, set out to classify the varieties of mankind and to show what significance was to be attached to the differences, physical and mental, which were supposed to exist between them. He insisted at the outset that no sharp distinctions could be made between peoples. Thus, he writes: "Although there seems to be so great a difference between widely separate nations, that you might easily take the inhabitants of the Cape of Good Hope, the Greenlanders, and the Circassians for so many different species of man, yet when the matter is thoroughly considered, you see that all do so run into one another, and that one variety of mankind does so sensibly pass into the other, that you cannot mark out the limits between them.

"Very arbitrary indeed both in number and definition have been the varieties of mankind accepted by eminent men." [45] A statement which stands with quite as great force today as when it was written nearly two centuries ago.

In the greatly enlarged and revised third edition of this work, published in 1795, Blumenbach concluded that "no variety of man-kind exists, whether of colour, countenance, or stature, etc., so singular as not to be connected with others of the same kind by such an imperceptible transition, that it is very clear they are all related, or only differ from each other in degree."

Not only did Blumenbach make clear the essential unity of mankind, but he also clearly recognized and unequivocally stated the fact that all classifications of the so-called "varieties" of mankind are

---

Churchill, I, p. 298. An attempt has been made to show that Herder was a racist; see Dover, "The Racial Philosophy of Johann Herder," *British Journal of Sociology,* III (1952), 124–33. But for a more reasonable evaluation of Herder's nationalism, see Schmidt, "Cultural Nationalism in Herder," *Journal of the History of Ideas,* XVII (1956), 407–17.

[45] Blumenbach, *On the Natural Variety of Mankind,* trans. and ed. by Thomas Bendyshe, in *The Anthropological Treatises of Johann Friedrich Blumenbach,* pp. 98–99 ff.

arbitrary. "Still," he remarked, "it will be found serviceable to the memory to have constituted certain classes into which the men of our planet may be divided." [46]

The history of physical anthropology, after the death of Blumenbach in 1840, may be described in terms of the gradual inversion of this genetic approach to the problem of the variety of mankind. The investigation of causes steadily gave way to the description of effects, as if the classification of mankind into as distinctive groups as it was possible to create were the proper function of a science of physical anthropology. The Darwinian conception of evolution, understood as dealing with continuous materials which, without *selection,* would remain unchanged, led anthropologists to believe that taxonomic exercises in the classification of mankind, both living and extinct, would eventually succeed in elucidating the relationships of the various groups of mankind to one another. We now know, however, that the materials of evolution are not continuous, but discontinuous, and that these materials are particulate, independent genes, which are inherently variable and unstable. Thus, classifications based on the shifting sands of morphological characters and physique can be extremely misleading.[47] How misleading may be gathered from the fact that in nature there actually exist many groups of individuals in different phyla which are distinct species in every sense but the morphological one.[48] The converse also is true, that is, individuals of the same species may exhibit morphological differences which the taxonomist would be led to assign to different specific rank. Such classificatory efforts belong to the pre-Mendelian era.[49] Then, as now, the concept of the continuity of species and the existence of transitional forms was associated with a belief in missing links. The anthro-

---

[46] *Ibid.*, p. 100.
[47] For a brilliant discussion of this subject see Hogben, "The Concept of Race," in his *Genetic Principles in Medicine and Social Science,* pp. 122–44. See also Boyd, *Genetics and the Races of Man.*
[48] Thorpe, "Biological Races in *Hyponemeuta padella* L.," *Journal of the Linnaean Society* (Zoölogy), XXXVI (1928), 621; Thorpe, "Biological Races in Insects and Allied Groups," *Biological Reviews,* V (1930), 177; Thorpe, "Ecology and the Future of Systematics," in Julian Huxley (ed.), *The New Systematics,* p. 358. Dobzhansky and Epling, *Contributions to the Genetics, Taxonomy, and Ecology of Drosophila pseudoobscura and Its Relatives.*
[49] For an admirable presentation of the new taxonomy see Mayr, *Systematics and the Origin of Species.*

pologist conceived his task to be to discover these links so that when they were all joined together we should have a complete Great Chain of Being leading from the most "primitive" to the most "advanced" forms of man.[50] In this manner was established a "racial" anthropology which sought to identify some of these links among existing peoples upon the basis of the physical differences which averaged groups of them were supposed to exhibit. As Linton has remarked, "unfortunately, the early guesses on these points became dogmas which still have a strong influence on the thought of many workers in this field."[51]

It may be noted here that at the beginning of the nineteenth century Cuvier had clearly foreseen the danger of such arbitrary procedures, and in the preface to his *Le Règne animal* (Paris, 1817) he explained; "It formed no part of my design to arrange the animated tribes according to gradations of relative superiority, nor do I conceive such a plan to be practical. I do not believe that the mammalia and the birds placed last are the most imperfect of their class; still less do I think that the last of the mammiferous tribes are superior to the foremost of the feathered race or that the last of the mollusca are more perfect than the first of the annelides or zoöphytes. I do not believe this to be, even if we understand the vague term *perfect* in the sense of 'most completely organized.' I have considered my divisions only as a scale of resemblance between the individuals classed under them. It is impossible to deny that a kind of step downward from one species to another may occasionally be observed. But this is far from being general, and the pretended scale of life, founded on the erroneous application of some partial remarks, to the immensity of organized nature, has proved essentially detrimental to the progress of natural history in modern times."[52]

Throughout Blumenbach's great work and the several editions which followed it the author carefully examined and rebutted, point by point, many of the arguments which had been brought forward to prove the inequality of the varieties of man, and most convincingly showed that there was no good reason to believe anything other than

---

[50] For a critical discussion of such terms as "advanced" and "primitive" see Montagu, "Some Anthropological Terms: A Study in the Systematics of Confusion," *American Anthropologist*, XLVII (1945), 119–33.

[51] Linton, *The Study of Man*, p. 22.

[52] Cuvier, *Le Règne animal*, I, pp. iv–vi.

that they were essentially equal. Thus the treatise, which is properly regarded as having laid the foundations of the science of physical anthropology, stood foursquare for the essential relative mental and physical equality of man. The writings which such works inspired were many and important.

For example, Blumenbach's pupil, the great Alexander von Humboldt, writes: "Whilst we maintain the unity of the human species, we at the same time repel the depressing assumption of superior and inferior races of men. There are nations more susceptible of cultivation, more highly civilized, more ennobled by mental cultivation than others—but none in themselves nobler than others. All are in like degree designed for freedom; a freedom which in the ruder conditions of society belongs only to the individual, but which in social states enjoying political institutions appertains as a right to the whole body of the community." And then Alexander quotes his brother Wilhelm, who writes: "If we would indicate an idea which throughout the whole course of history has ever more and more widely extended its empire—or which more than any other testifies to the much contested and still more decidedly misunderstood perfectibility of the whole human race—it is that of establishing our common humanity—of striving to remove the barriers which prejudice and limited views of every kind have erected amongst men, and to treat all mankind without reference to religion, nation, or colour, as one fraternity, one great community, fitted for the attainment of one object, the unrestrained development of the psychical powers. This is the ultimate and highest aim of society, identical with the direction implanted by nature in the mind of man towards the indefinite extension of his existence. He regards the earth in all its limits, and the heavens as far as his eye can scan their bright and starry depths, as inwardly his own, given to him as the objects of his contemplation, and as a field for the development of his energies . . . the recognition of the bond of humanity becomes one of the noblest leading principles in the history of mankind." [53] Such writings and the humanitarian efforts of the abolitionists[54] eventually told upon public opinion, and in 1808 Britain abolished the slave trade, while America soon followed suit. But

---

[53] Alexander von Humboldt, *Cosmos: A Sketch of a Physical Description of the Universe*, pp. 368–69; Wilhelm von Humboldt, *Über die Kawi-Sprache auf der Insel Java*, III, p. 426.

[54] See Appendix H, pp. 425–26.

slavery survived as an institution in the United States for almost sixty years more, and during that period the issue which it presented kept the subject of "race" differences always at white-hot temperature.

But to return to the beginning. When we examine the scientific literature of the seventeenth century with a view to discovering what beliefs were held concerning the variety of man, we find it was universally believed that mankind comprised a single species and that it represented a unitary whole. With one or two heretical exceptions, it was the accepted belief that all the children of mankind were one, and that all had a common ancestry in Adam and Eve. Physical differences were, of course, known to exist between groups of mankind, but what was unfamiliar was the notion that the differences exhibited by such peoples represented anything fundamental. Such differences, it was believed, could all be explained as due to the action of differing climatic and similar physiographic factors. Mankind was essentially one. Questions concerning the variety of mankind occurred to few thinkers during the seventeenth century. This was not because the known varieties of man were so few that they suggested no problem requiring solution, but principally, it would seem, because the conception of the "superiority" or "inferiority" of "races" which followed upon the increasing exploitation of other peoples had not yet developed to the point of creating a "race problem" and of thus focusing attention upon the significance of the variety presented by mankind. It was not until the economic relations of Europe and the peoples of other remote countries had given rise to the necessity of defining their place in nature that attempts were made to deal with this problem, and such attempts naturally first appeared toward the end of the eighteenth century. It was only then that Samuel Johnson, in *The Vanity of Human Wishes*, could write:

> Let observation with extensive view
> Survey mankind, from China to Peru.

By the middle of the nineteenth century "racism" had become an important ideological weapon of nationalistic and imperialistic politics.[55]

---

[55] For a valuable discussion of this aspect of the subject, see Arendt, *The Origins of Totalitarianism*. "It is highly probable that the thinking in terms of race would have disappeared in due time together with other irresponsible opinions of the nineteenth century, if the 'scramble for Africa' and the new era of imperialism had not exposed Western humanity to new and shocking

During the whole of the seventeenth century only five discussions relating to the varieties of mankind were published, and toward the end of the century Leibnitz, the great mathematician, summed up the prevailing view as to the nature of the peoples of the earth when he wrote: "I recollect reading somewhere, though I cannot find the passage, that a certain traveler had divided man into certain tribes, races, or classes. He made one special race of the Lapps and Samoyedes, another of the Chinese and their neighbors, another of the Caffres or Hottentots. In America, again, there is a marvelous difference between the Galibs, or Caribs, who are very brave and spirited, and those of Paraguay, who seem to be infants or in pupilage all their lives. That, however, is no reason why all men who inhabit the earth should not be of the same race, which has been altered by different climates, as we see that beasts and plants change their nature and improve or degenerate." [56]

The work which Leibnitz had in mind was a brief anonymous essay published in the *Journal des Scavans* in April, 1684, but it remained almost completely unnoticed.[57] "Race" was definitely not yet in the air. It was not until 1749 that Buffon introduced the word "race," in its zoological connotation, into the scientific literature.[58] It is commonly stated that Buffon classified man into six races. Buffon, who was the enemy of all rigid classifications, did nothing of the sort.[59]

---

experiences. Imperialism would have necessitated the invention of racism as the only possible 'explanation' and excuse for its deeds, even if no race-thinking had ever existed in the civilized world," pp. 183–84. See also "Racism and Imperialism" in Hofstadter, *Social Darwinism in American Thought, 1860–1915*, pp. 146–73; Curtin, "The Origins of the 'White Man's Burden,'" *The Listener*, LXVI (1961), 412–15.

[56] Leibnitz, *Otium Hanoveriana; sive, Miscellanea*, p. 37.

[57] [Bernier] "Nouvelle division de la Terre, par les différentes Espèces ou races d'homme qui l'habitent, envoyée par un fameux Voyageur à Monsieur ... à peu près en ces termes," *Journal des Scavans*, April 24, 1684, 85–89. In English translation this essay is reprinted in Bendyshe, "The History of Anthropology," in *Memoirs Read before the Anthropological Society of London*, I (1863–64), 360–64.

[58] Buffon, *Histoire naturelle, générale et particulière* (Paris, 1749). *Natural History, General and Particular*, trans. by William Smellie, corrected by William Wood (London, 1812), III, pp. 302 ff.

[59] Hrdlička, for example, lists six varieties as purporting to be "Buffon's classification." "The Races of Man" in Corrigan (ed.), *Scientific Aspects of the Race Problem*, p. 174.

What he did was to provide an account of all the varieties of man known to him in a purely descriptive manner. This is how he begins: "In Lapland, and on the northern coasts of Tartary, we find a race of men of an uncouth figure, and small stature." And this is the type of Buffon's description. Here the word "race" is used for the first time in a scientific context, and it is quite clear, after reading Buffon, that he uses the word in no narrowly defined, but rather in a general, sense.[60] Since Buffon's works were widely read and were translated into many European languages, he must be held at least partially responsible for the diffusion of the idea of a natural separation of the "races" of man, though he himself does not appear to have had such an idea in mind.

With the voyages of discovery of Bougainville (1761–66), of Wallis-Carteret (1766), of Captain Cook (1768–79), and many others in the eighteenth century, there were opened up to the view of Europe many new varieties of mankind—people hitherto undreamed of who thickly populated the islands of the South Seas, of Melanesia, and the Antipodes. Soon the inhabitants of the most distant parts of the world began to be described, pictured, and some of their skulls and handiwork were collected and put into museums. Meanwhile, the African slave trade had increased to enormous proportions. During the eighteenth century the slave trade was regarded as sanctioned by the Bible and as fully consistent with the good life.[61] "For what could be more godly than to deliver poor Negroes from heathen darkness and the certainty of damnation, by carrying them to a land where they would receive the 'blessings of Christianity.'"[62]

---

[60] The word "race" is of obscure origin. In English many uses of the word are set out in the *Oxford English Dictionary*, but it is clear that it was already in use in the sixteenth century. In France François Tant, in a book entitled *Thrésor de la langue française*, published in 1600, derived the word from the Latin *radix*, a root, and stated that "it alludes to the extraction of a man, of a dog, of a horse; as one says of good or bad race." See Topinard, "La Notion de race en anthropologie," *Revue d'Anthropologie*, 2d ser., II (1879), 590. Attempts have been made to derive the words from the Latin *ratio*, the Italian *razza* (14th century), the Spanish and Portuguese *raza*, and even from the Arabic *rās*. See Dover, "Race," *Man*, art. 95 (1951), 1.

[61] John Newton, captain of the slaver *African* in 1752, who afterwards aided Wilberforce in the campaign to abolish the trade, wrote, "During the time I was engaged in the slave trade I never had the least scruple as to its lawfulness." See Holt, *Walking Together*, p. 155.

[62] Jacks, *The Confessions of an Octogenarian*, pp. 137–38.

When, at the end of the eighteenth century, the traffic in slaves was for the first time seriously opposed and challenged, the question of the status and relation of the varieties of man became the subject of acrimonious debate. Long-term residents of lands in which Negroes were held in slavery published their beliefs concerning the mental and physical qualities of Negroes and the social arrangements they considered desirable as between whites and Negroes. Thomas Jefferson, for example, thought Negroes poor in mental endowment, but believed in their emancipation, with the qualification that when freed they were "to be removed beyond the reach of mixture." [63]

Edward Long's plausible but incautious remarks on the Negro, in which he compared the latter to an orangutan, were written after a five-year residence in Jamaica, and first published in England in 1774,[64] and in 1788 reprinted in *The Columbian Magazine*. Mentally, wrote Long, Negroes were void of genius, destitute of moral sense, and incapable of making progress in civilization or science. As plantation slaves they do their work "perhaps not better than an *orang-outang* might, with a little pains, be brought to do." [65]

There were innumerable publications of a similar kind during this period, as there were countless others presenting the opposite viewpoint. Perhaps the most remarkable of the latter was the Rev. Samuel Stanhope Smith's *Essay,* first published in 1787 and in a second edition in 1810.[66] Smith was a Presbyterian clergyman who became Professor of Moral Philosophy in 1779 at the College of New Jersey (afterwards Princeton University), and in 1795 seventh president of the college. Smith wrote, "If we compare together only those varieties of human nature by which the several sections of mankind differ most widely from one another, the difference is so great that, on the first view, it might very naturally lead to the conclusion that they must belong to distinct species. But, when we come to examine more particularly the intermediate grades which connect the extremes, and observe by what minute differences they approach, or recede from, one another;

---

[63] Jefferson, *Notes on the State of Virginia,* p. 662.

[64] [Long], *The History of Jamaica.*

[65] [Long], "Observations on the Gradation in the Scale of Being Between the Human and the Brute Creation. Including Some Curious Particulars Respecting Negroes," *The Columbian Magazine or Monthly Miscellany,* II (1788), 15.

[66] Smith, *An Essay on the Causes of the Variety of Complexion and Figure in the Human Species.*

and when we observe further, that each of these minute gradations can be traced to obvious and natural causes, forming so many links, as it were, in the great chain connecting the extremes, we are ready to call in question our first impressions, and perceive the necessity of subjecting them to a new and more vigorous examination." [67]

After citing evidence for the unity of the human species Smith concluded "that the denial of the unity of the human species tends to impair, if not entirely to destroy, the foundations of duty and morals, and, in a word, of the whole science of human nature." [68] Smith goes on to say, "It is a debt we owe to humanity to recognize our brethren in every class of men into which society is divided, and under every shade of complexion which diversifies their various tribes from the equator to the poles." [69]

In the discussion of the origins of modern racism it is necessary to recall that in America there was in existence a long tradition of antipathy toward the native "savages." Unable to civilize them their dispossessors determined to destroy them.[70] Of the American Indians Benjamin Franklin wrote in his *Autobiography,* "And indeed, if it be the design of Providence to extirpate these savages in order to make room for the cultivators of the earth, it seems probable that rum may be the appointed means." [71]

When the issue of emancipation was at last settled, in 1833, for the English colonies, it was far from being so for those of France and Holland. It was not until 1848 that the French emancipated their Negroes, and not until 1863 that the Dutch liberated their slaves. During all these years the monstrous "race" legend was continually being reinforced by the advocates of slavery, so that when the matter was finally settled in favor of the freedom of the slaves, the "race" legend nonetheless persisted. It served to solace the hearts of the

---

[67] *Ibid.,* 2d ed., p. 33

[68] *Ibid.*

[69] *Ibid.,* p. 34.

[70] For an account of this aspect of the subject, see Pearce, *The Savages of America.*

[71] Smyth (ed.), *The Writings of Benjamin Franklin,* I (1907), p. 376. In passing, it may be noted that in 1760 Franklin was admitted to membership in the English Anti-Slavery Society, and that when he was eighty-one years old Franklin became the president of the Pennsylvania Abolition Society. Nevertheless, Franklin's own slaves were not freed until after his death.

aggrieved supporters of slavery, while now, more than ever, they saw to it that the myths and legends which they had served to popularize would be perpetuated.

The idea of "race" was, in fact, the deliberate creation of an exploiting class which was seeking to maintain and defend its privileges against what was profitably[72] regarded as an inferior social caste. Ever since the commencement of the slave trade there had been those who had attempted to justify their conduct in it by denying the slaves the status of human beings. Montesquieu with devastating irony nicely put the view of such traders with their consciences as well as their slaves: "It is impossible for us to suppose these creatures to be men, because, allowing them to be men, a suspicion would follow, that we ourselves are not Christians." [73] Conversely, since they conceived themselves to be Christians, it followed that the slaves could not be men. The notion does not appear to have occurred to them that since men are equal in the sight of God they should also be equal in the sight of one another. More than two decades before the Civil War the most respected and influential Southern philosophers of slavery, Thomas R. Dew[74] and William Harper[75] (later supported by the leading American physical anthropologist, Josiah C. Nott,[76] who was teaching at the University of New Orleans), formulated the principles of the natural inequality of man. They codified, as it were, and openly avowed what Southern cotton planters had been thinking since the abolitionists had first challenged the "rights" upon which their economy was based.

Like Dew, Harper attacked and repudiated the philosophy of equality of Thomas Jefferson. "Is it not palpably nearer the truth,"

---

[72] As an investment the "inferior caste" yielded a profit which on the average amounted to 30 per cent. Klingberg, *The Anti-Slavery Movement in England*, p. 13.

[73] Montesquieu, *The Spirit of the Laws*, Book XV, Chapter V.

[74] Dew, *Review of the Debates in the Virginia Legislature of 1831–1832.* Dew's discussion first appeared in pamphlet form in Richmond in May, 1832, and was widely noticed in the Southern press.

[75] Harper, *A Memoir on Slavery* (Charleston, 1838).

[76] Nott, *Types of Mankind* (1854). In 1856 Nott contributed an appendix to Hotz's translation of Gobineau's *The Moral and Intellectual Diversity of Races*, in which he sought to provide the biological evidence for the natural inequalities of the various branches of mankind. See Carmichael, "Josiah Clark Nott," *Bulletin of the History of Medicine*, XXII (1948), 249–62.

he writes, "to say that no man was ever born free and that no two men were ever born equal? . . . Man is born to subjection. . . . The proclivity of natural man is to domineer or to be subservient." In the evolution of society each man or class of men comes to find the proper place and level, and the resulting differences are then crystallized and legalized by society. Laws are instituted to prevent outbreaks against this established order as well as to render the different classes contented and even ignorant—for "if there are sordid, servile, and laborious offices to be performed, is it not better that there should be sordid, servile, and laborious beings to perform them?" As William E. Dodd put it, "Society in the lower South was to be the realization unhindered of the social philosophy which began with the repudiation of the Declaration of Independence and ended with the explicit recognition of social inequality." [77]

Thomas Cooper characterized the rights of man as "a great deal of nonsense. Nothing can be more untrue; no human being ever was, now is, or ever will be born free." "Man has no inalienable rights," wrote another Southerner, "not even those of life, liberty, and the pursuit of happiness. . . . Instead of that 'glittering generality' which might serve as a motto for the wildest anarchy, the truth is that men and races of men have certain natural capacities and duties, and the right to use the one and discharge the other." [78]

After 1840, denials and attacks upon the principles of the Declaration of Independence become a staple practice in the proslavery literature of the South. A learned legal proslavery authority, Thomas Cobb, writing in 1858 cited such evidence as the following in order to contest the notion that slavery is contrary to the law of nature, that all men are free, and at birth entitled by nature to no higher rights and privileges than another: "The red ant will issue in regular battle array, to conquer and subjugate the black or negro ant . . . these negro slaves perform all the labor of the communities into which they are brought. . . . Upon this definition, therefore, of the law of nature, negro slavery would seem to be perfectly consistent with that law." [79] If, argues Cobb, the Negro were by nature equal to the white, enslave-

---

[77] Dodd, *The Cotton Kingdom*, p. 146; see also Chapter III, "The Social Philosophy of the Cotton Planter."

[78] Jenkins, *Pro-Slavery Thought in the Old South*, p. 125.

[79] Cobb, *An Inquiry into the Law of Negro Slavery*, pp. 8–9.

ment of the Negro would be wrong, for the law of nature imposes upon man in relation to his fellow man the obligation "so to shape his course as to attain the greatest happiness, and arrive at the greatest perfection of which his nature is susceptible. Consequently, whatever interferes with the attainment of this happiness and perfection does violence to the law of his nature, and whatever promotes and is consistent therewith is sanctioned by the law of his nature. In this view, *natural rights* depend entirely upon the nature of the possessor, not of the right." [80] It is, therefore, a matter of the greatest ease for Cobb to show that the nature of the Negro is such that his best interests and greatest happiness are secured by his enslavement to the white man.[81] The master is as necessary to the slave as the pilot is to the ship. By citing most of the leading authorities of the day Cobb has no difficulty in supporting his thesis. Cobb is transparently a man of great character, honesty, and worth. His learned book is written with dignity and sincerity—he is no ignorant rabble-rouser, nevertheless his book is a treasure house of most of the myths that have ever been uttered about the Negro. "In mental and moral development," says Cobb, "slavery, so far from retarding, has advanced the Negro race." [82] "Contact with the Caucasian is the only civiliser of the negro, and slavery the only condition on which that contact can be preserved." [83]

As Norlin has so well said, the slaveholding aristocracy of the South "rationalized their freedom to exploit and enslave. Even before the Civil War broke out, they had persuaded themselves that the institution of slavery was divinely ordained; that it was good for master and equally good for slave, and therefore worthy to be extended beyond the states where it was sanctified by law. They felt themselves to be the heaven-appointed shepherds of their flocks, being better able to care for their black wards than those outsiders who proposed by the tyranny of legislation to set bounds to their freedom of thought and action." [84] They would see to it, as one Virginian slaveholder wrote, that they continued to hold their property, "and for the right thereto, to be called in question by an unphilosophical set of

[80] *Ibid.*, pp. 16–17.
[81] *Ibid.*, p. 51.
[82] *Ibid.*, p. 49.
[83] *Ibid.*, p. 51.
[84] Norlin, *The Quest of American Life*, p. ix.

political mountebanks, under the influence of supernatural agency or deceit, is insufferable." [85]

It is not quite true to suggest, as R. H. Tawney has done, that the one thing these political philosophers omitted to ask themselves was on what grounds the view could be sustained that inequalities in intelligence or biology justified the penalty of slavery. The fact is that they were asked and asked themselves this question ceaselessly, and they made answer, as Aristotle had done before them, that some men were born to be masters and others to be slaves. Like Aristotle, they deliberately invented a theory to justify social discrimination. As early as the year 1700 we find the Puritan Judge John Saffin, of Boston, writing "to prove that all men have equal right to Liberty, and all outward comforts of this life . . . [is] to invest the Order that God hath set in the World, who hath Ordained different degrees and orders of men, some to be High and Honorable, some to be Low and Despicable; some to be Monarchs, Kings, Princes and Governors, Masters and Commanders, others to be Subjects and to be Commanded; Servants of sundry sorts and degrees, bound to obey; yea, some to be born Slaves, and so to remain during their lives, as hath been proved." [86]

From 1830 to 1860 vigilance committees were established throughout the South to punish anyone who in any way exhibited antislavery or pro-emancipation tendencies. Russel Nye has given an account of such cases in his book *Fettered Freedom*. Here are but two typical cases from the month of January, 1850. Elijah Harris, an itinerant schoolteacher, from Dumbarton, New Hampshire, was arrested on a writ issued by the justice of the peace of Clinton, Barnwell District, South Carolina. He was arraigned before the local committee of safety, and convicted of carrying in his trunk an antislavery sermon by a New Hampshire minister. The committee shaved his head, tarred and feathered him, and gave him twelve hours to leave town. [87]

---

[85] Quoted from Apthekar, *Essays in the History of the American Negro*, p. 139.

[86] Saffin, *A Brief and Candid Answer to a Late Printed Sheet, Entitled, The Selling of Joseph*. Quoted from Moore, *Notes on the History of Slavery in Massachusetts*, p. 251. In our own time this doctrine has been even more efficiently preached by Protestant theologians of the Dutch Reformed Church of South Africa.

[87] *The National Anti-Slavery Standard*, January 28, 1850.

Robert Esmond, a resident of Charleston, South Carolina, during the same month, was tarred and feathered on suspicion of teaching Negroes to read.[88]

For the slaveholders the strategic elaboration of erroneous notions which had long been held presented no great difficulty. In order to bolster up their self-appointed rights the superior caste did not have far to seek for reasons which would serve to justify its conduct. The artificially maintained illiteracy and the alleged spiritual benighted-ness of the slaves supplied abundant material for elaboration on the theme of their essential inferiority. Their different physical appearance provided a convenient peg upon which to hang the argument that this represented the external sign of more profound ineradicable mental and moral inferiorities. It was an easily grasped mode of reasoning, and in this way the obvious difference in their *social* status, in caste status, was equated with their obviously different *physical* appearance, which, in turn, was taken to indicate a fundamental *biological* difference. Thus was a culturally produced difference in social status converted into a difference in biological status. What had once been a social difference was now transformed into a bio-logical difference which would serve, it was hoped, to justify and maintain the social difference.[89]

This was a most attractive idea to many members of a society in which the classes were markedly stratified, and it was an idea which had a special appeal for those who were beginning to take an active

---

[88] *The Anti-Slavery Bugle,* January 12, 1850.

[89] It is of interest to note here that in what is undoubtedly the most important study of the problem of the American Negro in America which has ever been made, the author's independent analysis of the historical facts has led him to practically identical conclusions: "The biological ideology had to be utilized as an intellectual explanation of, and a moral apology for, slavery in a society which went out emphatically to invoke as its highest principles the ideas of the inalienable rights of all men to freedom and equality of opportunity." Myrdal, *An American Dilemma: The Negro Problem and Modern Democracy,* pp. 83–89. "The *correct* observation that the Negro is inferior [i.e., socially inferior] was tied up to the *correct* belief that man belongs to the biological universe, and, by twisting logic, the *incorrect* deduction was made that the inferiority is biological in nature." *Ibid.,* p. 97. For a valuable discussion of the subject see Greene, "The American Debate on the Negro's Place in Nature," *Journal of the History of Ideas,* XV (1954), 384–96.

interest in the scientific study and classification of the "races" of mankind.[90] For the term "race," taken over from Buffon with all the emotional connotations which had been added to it, had by now become
established. It was with this tremendous handicap of a term in which
the very question it was attempted to ask had from the outset already
been begged that most anthropologists of the nineteenth century embarked on their researches. The question they had begged was the
one which required to be proved, namely, that mental and moral
differences were associated with "racial" external physical differences.
As Wundt once remarked in another connection, "in the seventeenth
century God gave the laws of Nature; in the eighteenth century
Nature did this herself; and in the nineteenth century individual
scientists take care of that task." [91] And we may add that in the
twentieth century the tasks determine for the scientists, and others,
what the laws of nature shall be.

The allegedly scientific presentation of the case for slavery was
produced by Josiah C. Nott, and published in 1854 under the title
Types of Mankind. This 738-page volume, which enshrined most of
the prejudices and pseudoscience of the day, was embellished with
an essay contributed by Louis Agassiz, Professor of Zoology at Harvard, in which he identified himself with the pluralist position of the

[90] We may refer, for example, to the case of the president of the Anthropological Society of London, Dr. James Hunt. On November 17, 1863, Dr. Hunt
read a paper before the society entitled "The Negro's Place in Nature," in
which he asserted the essential inferiority in every way of the Negro to the
white man. "The Negro's Place in Nature," *Memoirs of the Anthropological
Society* (London), I (1863), 1–64. This paper was discussed at the meeting in
a very dignified manner by everyone but the egregious and insolent Dr. Hunt,
who wound up his reply to his critics with the remark that "all he asked was
that scientific evidence of this character should be met by scientific argument,
and not by poetical clap-trap, or by gratuitous and worthless assumptions." *Anthropological Review* (London), I (1863), 391. The paper was the immediate
cause of many acrimonious debates, and it was, of course, received with much
applause by the proslavery party. When, in 1869, Dr. Hunt died, a New York
paper wrote that "Dr. Hunt, in his own clear knowledge and brave enthusiasm, was doing more for humanity, for the welfare of mankind, and for the
glory of God, than all the philosophers, humanitarians, philanthropists, states-
men, and, we may say, bishops and clergy of England together." This last
quotation is taken from Haddon's *History of Anthropology*, p. 45.
[91] Wundt, *Philosophische Studien*, Vol. III.

authors, and thus lent them and their views the prestige of his great authority as a scientist.[92] This work was not without some influence in the world, and all of it for the worse. Henry Schoolcraft, the great authority on the American Indians wrote, in September, 1854, of this work, "The types are . . . the fruits of the mountain that was in labor. From one end of the land to the other subscribers have been drummed up for this work, and when it came forth it is a patch-work of infidel papers . . . if this be all that America is to send back to Europe . . . it were better that the Aborigines had maintained their dark empire undisturbed." [93]

As an independent student of the evidence has put it: "When between the years 1859 and 1870, anthropological societies were established successively in Paris, London, New York, Moscow, Florence, Berlin and Vienna, the attention of anthropologists was in the first place directed mainly to the statement and exploration of problems of racial divergence and distribution. The need for such a preliminary investigation was great. Popular opinion drew a rough but ready distinction between men of white, black, yellow and red colour, vaguely supposed to be native to the continents of Europe, Africa, Asia and America respectively. Differences of average stature, of physiognomy, of growth and texture of hair were recognized; certain combinations of these characters were supposed to be typical of certain ultimate stocks. There was the self-satisfied view, influenced by an uncritical acceptance of the Biblical account of the Creation, Flood, dispersion of its survivors, selection of a favoured race, which either alone or [together] conspicuously expressed divine purpose, that divergence from European standard[s] should ultimately be explained in terms of degradation." [94]

It was not principally the scientific student of the varieties of man who influenced European thought along these lines, but an aristocrat of the Second Empire, an amateur orientalist and professional diplomat, Count Joseph Arthur de Gobineau. Gobineau was a reactionary littérateur who rejected the principles of the French Revolution,[95] and

---

[92] See Lurie, "Louis Agassiz and the Races of Man," *Isis*, XLV (1954), 227–42; Stanton, *The Leopard's Spots: Scientific Attitudes Toward Race in America, 1815–59.*

[93] See Bachman, *John Bachman*, p. 317.

[94] Foster, *Travels and Settlements of Early Man*, p. 31.

[95] For an account of Gobineau and a distillation of the essence of Gobineau-

looked upon the egalitarian philosophy of the Revolution as the hopelessly confused expression of a degraded rabble. If the founders of
the First Republic had believed in the liberty, equality, and fraternity
of mankind, this scion of the Second Empire would show that, on
the contrary, a man was not bound to be free, that the idea of the
brotherhood of man was a vain and empty dream, a repugnant dream
which could never be realized because it was based upon a fallacious
belief in the equality of man.[96] These views were fully set out by
Gobineau in his four-volume work entitled *Essai sur l'inégalité des
races humaines* (Paris, 1853–55). In 1856 an American translation of
the first two volumes under the title *The Moral and Intellectual
Diversity of Races* was published at Philadelphia. This was the work
of H. Hotz, of Montgomery, the pious Alabama proslavery propa-
gandist. At the invitation of either Gobineau or Hotz, Josiah C. Nott,
the proslavery anthropologist, contributed an anthropological appendix to the translation. Gobineau returned the compliment by sub-
scribing to Nott and Gliddon's *Indigenous Races of the Earth,* which
appeared in the following year, 1857, from the same publishing house
which had issued the translation of the *Essai.* As Finot has pointed
out, Gobineau never attempted to conceal or dissimulate the motives
which led him to write the *Essai.* For him "it was only a matter of
bringing his contributions to the great struggle against equality and
the emancipation of the proletariat. Imbued with aristocratic ideas
... he thought it useful to oppose to the democratic aspirations of his
time a number of considerations on the existence of natural castes in

---

ism by an apostle of both Gobineau and Nietzsche, Dr. Oscar Levy, see Gobineau, *The Renaissance,* trans. by Paul V. Cohn. The introductory essay of
some sixty pages by Dr. Levy is an amazing thing.

[96] Observe how, from the same motives, this reaction expresses itself in the
more recent writings of one of the most confused of American racists, namely
in Madison Grant's *The Passing of the Great Race.* He writes: "There exists
to-day a widespread and fatuous belief in the power of environment, as well
as of opportunity, to alter heredity, which arises from the dogma of the brotherhood of man, derived in turn from those loose thinkers of the French Revolution and their American mimics. Such beliefs have done much damage
in the past, and if allowed to go uncontradicted, may do much more serious
damage in the future" (p. 14). It may be remarked here that the history of
Europe during the past hundred and sixty years could well be written in
terms of reaction to the principles of the French Revolution. This would be
a theme well worth the attention of serious historians.

humanity and their beneficial necessity." [97] Ever since their publication Gobineau's works have enjoyed a great reputation among reactionaries and demagogues of every kind. Among others they gave the composer Richard Wagner a "scientific" basis for his racist prejudices, fortifying him and encouraging him in the production of his virulent and influential racist writings.[98] Some forty-five years later the views originally expressed in Gobineau's works were taken over lock, stock, and barrel by Wagner's son-in-law, Houston Stewart Chamberlain, and elaborated in his *Grundlagen des neunzehnten Jahrhunderts*.[99] This work, which has been accurately described as "one of the most foolish books ever written,"[100] enjoyed an enormous popularity in Germany. Kaiser Wilhelm II called it "my favorite book," and distributed it widely among libraries, the military, the nobility, and his friends.

Both Gobineau and Chamberlain's works may be regarded as the spiritual progenitors of Hitler's *Mein Kampf*. In this connection the words of John Oakesmith, written during World War I, are of interest to all who, by forces similar to those which were operative then, have since been plunged into far more horrible wars. Oakesmith writes: "The essence of the racial theory, especially as exhibited by the writers of the school of Houston Stewart Chamberlain, is profoundly immoral, as well as unnatural and irrational. It asserts that by virtue of belonging to a certain 'race,' every individual member of it possesses qualities which inevitably destine him to the realization of certain ends; in the case of the German the chief end being universal dominion, all other 'races' being endowed with qualities which

---

[97] Finot, *Race Prejudice*, p. 7. For a brilliant analysis of Gobineau and his views see Cassirer, *The Myth of the State*, pp. 225–47.

[98] For a valuable account of these writings and their influence, see Stein, *The Racial Thinking of Richard Wagner*.

[99] Chamberlain, *Die Grundlagen des neunzehnten Jahrhunderts* (1899); trans. by John Lees as *The Foundations of the Nineteenth Century* (1910).

[100] Oakesmith, *Race and Nationality*, p. 58. "It is false in its theories; ludicrously inaccurate in its assertions; pompous and extravagant in its style; insolent to its critics and opponents. . . . He frequently uses the term 'lie' and 'liar' of others, while claiming that he is himself constitutionally incapable of lying . . . he is a violent and vulgar charlatan all the time. We say, and say it deliberately, that he is the only author we have read to whose work Sidney Smith's phrase, 'the crapulous eructations of a drunken cobbler,' would appropriately be applied." A judgment, I believe, which all impartial critics would share.

as inevitably destine them to submission and slavery to German ideals and German masters. This essentially foolish and immoral conception has been the root-cause of that diseased national egotism whose exhibition during the war has been at once the scorn and the horror of the civilized world." [101]

In the Western world the German people have especially excelled in the art of creating myths. Luther, to a large extent, successfully destroyed the mythological element in Christianity for them, and from the date of that event to the advent of the Nazi Party the Germans had been seeking for some new mythology wherewith to replace what they had lost. When he cleared the way for a more purely rational interpretation of the world, Luther failed to foresee that by withdrawing the experience of the mystical, the poetic, the metaphysical, and the dramatic, he was building for a time when the people would be glad to embrace a mythology whose barbarity would have appalled him. One may never deprive a people of its feeling of unity with the world, with nature, and with man without providing another set of such metaphysical beliefs—unless one is ready to brook disaster. We may recall the words of Ernest Renan, written in 1848: "The serious thing is that we fail to perceive a means of providing humanity in the future with a catechism that will be acceptable henceforth, except on the condition of returning to a state of credulity. Hence, it is possible that the ruin of idealistic beliefs may be fated to follow hard upon the ruin of supernatural beliefs and that the real abasement of the morality of humanity will date from the day it has seen the reality of things.[102] Chimeras have succeeded in obtaining from the good gorilla an astonishing moral effort; do away with the chimeras and part of the factitious energy they aroused will disappear." [103]

After World War I the Germans found themselves particularly frustrated and alone. By providing them with a new mythology and making the Germans feel that they belonged to a "superior race," the "Herrenvolk," Hitler endowed them with a completely acceptable *Weltanschauung*. The fact that the Nazi "race" theories represented the most ludicrous and vicious mythology that had ever been perpe-

---

[101] *Ibid.*, p. 50.

[102] Almost a hundred years later we find Sigmund Freud writing, a little querulously, "Because we destroy illusions, we are reproached with endangering ideas."

[103] Renan, *The Future of Science*, p. xviii.

trated upon a people did not, as we know, prevent those myths from functioning as if they were perfectly true. "If one asks," as Bonger has done, "whether these partisans are even partially successful in proving their thesis, then the answer must be a decided No. It is really no theory at all but a second-rate religion. Things are not proved but only alleged. It resembles the commonly witnessed phenomenon of persons who, quite without reason, fancy themselves (and often their families also) to be more exalted than others. But now it is carried out on a much larger scale, and with much greater detriment to society, since it affects wide-spread groups." [104]

What Hitler is said actually to have thought about "race" is reported from a personal conversation by Hermann Rauschning. "I know perfectly well," Hitler said to Rauschning, "just as well as all those tremendously clever intellectuals, that in the scientific sense there is no such thing as race. But you, as a farmer and cattle-breeder, cannot get your breeding successfully achieved without the conception of race. And I as a politician need a conception which enables the order which has hitherto existed on historic bases to be abolished and an entirely new and anti-historic order enforced and given an intellectual basis. . . . With the conception of race, National Socialism will carry its revolution abroad and recast the world." [105]

Lord Bryce, writing in 1915 during World War I, remarked: "Whatever condemnation may be passed—and justly passed—upon reckless leaders and a ruthless caste that lives for and worships war, it is the popular sentiment behind them, the exaggeration of racial vanity and national pretensions, that has been and is the real source of the mischief, for without such sentiments no caste could exert its baleful power. Such sentiments are not confined to any single nation, and they are even more widespread in the wealthier and more educated classes than in the humbler. As it is largely by the educated, by students and writers as well as by political leaders, that the mischief has been done, more or less everywhere, even if most conspicuously in one country, so it should be the function and the privilege of thinkers and writers as well as of practical men to enforce a broader, saner, and more sympathetic view of the world as a vast community, in which every race has much to give and much to receive, to point

---

[104] *Race and Crime,* p. 11. For an admirable account of the rise of racism in Germany see Massing, *Rehearsal for Destruction.*
[105] Rauschning, *The Voice of Destruction,* p. 232.

out that it is by the co-operation, unconscious but unceasing, by the reciprocal teaching and learning of the more gifted races, that all progress has been achieved. Perfection is obtained not by the ascendancy of any one form of excellence, but by the blending of what is best in many different forms." [106]

How much more true are these words today than when they were written. We all know only too well to what horrors the reckless "führers" of the Axis nations and their ruthless conduct have led the world, and we have witnessed the exaggeration of "racial" vanity and national pretensions assuming the form of a national religion and serving as an incentive to the common people to follow wherever their "führers" lead. We have seen the virus of the disease spread throughout the greater part of the civilized world in the form of "racism," and in the United States we have heard the word "race" bandied about over the ether waves, on the screen, from the pulpit, in our houses of legislature, our Supreme Court, and used by demagogues in various mischievous ways. In the press, in books of all sorts, and in the magazines the same mischievous looseness of usage is observable. Today, more than at any previous time in the history of man, it is urgently necessary to be clear as to what this term is and what it really means.

The fact is that the modern concept of "race" is a product of emotional reasoning, and, as we have seen, from their inception "racial" questions have always been discussed in an emotional atmosphere. It might almost be called "the atmosphere of the scapegoat" or, possibly, "the atmosphere of frustration or fear of frustration." As a writer in the leading organ of British science, *Nature*, remarked: "It is a matter of general experience that racial questions are rarely debated on their merits. In the discussion of the effects of inter-racial breeding among the different varieties of the human stock, the issue is commonly determined by prejudice masquerading as pride of race or political and economic considerations more or less veiled in arguments brought forward in support of a policy of segregation. No appeal is made to what should be the crucial factor, the verdict of science." [107]

---

[106] Bryce, *Race Sentiment as a Factor in History*, p. 31. For an excellent study of the "mischief" done by educated writers see Faverty, *Matthew Arnold the Ethnologist*.

[107] "Miscegenation in South Africa," *Nature*, No. 3698 (1940), 357. The above

And what is the verdict of science? It will be our purpose to make that verdict clear in the following pages. The older school of anthropologists,[108] some of whom are still with us, grappled with the problem unsuccessfully, and the great number of conflicting viewpoints they presented shows that they were, as a whole, never quite clear as to what was to be meant by the term "race." They were, indeed, something less than clear, if not altogether confused.[109] In the following chapter a brief attempt will be made to show how it came about that so many past and some present anthropologists came to be confused upon the subject of "race."

remarks refer to the official report of the commissioners appointed by the Union of South Africa under the title *Report of the Commission on Mixed Marriages in South Africa* (Pretoria, Government Printer, 1939). This document provides an interesting case study of "race" prejudice in action at high governmental level. American precedents, laws, and decisions relating to intermarriage are heavily drawn upon. So was the way prepared for apartheid.

[108] In using the term "anthropologist" here and in succeeding chapters, I am referring to the physical anthropologist as distinguished from the cultural or social anthropologist. Possibly because of their wider and more intimate acquaintance with a variety of different peoples, particularly in the more isolated parts of the world, cultural anthropologists have generally been somewhat more sound on the subject of "race" than have most physical anthropologists.

[109] See the UNESCO report *The Race Concept.*

2

The Meaninglessness of the Older Anthropological
Conception of "Race"

IT IS SAID that when the theory of evolution was first announced
it was received by the wife of the canon of Worcester Cathedral
with the remark, "Descended from the apes! My dear, we will hope
it is not true. But if it is, let us pray that it will not become generally
known."

The attempt to deprive the classical anthropologist of his belief in
"race" may by some be construed as a piece of cruelty akin to that
which sought to deprive the canon's wife of her belief in the doctrine
of special creation. Indeed, the older anthropological conception of
"race" and the belief in special creation have much in common, for
"race" is, to a large extent, the special creation of the anthropologist.
Most anthropologists have until recently taken it for granted that
"race" corresponds to some sort of physical reality in nature. Indeed,
the concept of "race" is one of the fundamental ideas with which the
anthropologist has habitually worked. To question the validity of
this basic concept upon which he was intellectually nurtured as if it
were an axiom is something which scarcely occurred to him. One
doesn't question the axioms upon which one's science and one's
activity in it are based—at least, not usually. One simply takes them
for granted.

But in science, as in life, it is a good practice to attach from time
to time a question mark to the facts one takes most for granted, to
question the fundamental postulates or facts which require no demonstration; for a fact as a postulate is largely the opinion of those who
should know—and those who should know are but human, and therefore liable to err. In science such questioning is important, because

without it there is a very real danger that certain erroneous or arbitrary ideas, which may originally have been used merely as a convenience, may become so fortified by technicality and so dignified by
time that their original infirmities may eventually be wholly concealed.

So with the older or classical anthropological conception of "race."
It was, indeed, nothing but a whited sepulcher, a conception which in
the light of modern field and experimental genetics proved utterly
erroneous and meaningless; "an absolutist system of metaphysical beliefs," as it has been called.[1] As such, it has been suggested that the
term be dropped from the anthropological as well as from the popular
vocabulary, for it is a tendentious term which has done an infinite
amount of harm and no good at all.

The development of the anthropological conception of "race" may
be traced from the scholastic naturalization of Aristotle's doctrine of
the predicables of genus, species, difference, property, and accident.
From the Middle Ages through the seventeenth century it may be followed to the early days of the Age of Enlightenment, when Linnaeus,
in 1735, took over the concepts of class, genus, and species from the
theologians to serve him as systematic tools.[2] As we have already seen,
the term *race* was first introduced into the literature of natural history by Buffon in 1749. But Buffon did not use the term in a classificatory sense; this was left to Blumenbach.

As used by Blumenbach, the term "race" merely represented an
extension of the Aristotelian conception of species; that is to say, it
was a subdivision of a species. Like Buffon, Blumenbach recognized
that all human beings belong to a single species, as did Linnaeus, and
he considered it merely convenient to distinguish between certain
geographically localized groups of man. Thus, when with Blumenbach, in the late eighteenth century, the term assumed a classificatory
value, it was understood that that value was purely arbitrary and no
more than a simple convenience. It had no other meaning than that.

The Aristotelian conception of species, the theological conception
of special creation, and the natural history of the Age of Enlightenment, as represented particularly by Cuvier's brilliant conception of
unity of type, namely, the idea that animals can be grouped and classi-

---

[1] Myrdal, *An American Dilemma: The Negro Problem and Modern Democracy*, p. 116.
[2] Linnaeus, *Systema naturae*.

fied upon the basis of assemblages of structural characters which, more or less, they have in common—these three conceptions fitted together extremely well and yielded the idea of the fixity of species, an idea which, in spite of every indication to the contrary in the years which followed, was gradually extended to the concept of "race."

The Darwinian contribution showed that species were not so fixed as was formerly believed and that under the action of natural selection one species might give rise to another; that all animal forms might change in this way. It is, however, important to remember that Darwin conceived of evolution as a process involving continuous materials which, without the operation of natural selection, would remain unchanged. Hence, under the Darwinian conception of species it was still possible to think of species as relatively fixed and immutable, with the modification that under the slow action of natural selection they were capable of change. For the nineteenth-century anthropologist, therefore, it was possible to think of "race" or "races," not as Blumenbach did in the eighteenth century, as an arbitrary convenience in classification, but as Cuvier did at the beginning of the nineteenth century for all animals, as groups which could be classified on the basis of the fact that they possessed an aggregate of common physical characters, and, as Darwin later postulated, as groups which varied only under conditions of natural selection, but which otherwise remained unchanged.

This is essentially a scholastic conception of species with the one fundamental difference that a species is considered to be no longer fixed and immutable. As far as the older anthropological conception of "race" is concerned, a few anthropologists, still unaware of the significance of the findings of modern genetics, continue to think of "race" as the scholastics thought of species, as a knowable, even though mutable, fixed whole, the essence of which could be defined *per genus, species, propria, et differentia.*

In fact, the anthropologist had simply taken over a crude eighteenth-century notion which was originally offered as a general term with no more than an arbitrary value—a convenient aid to the memory in discussing various groups of mankind—and, having erected a tremendous terminology and methodology about it, deceived himself in the belief that he was dealing with an objective reality.[3]

---

[3] As Boas remarked, "we talk all the time glibly of races and nobody can give us a definite answer to the question what constitutes a race." Speaking of his

An illuminating reflection of a persisting anthropological view-point occurs in an attractive book by a student of anthropology. In explaining the object of her investigations, she writes: "The purpose of these anthropometric measurements is the establishment of various physical types. The more generalized characteristics of any one locality can be determined, the resemblances to and differences from their near and remote neighbours, the ideal being to discover the various strains which are there combined. In anthropology there is as much information to be gathered from these physical measurements as from the study of social habits and customs." [4] This represents a fair state-ment of the older anthropological viewpoint: "the purpose of these anthropometric measurements is the establishment of various physical types."

For more than a century anthropologists have been directing their attention principally toward the task of establishing criteria by means of which "races" of mankind might be defined—a diverting parlor game in which by arbitrarily selecting the criteria one could nearly always make the "races" come out exactly as one thought they should. As Boyd writes, "Those of the proposed criteria which were adopted are evidently those which were found to give 'reasonable results'—that is, they brought home the bacon; so that in cases where the anthro-pologist was convinced race differences ought to exist, these criteria proved that they did. Unobliging criteria which seemed to show no differences between races 'obviously' distinct, or which indicated differences within groups 'obviously' homogeneous, have been tact-fully relegated to the scrap heap." [5] In this observation we probably have the crux of the whole problem. Only those methods of "race" classification which indicated the "right sort" of "race" differences were encouraged and utilized.

Most anthropologists took completely for granted the one thing which required to be proved, namely, that the concept of "race" corre-

---

earliest days as a physical anthropologist, Boas says: "When I turned to the consideration of racial problems I was shocked by the formalism of the work. Nobody had tried to answer the questions why certain measurements were taken, why they were considered significant, whether they were subject to other influences." Boas, "History and Science in Anthropology: a Reply," *American Anthropologist*, XXXVIII (1936), 140.

[4] Crockett, *The House in the Rain Forest*, p. 29.

[5] Boyd, *Genetics and the Races of Man*, p. 195.

sponds with a reality which can actually be measured and verified and descriptively set out so that it can be seen to be a fact[6]—in short, that the anthropological conception of "race" is true, which states that in nature there exist groups of human beings comprised of individuals each of whom possesses a certain aggregate of characters which individually and collectively serve to distinguish them from the individuals in all other groups.

Stated in plain English, this is the conception of "race" which most anthropologists have held and practically everyone else, except the geneticist, accepts. When, as in recent years, some anthropologists have admitted that the concept cannot be strictly applied in any systematic sense, they have thought to escape the consequences of such an admission by calling the term a "general" one and have proceeded to play the old game of blindman's buff with a sublimity which is almost enviable. For it is not vouchsafed to everybody completely to appreciate the grandeur of the doctrine here implied. The feeling of dissatisfaction with which the older anthropologists had viewed the many laborious attempts at classification of human groups had not, on the whole, succeeded in generating the disloyal suspicion that something was probably wrong somewhere. If there was a fault, it was generally supposed, it lay not with the anthropologist, but with the material, with the human beings themselves who were the subject of classification, and who always varied so much that it was difficult to put them into the group where they were conceived properly to belong. This was definitely a nuisance, but, happily, one which could be overcome by the simple expedient of "averaging"—the principal occupation of the student of "race."

The process of averaging the characters of a given group, of knocking the individuals together, giving them a good stirring, and then serving the resulting omelet as a "race" was, until recently, essentially the anthropological process of race-making. It may have been good

---

[6] T. H. Huxley, in his essay, published in 1865, "On the Methods and Results of Ethnology" (reprinted in *Man's Place in Nature*), refused to use the terms "stocks," "varieties," "races," or "species" in connection with man, "because each of these last well-known terms implies, on the part of its employer, a preconceived opinion touching one of those problems, the solution of which is the ultimate object of the science; and in regard to which, therefore, ethnologists are especially bound to keep their minds open and their judgments freely balanced."

cooking, but it was not science, since it served to confuse rather than to clarify. When an omelet is done it has a fairly uniform character, though the ingredients which have entered into its making have been varied. So it was with the anthropological conception of "race." It was an omelet which corresponded to nothing in nature: an indigestible dish conjured into being by an anthropological chef from a number of ingredients which were extremely varied in character. This omelet conception of "race" had no existence outside the statistical frying pan in which it had been reduced by the heat of the anthropological imagination.

It is this omelet conception of "race" which is so meaningless—meaningless because it is inapplicable to anything real. When, recently, anthropologists began to realize that the proper description of a group does not consist in the process of making an omelet of it, but in the analysis and description of the character of the variability of the elements entering into it—its ingredients—they discovered that the fault lay not with the materials but with the conceptual tool with which they had approached their study.

That many differences exist between different groups of human beings is obvious; but the older anthropological conception of these was erroneous, and the classical anthropological approach to the study of their relationships was unscientific and pre-Mendelian. Taxonomic exercises in the classification of assemblages of phenotypical (external) characters will never succeed in elucidating the relationships of different groups of mankind to one another, for the simple reason that it is not assemblages of characters which undergo changes in the formation of the individual and the group but the single units which are physiologically associated with those characters. One of the great persisting errors involved in the anthropological conception of "race" has been due to the steady refusal to recognize this fact. The fact is that it is not possible to classify the various groups of mankind by means of the characters which the older anthropologists customarily used, because those characters do not behave as the pre-Mendelian anthropologists thought they should behave, namely, as complexes of characters which are relatively fixed and are transmitted as complexes, but instead they behave in a totally different manner, as the expression of the many independent units, linked and unlinked, which have entered into their formation.

The parallel in the history of biology is striking here and has been well illustrated by Dobzhansky, who writes: "Many studies on hy-bridization were made before Mendel, but they did not lead to the discovery of Mendel's laws. In retrospect, we see clearly where the mistake of Mendel's predecessors lay: they treated as units the com-plexes of characteristics of individuals, races, and species, and at-tempted to find rules governing the inheritance of such complexes. Mendel was first to understand that it was the inheritance of separate traits, and not complexes of traits, which had to be studied. Some of the modern students of racial variability consistently repeat the mis-takes of Mendel's predecessors." [7]

The materials of evolution are not represented by continuous ag-gregates of characters, but by discontinuous packages of chemicals, each of which is more or less independent in its action and may be only partially responsible for the expression of any character. These chemical packages are the genes, situated mostly within the chromo-somes, structures with which many anthropologists were until recently scarcely on terms of a bowing acquaintance. The genes retain both their independence and their individual character more or less in-definitely, although probably they are all inherently variable and, in time, may undergo mutation. For these reasons any conception of "race" which operates as if inheritance were a matter of transmitting gross aggregates of characters is both erroneous and meaningless. To quote Dobzhansky once more: "The difficulty . . . is that . . . the con-cept of race as a system of character averages logically implies a theory of continuous, rather than of particulate, germ plasm. Such a concept is obviously outmoded and incapable of producing much insight into the causative factors at work in human populations. Although the genic basis of relatively few human traits is known, it seems that following up the distribution of these traits could tell us more about the 'races' than a great abundance of measurements." [8]

The principal agencies of evolutionary change in man are primarily gene variability and gene mutation. Evolutionary changes are brought about through the rearrangements in the combinations of genes in consequence of the operation of many secondary factors, physical and cultural, and changes in the character of genes themselves. In order to appreciate the meaning of the variety presented by mankind today it

---

[7] Dobzhansky, *Genetics and the Origin of Species,* 2d ed., p. 78.
[8] *Ibid.,* p. 359.

is indispensably necessary to understand the manner in which these agencies work. Thus, in man it is practically certain that some forms of hair and skin color are due to mutation, while still other forms are due to various combinations of these mutant forms with one another, as also with nonmutant forms. The rate of mutation for different genes in man varies. It has been calculated that the gene for normal clotting mutates, for example, to the gene for hemophilia in one out of less than 10,000 individuals per generation. It is highly probable, for example, that such a mutation occurred in the person of Queen Victoria's father,[9] a fact which in the long run may perhaps constitute both his and her chief claim to fame. The rate of mutation of the blood group genes, however, appears to be low.[10] Mutation of skin-color genes also is infrequent, while mutation of hair-form genes is somewhat more frequent.

If anthropologists are ever to understand how the different groups of mankind came to possess such characters as distinguish the more geographically isolated of them, and those of the less isolated, more recently mixed, and therefore less distinguishable groups, it should be obvious that they must cease making omelets of the very ingredients, the genes, which it should be our purpose to isolate and to map. What must be studied are the frequencies with which such genes occur in different groups of populations. The gene frequency method for the study of the distribution of human genes is a simple one and has now been available for some time,[11] as likewise has been the method for the study of genetic linkage in man.[12] If, roughly speaking, one gene be arbitrarily assigned to every component of the body, it should be fairly clear that as regards the structure of man we are dealing with many thousands of genes. In the fruit fly *Drosophila melanogaster,* in which there are four pairs of chromosomes, it has been estimated that

[9] Haldane, *Heredity and Politics,* p. 88.

[10] See Montagu, *Human Heredity.*

[11] For a clear exposition of the facts see Boyd, *Genetics and the Races of Man;* Stern, *Principles of Human Genetics;* Strandskov, "The Distribution of Human Genes," *Scientific Monthly,* LII (1942), 203–15, and "The Genetics of Human Populations," *American Naturalist,* LXXVI (1942), 156–64.

[12] Finney, "The Detection of Linkage," *Journal of Heredity,* XXXIII (1942), 156–60; Kloepfer, "An Investigation of 171 Possible Linkage Relationships in Man," *Annals of Eugenics,* XIII (1946), 35–71; Mather, *The Measurement of Linkage in Heredity.*

there are no less than 5,000 genes. Man has 23 pairs of chromosomes; if we award him the same number of genes as *Drosophila* may be assumed to have on each chromosome, namely, 1,250, then man has at least 28,750 genes in the chromosomes of his sex cells. But altogether apart from this in a single mating the theoretical possible combinations between the 23 chromosomes of the male and those of the female are 8,388,608, or 2 raised to the 23rd power, and the chance of any one such combination being repeated more than once is one in 70,000,-000,000,000, or $2^{23} \times 2^{23}$. It will be seen that the different combinations that a 30,000-gene system can take reach a stupendous figure. This is on a purely numerical basis. By totally different methods Spuhler has arrived at the figure of about 34,000 genes in man,[13] and Evans at an estimate of between 10,000 and 100,000 genes in man.[14] If we consider the newer concepts, which recognize that the adult individual represents the end point in the interaction between all these genes, under the influence of the environments in which they have undergone development, the complexities become even greater.[15] The morphological characters which anthropologists have relied upon for their "racial" classifications have been few indeed, involving a minute fraction of the great number of genes which it would actually be necessary to consider in attempting to make any real—that is to say, genetically analytic—classification of mankind.

To sum up, the indictment against the older, or classical, anthropological conception of "race" is that: (1) it is artificial, (2) it does not correspond with the facts, (3) it leads to confusion and the perpetuation of error, and finally, (4) for all these reasons it is meaningless, or rather, more accurately, such meaning as it possesses is false. Based as it is on unexamined facts and unjustifiable generalizations, it were better that the term "race," being so weighed down with false meaning, be dropped altogether from the vocabulary.

If it be agreed that the human species is one and that it consists of a group of populations which, more or less, replace each other geographically or ecologically and of which the neighboring ones in-

---

[13] Spuhler, "An Estimate of the Number of Genes in Man," *Science,* CVIII (1948), 279.
[14] Evans, "Quantitative Inferences concerning the Genetic Effects of Radiation on Human Beings," *Science,* CIX (1949), 299–304.
[15] See Montagu, *The Biosocial Nature of Man;* Montagu, *Prenatal Influences.*

tergrade or hybridize wherever they are in contact, or are potentially capable of doing so,[16] then it should be obvious that the task of the student interested in the character of these populations must be to study the frequency distribution of the genes which characterizes them—not entities which are purely imaginary.

Physical anthropologists must recognize that they have unwittingly played no small part in the creation of the myth of "race," which in our time has assumed so dangerous a form. It is encouraging to be able to say that since the appearance of the first edition of this book in 1942 most anthropologists have seen their responsibility clearly and are taking active steps to exorcise the monster of "race" and deliver the thought and conduct of mankind from its evil influence.[17] Dr. G. M. Morant, in delivering the address on physical anthropology at the centenary meeting of the Royal Anthropological Institute, said: "It seems to me that the time has come when anthropologists must fully recognize fundamental changes in their treatment of the problem of racial classification. The idea that a race is a group of people separated from all others on account of the distinctive ancestry of its members is implied whenever a racial label is used, but in fact we have no knowledge of the existence of such populations to-day or in any past time. Gradations between any regional groups distinguished, and an absence of clear-cut divisions, are the universal rule. Our methods have never been fully adapted to deal with this situation." [18]

---

[16] Mayr, "Speciation Phenomena in Birds," *Biological Symposia*, II (1941), 66, and *Systematics and the Origin of Species*, pp. 154 ff.; Mayr, *Animal Species and Evolution*.

[17] For a cogent criticism, by a cultural anthropologist, along similar lines, see the chapter on "race" in Linton, *The Study of Man*, pp. 22–45. See also Krogman, "The Concept of Race," in Linton (ed.), *The Science of Man in the World Crisis*, pp. 38–62.

[18] Morant, "The Future of Physical Anthropology," *Man*, XLIV (1944), 17.

3

The Genetical Theory of "Race"

THE CLASSICAL anthropological practice of describing the end effects of complex variations without in the least attempting to consider the nature of the conditions responsible for them can never lead to any understanding of their real meaning. In order to understand the end effects with which the physical anthropologist has been so much concerned it is necessary to investigate the causes producing them, and this can only be done by studying the conditions under which they come into being, for it should be obvious that it is the conditions *producing* the end effects which must be regarded as the efficient causes of them.

Comparing numerous series of metrical and nonmetrical characters relating to different varieties of man may provide us with some notion of their likenesses and differences and tell us something of the variability of their characters; this is necessary and important, but no amount of detailed description and comparison will ever tell us how such groups came to be as we now find them, unless a serious attempt be made to discover the causes operative in producing them.

Such causes are at work before our eyes at the present time. In this country and in many other parts of the world where different "racial" groups have met and interbred, determinate sequences, if not the actual mechanism, of "racial" change may be studied. The discoveries of geneticists concerning the manner in which genetic changes are brought about in other organisms and what little is known of human genetics render it perfectly clear that the genetic systems of all living things behave fundamentally according to the same laws. If this is true, it then becomes possible, for the first time in the history of man, to envisage the possibility of an evolution in genetical terms of the

73

stages through which man, as a variable species, must have passed in order to attain his present variety of form and also, in the same terms, to account for that variety.

The principles involved in the genetic approach to the study of the evolution of the variety of mankind cannot be fully discussed here, because such a discussion would demand a treatise in itself, and because such treatises are already available elsewhere.[1] Here we have space only for a very condensed statement of the genetical theory of "race."

The conception of "ethnic group differences" here proposed is based upon the following fundamental postulates: (1) that the original ancestral species population was genetically relatively homogeneous; (2) that by migration away from this original ancestral group, individual families became dispersed over the earth; (3) that some of the groups thus dispersed became geographically isolated from one another and remained so isolated for more or less considerable periods of time; (4) that upon all these isolated groups several of the following factors came into play as conditions leading to evolutionary change: (a) the genetic drift or inherent variability of the genotypic materials composing each individual member of the group, and (b) physical change in the action of a gene associated, in a partial manner, with a particular character, that is, gene mutation.

Genetic drift describes the fact that, given a genetically heterogeneous or heterozygous group, spontaneous random variations in gene frequencies will, in the course of time, occur, so that such originally relatively homogeneous groups will come to exhibit certain differences from other isolate groups which started with the same genetic equipment.

Mutation defines the condition in which a particular gene undergoes a permanent change of some sort, and its action expresses itself in the appearance of a new trait or new form of an old character. Mutations have almost certainly occurred independently in different human isolate groups, at different times and at different rates, and have affected different characters. Thus, for example, in one part of a population mutant dominant genes leading to the development of kinky hair may have appeared and have ultimately become scattered throughout the population, as among Negroes. We cannot, however,

---

[1] Boyd, *Genetics and the Races of Man;* Dobzhansky, *Mankind Evolving.*

make a similar assumption for all or many of the characters which distinguish the four major groups of man from one another. Skin color, for example, cannot be so simply explained, for the probabilities are high that even in early man there were already in existence various skin colors and also, incidentally, hair colors.[2] Selection has undoubtedly played an important role here.

Up to this point we have seen that it is possible to start with a genetically heterogeneous, but otherwise relatively homogeneous, population from which independent groups have migrated and become isolated from one another and that by random variation in gene frequencies and the change in the action of genes themselves—disregarding for the moment the operation of such factors as selection of various sorts—new genetic combinations of characters have appeared which, in so far as they differ from those which have appeared in other groups, define the differences existing between such groups. In brief, random variation in gene frequency and the action of mutant genes are the primary agencies responsible for the production of physical differences between human groups. In fact, these constitute the basic processes in the evolution of all animal forms. But there are also other factors involved which, though secondary in the sense that they act upon the primary factors and influence their operation, are not less important in their effects than the primary factors. Indeed, these secondary factors, ecological, natural, social, and sexual selection, inbreeding, outbreeding, or hybridization, and so forth, have been unremitting in their action upon the primary factors, but the character of that action has been very variable. The action of these secondary factors does not require any discussion here (hybridization is discussed in Chapter 10). I wish here to emphasize principally that in the character of the action of the two primary factors, genetic drift and gene mutation, we have the clear demonstration that the variation of all human groups is a natural process which is constantly proceeding. The genetic and physical differences that characterize populations, the so-called "races," merely represent an expression of

---

[2] Among apes of the present day, for example, one encounters animals that are completely white skinned, others that are completely black or brown skinned; still others are mixed or differently colored, thus the face and hands and feet may be black and the remainder of the body white or brown. The hair on the crown of a gorilla's head may contain almost every color that is to be found among men today.

the process of genetic change within a definite ecologic area. "Race" is a dynamic, not a static condition; the populations so described become static and classifiable only when a taxonomically minded anthropologist arbitrarily delimits the process of change at his own time level.

In short, the so-called "races" are populations that merely represent different kinds of temporary mixtures of genetic materials common to all mankind. As Shelley wrote,

> Man's yesterday may ne'er be like his morrow;
> Naught may endure but mutability.

Over a sufficient length of time, all genes will, presumably, mutate. The frequency with which various genes have undergone change or mutation in human groups is at present unknown, but when anthropologists address themselves to the task of solving the problem of gene variability in different human groups, important discoveries may be expected. The immediate task of the physical anthropologist interested in the origins of human variety should be to investigate the problem presented by that variety, not as a taxonomist but as a geneticist, since the variety which is loosely termed "race" is a process which can be described accurately only in terms of the frequencies with which the individual genes occur in groups representing adequate geographic isolates.

If between populations variability can best be described in terms of gene frequencies, then one of the most important tasks of the anthropologist must be the discovery of the roles played by the primary and secondary factors in producing that variability. The approach to the solution of this problem is twofold: first, through the analysis of the character of the variability itself in definitely localized groups; and, second, through the study of the effects of "race" mixture among living peoples. Such studies as those of Boyd, Birdsell, and Coon, Garn and Birdsell, have already shown what can be achieved by means of the genetic approach.[3] As Dobzhansky has pointed out, "the funda-

---

[3] Boyd, *Genetics and the Races of Man;* Birdsell, "Some Implications of the Genetical Concept of Race in Terms of Spatial Analysis," *Cold Spring Harbor Symposia on Quantitative Biology,* XV (1950), 259–314; Birdsell, "The Problem of the Early Peopling of the Americas as Viewed from Asia," in William S. Laughlin (ed.), *Papers on the Physical Anthropology of the American Indian,* pp. 1–68a; Coon, Garn, and Birdsell, *Races, a Study of the Problems of Race Formation in Man.*

mental units of racial variability are populations and genes, not complexes of characters which connote in the popular mind a racial distinction." [4] It is with such complexes that the old-fashioned type of anthropologist has been fruitlessly dealing for so long. And as Dobzhansky so cogently put it in a previously quoted passage which, however, cannot be too often repeated, the error of the pre-Mendelians lay in the fact that "they treated as units the complexes of characteristics of individuals, races, and species, and attempted to find rules governing the inheritance of such complexes. Mendel was first to understand that it was the inheritance of separate traits, and not of complexes of traits, which had to be studied. Some of the modern students of racial variability consistently repeat the mistakes of Mendel's predecessors." [5]

In man the process of differentiation between populations is genetically best understood in terms of the frequency with which certain genes become differentiated in different groups derived from an originally somewhat heterogeneous species population and subsequently undergo independent development. We have already seen that the mechanisms involved in differentiating a single collective genotype into several separate genotypes, and the subsequent development of a variety of phenotypes within these genotypes, are primarily genetic drift or gene variability and gene mutation, and secondarily, the action of such factors as environment, natural, social, and sexual selection, inbreeding, outbreeding, and the like.

Many of the physical differences existing between the living populations of mankind probably originally represent the end effects of small gene mutations fitting harmoniously into gene systems which remain relatively unaltered. Judging from the nature of their likenesses and differences, and from the effects of intermixture, the number of genes involved would appear to be relatively small in number, each being for the most part independent in its action.

Quite as important as the primary factors in the production of the genetic variety of mankind are the secondary factors, such as migration, social and sexual selection, inbreeding, outbreeding, and the like. [6] These processes are akin to those practiced in the production

---

[4] Dobzhansky, *Genetics and the Origin of Species,* 3rd ed., p. 177.
[5] *Ibid.*
[6] See Montagu (ed.), *Culture and the Evolution of Man;* Spuhler (ed.), *The Evolution of Man's Capacity for Culture.* One form of inbreeding, namely,

of domestic breeds of animals from wild types, in whom generic, specific, and racial characters which, under natural conditions, in the secular period of time concerned, would have remained stable, are rendered markedly unstable, as in our artificially produced varieties of cats, dogs, horses, and other domesticated animals.

Considering the roles of mutation, inbreeding, crossbreeding, and selection in the evolution of lower animals, Sewall Wright has arrived at a judgment concerning the conditions for evolution based on the statistical consequences of Mendelian heredity which, allowing for the modifying effects of the secondary factors arising out of man's social activities, may be applied to man. "The most general conclusion is that evolution depends on a certain balance among its factors. There must be gene mutation, but an excessive rate gives an array of freaks, not evolution; there must be selection, but too severe a process destroys the field of variability, and thus the basis for further advance; prevalence of local inbreeding within a species has extremely important evolutionary consequences, but too close inbreeding leads merely to extinction. A certain amount of crossbreeding is favorable, but not too much. In this dependence on balance the species is like a living organism. At all levels of organization life depends on the maintenance of a certain balance among its factors.

"More specifically, under biparental reproduction a very low rate of mutation balanced by moderate selection is enough to maintain a practically infinite field of possible gene combinations within the species. The field actually occupied is relatively small though sufficiently extensive that no two individuals have the same genetic con-

---

own mother's brother's daughter—own father's sister's son—marriage, that is cross-cousin marriage, is probably very ancient and is still widely practiced throughout the world. In this connection Buxton has observed that "herein may lie one of the explanations of the slight differences which appear in the physique of different groups of mankind. If two groups exist side by side, do not intermarry, but each practice within their own group some form of consanguineous marriage, provided it be physical and not classificatory consanguinity, each will tend to become a pure strain, but according to the laws of chance each of these pure strains will tend to get those differences in physique between neighboring tribes which are often so puzzling to the physical anthropologist. Once the pure strains have become established, so long as outside blood is not introduced into the tribe, this difference will tend to be perpetuated," Buxton, "Cross Cousin Marriages, the Biological Significance," in Rattray, *Religion and Art in Ashanti*, p. 343.

stitution. The course of evolution through the general field is not controlled by direction of mutation and not directly by selection, except as conditions change, but by a trial and error mechanism consisting of a largely nonadaptive differentiation of local races (due to inbreeding balanced by occasional crossbreeding) and a determination of longtime trend by intergroup selection. The splitting of species depends on the effects of more complete isolation, often made permanent by the accumulation of chromosome aberrations, usually of the balanced type. Studies of natural species indicate that the conditions for such an evolutionary process are often present." [7]

Precisely similar conditions have been operative, we may be sure, in the evolution and diversification of man. The variety of characters exhibited by the different ethnic groups of man almost certainly owe their being to the operation of the factors so well described by Sewall Wright. The common definition of "race," however, is based upon an arbitrary and superficial selection of characters, a statement which applies to the use of the term by animal breeders as well as to those who use it in connection with man. As Kalmus has pointed out, "Breeders of the old school rarely distinguish between the characters which are due to single gene differences and those which are due to many, and their use of the word race still remains rather vague. The term used by modern geneticists to take the place of race is strain, which has a more precise meaning; it is applied to forms which differ from the commonly found wild type by one or several precisely defined hereditary characters which usually breed true. For instance, there may be a strain of white sweet peas, or of peaches without hairs (nectarines), or of sheep without horns." [8] At its best the term "race" may, in genetic terms, be redefined as a group of individuals of whom an appreciable majority, taken at a particular time level, is characterized by the possession through a common heredity of a certain number of genes phenotypically (that is, on the basis of certain visible or measurable characters) selected as marking "racial" boundaries between them and other groups of individuals of the same species population not characterized by so high a degree of frequency of these particular genes.

[7] Wright, "The Roles of Mutation, Inbreeding, Crossbreeding, and Selection in Evolution," *Proceedings of the Sixth International Congress of Genetics,* I (1932), 356–66.
[8] Kalmus, *Genetics,* p. 46.

This is, perhaps, granting the common conception of "race" too much credit for either significance or intelligibility, but it should be obvious that such a definition represents a rather fatuous kind of abstraction, a form of extrapolation for which there can be little place in scientific thought. What, for instance, does "an appreciable majority" refer to? What are the characters which are to be exhibited by this "appreciable majority"? And upon what grounds are such characters to be considered as significantly defining a "race"? As Dobzhansky points out, "the geographical distributions of the separate genes composing a racial difference are very frequently independent." [9] Thus, blood group distributions are independent of skin color or cephalic index distributions, and so forth. What aggregation, then, of gene likenesses and differences constitutes a "race" or ethnic group?

The answer to this question awaits further research. Meanwhile, we may venture, in a very tentative manner, a definition of an ethnic group here (see Appendix B, p. 372 for a more extended discussion of this definition). An ethnic group represents part of a species population in process of undergoing genetic differentiation; it is a group of individuals capable of hybridizing and intergrading with other such ethnic groups to produce further genetic recombination and differentiation.

In an expanded form this definition may be written as follows: An ethnic group represents one of the complex of populations comprising the single species *Homo sapiens* which individually maintain their differences, physical and cultural, by means of isolating mechanisms such as geographic and social barriers. These differences will vary as the power of the geographic and social barriers, acting upon the original genetic and cultural differences, vary. Where these barriers are of low power, neighboring groups will intergrade or hybridize with one another. Where these barriers are of high power, such ethnic groups will tend to remain distinct or to replace each other geographically or ecologically.[10]

---

[9] Dobzhansky, *Genetics and the Origin of Species,* 2d ed., p. 77.

[10] The conception of an ethnic group was clearly stated as early as 1844 by Alexander von Humboldt; he writes: "The distribution of mankind is . . . only a distribution into *varieties,* which are commonly designated by the somewhat indefinite term *races.* As in the vegetable kingdom, and in the natural history of birds and fishes, a classification into many small families is based on a surer foundation than where large sections are separated into a few but

An example will perhaps help to clarify this definition. When American Negroes marry and have a family, their children more closely resemble other American Negroes, as well as Negroes elsewhere in the world, than they do American or other whites. This merely means that the offspring have drawn their genes from a local group in the population in which certain genes, say for skin color, were present that were not present in other local groups of the American population. Now, the manner in which such genes are distributed within a population such as the United States is determined not so much by biological factors as by social factors. This may be illustrated by means of a homely example. If Negroes were freely permitted to marry whites, the physical differences between Negroes and whites would eventually be completely eliminated through the more or less equal distribution of their genes throughout the population. That this has not occurred to any large extent is due principally to the erection of social barriers against such "miscegenation." These are essentially caste barriers. Such social, or caste, barriers tend to keep the stocks with white and black genes separate. In this way such barriers act as isolating factors akin to natural geographic isolating factors, which have the same effect in maintaining the homogeneity of genetic characters within the isolated group.

Is it not clear, then, that the frequency distributions of certain genes within a population—no matter how these genes have arisen—which serve to distinguish one ethnic group from another for the most part represent the effects of the action of different isolating agents upon a common stock of genetic materials? Such agencies as natural, social, and sexual selection result in different frequency distributions of genes among local groups and populations. Such, from the standpoint of the naturalist, is an ethnic group.

It will be observed that such a definition emphasizes the fact that so-called "racial" differences simply represent more or less temporary

---

large divisions; so it also appears to me, that in the determination of races a preference should be given to the establishment of small families or nations. Whether we adopt the old classification of my master, Blumenbach . . . or that of Prichard . . . we fail to recognize any typical sharpness of definition, or any general or well established principle, in the division of these groups. The extremes of form and colour are certainly separated, but without regard to the races, which cannot be included in any of these classes." *Cosmos: A Sketch of a Physical Description of the Universe,* pp. 365–66.

or episodic expressions of variations in the relative frequencies of genes in different parts of the species population and rejects altogether the all-or-none conception of "race" as a static immutable process of fixed differences. It denies the unwarranted assumption that there exist any hard and fast genetic boundaries between any groups of mankind and asserts the common genetic unity of all groups. Such a conception of "race" cuts across all national, linguistic, religious, and cultural boundaries and thus asserts their essential independence of genetic factors.

4

The Biological Facts

CONCERNING THE ORIGIN of the living varieties of man we can say little more than that there are many reasons for believing that a single stock gave rise to all of them. All varieties of man belong to the same species and have the same remote ancestry. This is a conclusion to which all the relevant evidence of comparative anatomy, paleontology, serology, and genetics, points. On genetic grounds alone it is virtually impossible to conceive of the varieties of man as having originated separately as distinct lines from different anthropoid ancestors. Genetically the chances against such a process ever having occurred are, in terms of probability, of such an order as to render that suggestion inadmissible. On purely physical grounds it is, again, highly improbable that starting from different ancestral stocks the varieties of man would have independently come to resemble one another as closely as they do. This is demanding too much from convergence.

In October, 1962, Professor Carleton S. Coon published a book entitled *The Origin of Races,* in which he attempts to trace the evolution of the five races which he calls Australoids, Mongoloids, Caucasoids, Capoids, and Congoids. The theory he presents is "that at the beginning of our record, over half a million years ago, man was a single species, *Homo erectus,* perhaps already divided into five geographic races or subspecies. *Homo erectus* then evolved into *Homo sapiens* not once but five times, as each subspecies, living in its own territory, passed a critical threshold from a more brutal to a more sapient state." [1]

[1] Coon, *The Origin of Races,* p. 656.

The reference to the "more brutal" state of the assumed five sub-species of *Homo erectus* than of their descendants of sapient state is capable of several meanings in such a context, and when juxtaposed to "sapient" perpetuates pejorative and odious comparisons which are out of place in scientific discussions, unless they can be justified. There is absolutely no reason to believe that early man was any more brutal, even though he was morphologically and culturally less developed, than contemporary man. It is a question whether he was, in fact, as brutal.

The idea that five subspecies or geographic races of *Homo erectus*, (which refers to early man of the pithecanthropoid type), in isolation from one another, "evolved independently into *Homo sapiens* not once but five times," at different times and in different places, is a very dubious one. The theory simply doesn't square with the biological facts. Species and subspecies simply don't develop that way. The transmutation of one species into another is a very gradual process, and the development of the subspecies reflects the biological history of the species as a whole. However few or many subspecies of *Homo erectus* there may have been, all of them, at one time or another, probably participated in the development of *sapiens* subspecies. Subspecies of one species do not usually become transformed into subspecies of another single species. On the contrary, independent subspecies of a single species, as incipient species, tend to speciate into different species. If Coon were right the living so-called "races" or "subspecies" of man would present the most remarkable example of parallel or convergent evolution in the history of animated nature. The human species is a species because all its members have shared a more or less common biological history—making allowance for all the differences in that history which each population or so-called "race" or "subspecies" has undergone. Coon implies that that history has been essentially and independently different for his five assumed races, and further implies that in isolation the genetic direction of *Homo erectus* was predetermined—that each of the subspecies occupying their separate ecologic niches would inevitably have developed into *sapiens*. But the evolutionary process, even for man the cultural creature, does not work like that, as is abundantly testified by the biological history of man himself. For if the subspecies of man had developed in the kind of independent isolation Coon postulates they would have exhibited, owing, among other things, to the inherent variability of the genetic constitution, far greater differences in their earlier and more recent forms than they, in fact, do.

What is so remarkable about the varieties of man is their likenesses, not their differences. It would be putting too much of a strain upon and demanding too much of any theory to require it to make out a case for an independent and parallel and convergent evolution of varieties of any kind as like one another as are the so-called "races" of man.

Were this all, Coon's book could be written off as just another of those attempts which are made from time to time to unravel the tangled skein of man's biological history, and it could be dismissed as the failure it is, were it not for the fact that the author of *The Origin of Races* delivers himself of opinions as if they were facts, and these of a kind which are likely to be misunderstood by the unwary, or understood for what they are not, and used by racists and others for their own nefarious purposes.

From the very first page of his book Coon makes statements of the following kind: "Each major race had followed a pathway of its own through the labyrinth of time. Each had been molded in a different fashion to meet the needs of different environments, and each had reached its own level on the evolutionary scale." [2] There can be no doubt about the meaning here: Each of the races occupies a different evolutionary level on the ladder of development, for that is what "evolutionary scale" means. That means, of course, as we shall see, that some "races" stand higher in the scale of evolution than others. And this is exactly what Coon implies.

Coon regrets that "dead men can take no intelligence tests," thus revealing a rather misplaced faith in the value of intelligence tests, and an obvious failure to understand the worthlessness of intelligence tests when applied cross-culturally or "racially." "However," he goes on to say, "it is a fair inference that fossil men now extinct were less gifted than their descendants who have larger brains, that the subspecies that crossed the evolutionary threshold into the category of *Homo sapiens* the earliest have evolved most, and that the obvious correlation between the length of time a subspecies has been in the *sapiens* state and the levels of civilization attained by some of its populations may be related phenomena." [3]

---

[2] *Ibid.*, p. vii.
[3] *Ibid.*, pp. ix–x.

This, again, reveals a rather naive faith in the value of brain size as a measure of mental capacity. Was Neanderthal man, with a mean cranial capacity of 1,550 cc., brighter than contemporary white men with a mean cc. of 1,400? If not, then why should white men be any more gifted than many of their extinct ancestors with smaller brains than theirs? The statement that the subspecies which has been in the *sapiens* state longer than another—allowing for a moment that such a statement makes any sense at all—must therefore have evolved the most and have a correspondingly higher level of civilization is just the kind of thing that was being said by racist anthropologists a hundred years ago. Professor Coon is in the direct line of Nott and Gliddon. Altogether apart from the fact that there are differences in biological rates of development, and that there is such a thing as "cultural" or "social time," [4] facts which would alone be sufficient to take care of Coon's "fair inference"(s), there is not the very slightest ground for believing that any of the varieties of man attained the *sapiens* state either earlier or later than another. Supposing one subspecies had arrived at the *sapiens* state later than another, such a subspecies could very well, under favorable conditions, have far outdistanced the earlier subspecies in cultural development. The fact is that grandchildren often have a way of excelling their grandparents! But this is all an argument *in vacuo*.

Since, according to Coon, the Negroes were the last of the subspecies of *Homo erectus* to be transformed into *sapiens*,[5] the level of civilization attained by them is "explained"—they simply don't have as long a history as *sapiens,* as do Caucasoids and, interestingly enough, nor have the archaic Australoids (Australian aborigines, Papuans, Melanesians, Negritos, and the like), so it is not to be wondered at that we are as *we* are, and they as *they* are. And if the reader desires to observe what one of the latest to be developed sapientes looks like when compared with one of the earliest to be developed sapient types, he has only to consult Plate XXXII, in which he will see the photographic reproduction of an Australian aboriginal woman above and of a Chinese scholar below. The caption reads as follows: "The Alpha and Omega of *Homo sapiens*: An Australian aboriginal woman with a cranial capacity of under 1,000 cc. (Topsy a Tiwi); and a Chinese

---

[4] Montagu, "Social Time: a Methodological and Functional Analysis," *American Journal of Sociology,* XLIV (1938), 282–84.

[5] Coon, *op. cit.,* pp. 655–56.

sage with a brain nearly twice that size (Dr. Li Chi, the renowned archaeologist and director of Academia Sinica)." "Alpha and Omega," the first and the last. "Obviously," Topsy just growed, and is what she is, a poor benighted Australian aboriginal primarily because she has a brain of 1,000 cc., and Dr. Li Chi is primarily what he is because he has a brain nearly twice that size. Of course, there are cultural differences, but the implication is clear: no matter what cultural advantages Topsy or any of her children had been afforded, neither she nor they could have achieved what Dr. Li Chi had achieved.

This seems to me a really shocking example of scientific illiteracy. Apart from the demonstrable biologistic fallacies involved in this sort of argument, does it really have to be re-proven every year that brain size within the normal range of variation characteristic of the human species at the *sapiens* level, and characteristic of every human population, in which a brain size of 850 cc. in a perfectly normally intelligent European is occasionally encountered,[6] in a land area in which one may also encounter an Anatole France with a brain size no larger than Topsy's, has nothing whatever to do with mental capacity?[7] But then, according to Coon, the Australian aborigines "come closest of any living peoples, to the *erectus-sapiens* threshold."[8] So they ought to be "less gifted" than Caucasoids and the large-brained Mongoloids. And by the same token (though Coon omits any reference to this), the large-brained Mongoloids, having larger brains, on the average, than Caucasoids, ought to be "more gifted" than the latter.

"The genetic basis for high intelligence," Coon tells us, "has been acquired independently in different taxonomic categories of primates. There is no evidence that the most successful populations within several different human races have not also become bright independently."[9] In other words, different human races are likened to the different monkeys, orangutans, chimpanzees, and gorillas, and there

---

[6] Hechst, "Über einen Fall von Mikroencephalie ohne Geistigen Defekt," *Archiv für Psychiatrie und Nervenkrankheiten*, XCVII (1932), 64–76.

[7] Paterson, *Physique and Intellect*, pp. 80–123. Guillaume–Louis and Dubreil–Chambardel, "Le Cerveau d'Anatole France," *Bulletin de l'Academie de Médecine (Paris)*, XCVIII (1927), 328–36. See also pp. 100–06 of the present volume.

[8] Coon, *op. cit.*, p. 427.

[9] *Ibid.*, p. 184.

is "no evidence" that just as these different "taxonomic categories of primates" had independently acquired their different mental capacities, that the different human "races" had not likewise independently done so. It hardly needs to be pointed out that the "races" of man are not equatable with the "different taxonomic categories of primates," and that, in any event, the evolution of man's intelligence has proceeded upon very different lines from that of any other taxonomic category of primate. But this is a subject to which we shall return at some length in the next chapter.

Coon also finds that "Human beings vary in temperament. It is a common observation among anthropologists who have worked in many parts of the world in intimate contact with people of different races that racial differences in temperament also exist and can be predicted." [10] This will be news to many anthropologists, among whom it is the common observation that the more one gets to know "people of different races" the more fundamentally alike they appear to be beneath the surface of the superficial differences. It is the present belief of many anthropologists and others that this discovery constitutes one of the principal contributions made by anthropology to the understanding of man.

The African Negroes—Coon's "Congoids"—would almost seem to have been specially created, according to Coon's findings. "As far as we know now," he writes, "the Congoid line started on the same evolutionary level as the Eurasiatic ones in the Early Middle Pleistocene and then stood still for half a million years, after which Negroes and Pygmies appeared as if out of nowhere." [11] Of course, the joker lies in the "As far as we know now." And what we know now is precisely so unilluminatingly little relating to the physical evolution of Negroes, that the half a million years of standing still, mentioned by Coon, represents nothing more than the standstill in our knowledge concerning the Negro's physical evolution. Even the surface of the subject has not yet been scratched, for the materials which would enable us to reconstruct the barest outline of Negro evolution or, for that matter, that of any other ethnic group, are simply not available. In any event, the top-drawer people didn't originate in "the Dark Continent." The Children of Light originated elsewhere. "If Africa was the cradle of mankind," we are told, "it was only

[10] *Ibid.*, p. 116.
[11] *Ibid.*, p. 658.

an indifferent kindergarten. Europe and Asia were our principal schools." [12]

"Genes in a population," Coon tells us, "are in equilibrium if the population is living a healthy life as a corporate entity. Racial intermixture can upset the genetic as well as the social equilibrium of a group, and so, newly introduced genes tend to disappear or to be reduced to a minimum percentage unless they possess a selective advantage over their local counterparts." [13]

The population genetics of these statements are entirely erroneous, in fact they are preposterous, and far from reflecting the facts, the truth is that under the ordinarily prevailing conditions newly introduced genes can establish themselves rapidly, especially within small breeding populations. As for racial intermixture upsetting the genetic equilibrium of a group, the evidence of everyday experience throughout the world and of field investigations is entirely contrary to this statement, as we shall abundantly see in Chapter 10.

Coon finally tells us that had it "been in the evolutionary scheme of things, and had it not been advantageous to each of the geographical races for it to retain, for the most part, the adaptive elements in its genetic *status quo*" we would all have been "homogenized" by now.[14]

It is a common practice of men to confuse their own views with the laws of nature. It would appear that Coon has fallen into the same error. In any event, he is not a reliable guide to "the evolutionary scheme of things." "The evolutionary scheme of things" is not some mystical process which has kept men apart from one another, from being "homogenized," to use Coon's exceedingly unpleasant word. The evolutionary process has no scheme, and it has not schemed to keep men apart for adaptive or any other reasons. What has kept men apart have been physiographic and social barriers, principally the former, and this is why "the geographical races," being separated by geography and similar barriers, have not been "homogenized."

I have thus far said nothing about the anthropological conception of "race" because this is to some extent yielding to genetic pressure, and because the future of what used to be called the study of "race" lies, in my view, largely in the direction of population genetics. The

[12] *Ibid.*, p. 656.
[13] *Ibid.*, p. 661.
[14] *Ibid.*, p. 662.

older anthropological conception of "race" still occasionally lingers on, suggesting that it is perhaps beyond the reach both of scientific judgment and mortal malice. Insofar as the genetic approach to the subject is concerned, many anthropologists are, as it were, self-made men and only too obviously represent cases of unskilled labor. However, my feeling is that they should be praised for trying rather than blamed for failing. The new anthropology is on the right track.

Recently Garn and Coon have attempted to adapt the terms "geographic race," "local race," and "microgeographical race," for use in the human species. They define, for example, "a geographical race" as, "in its simplest terms, a collection of (race) populations having features in common, such as a high gene frequency for blood group B, and extending over a geographically definable area." [15]

In this definition I think we can see, in high relief as it were, what is wrong with the continuing use of the term "race." The term "geographical race" immediately delimits the group of populations embraced by it from others, as if the so-called "geographical race" were a biological entity "racially" distinct from others. Such a group of populations is not "racially" distinct, but differs from others in the frequencies of certain of its genes. It was suggested by the UNESCO group of geneticists and physical anthropologists that such a group of populations be called a "major group." [16] This suggestion was made precisely in order to avoid such difficulties as are inherent in the term "geographical race." Since Garn and Coon themselves admit that "geographical races are to a large extent collections of convenience, useful more for pedagogic purposes than as units for empirical investigation," [17] it seems to me difficult to understand why they should have preferred this term to the one more closely fitting the situation, namely, "major groups." It is a real question whether spurious precision, even for pedagogical purposes, or as an "as if" fiction, is to be preferred to a frank acknowledgment, in the terms we use, of the difficulties involved. Garn and Coon are quite alive to the problem, but it may be questioned whether it contributes to the student's clearer understanding of that problem to use terms which not only do not fit the conditions, but which serve to contribute to making the

---

[15] Garn and Coon, "On the Number of Races of Mankind," *American Anthropologist,* LXVII (1955), 997.

[16] See Appendix A, pp. 361–71.

[17] *Op. cit.,* p. 1,000.

student's mind a dependable instrument of imprecision, especially in view of the fact that a more appropriate term is available.

The principle of "squatter's rights" apparently applies to words as well as to property. When men make a heavy investment in words they are inclined to treat them as property, and even to become enslaved by them, the prisoners of their own vocabularies. High walls may not a prison make, but technical terms sometimes do. This, I would suggest, is another good reason for self-examination with regard to the use of the term "race."

Commenting on Garn's views on race, Dr. J. P. Garlick has remarked, "The use of 'race' as a taxonomic unit for man seems out of date, if not irrational. A hierarchy of geographical, local and micro-races is proposed, with acknowledgments to Rensch and Dobzhansky. But the criteria for their definition are nowhere made clear, and in any case such a scheme could not do justice to the many independent fluctuations and frequency gradients shown by human polymorphic characters. Surely physical anthropology has outgrown such abstractions as 'Large Local Race. . . . Alpine: the rounder-bodied, rounder-headed, predominantly darker peoples of the French mountains, across Switzerland, Austria, and to the shores of the Black Sea.' " [18]

Garn and Coon do not define "local races" but say of them that they "can be identified, not so much by average differences, but by their nearly complete isolation." In that case, as Dahlberg[19] long ago suggested, why not call such populations "isolates"?

"Microgeographical races" also fail to receive definition, but are described as differing "only qualitatively from local races." In that case, why not use some term which suggests the difference?

In short, it is our opinion that taxonomies and terms should be designed to fit the facts, and not the facts forced into the procrustean rack of pre-determined categories. If we are to have references, whether terminological or taxonomical, to existing or extinct populations of man, let the conditions as we find them determine the character of our terms or taxonomies, and not the other way round.

Up to the present time no satisfactory classification of the varieties of mankind has been devised, and it is greatly to be doubted whether such classification is possible in any manner resembling the procedure

---

[18] Garlick, Review of *Human Races* and *Readings on Race* by S. M. Garn, *Annals of Human Genetics,* XXV (1961), 169–70.

[19] Dahlberg, *Race, Reason and Rubbish; a Primer of Race Biology.*

of the purely botanical or zoological taxonomist. The reason for this is that all human varieties are much more mixed than are plant or animal forms, hence there is a greater dispersion or scattering of characters, which has the effect of producing a considerable amount of intergrading between ethnic groups or varieties. The more or less great variability of all ethnic groups constitutes a genetic proof of their mixed character. From the biological standpoint the physical differences which exist between the varieties of mankind are so insignificant that when properly evaluated they can be described mainly in terms of a particular expression of an assortment of genes which are common to mankind as a whole. At most, human varieties probably differ from one another only in the distribution of a comparatively small number of genes. This one may say much more definitely of man than one could say it of the differences exhibited by any of our domesticated varieties of cats, dogs, or horses. There are numerous varieties of cats, dogs, and horses, many of which represent highly selected strains of animals which have been developed as more or less homogeneous strains and domesticated by man. Man, too, is to some extent a domesticated, a self-domesticated, animal but, unlike our domestic animals, man exhibits varieties that are much mixed and far from representing homogeneous breeds. The range of variation in all human varieties for most characters is considerably greater than that which is exhibited by any group of animals belonging to a comparatively homogeneous breed. All the evidence indicates that the differences between the so-called "races" of man to a large extent represent a random combination of variations derived from a common source, which, by inbreeding in isolated groups, have become scattered and more or less stabilized and hereditary in a large number of the members of such groups. Furthermore, the evidence suggests that such selection of variations as has occurred in different groups has been primarily restricted to physical characters. There is no evidence among the ethnic groups of mankind that any process of mental selection has ever been operative which has acted differentially upon mankind to produce different types of mind. The conception of differential selection for mental qualities seems to be a peculiarly modern one, adapted to modern prejudices. The evolution of man's mental characters and the mental capacities of mankind are discussed in the next chapter.

Man has bred dogs for certain temperamental qualities useful in the hunt for many centuries. The Irish setter, for example, is always red-haired, but his red hair has no connection with his temperamental qualities. The Irish setter has the same kind of temperament as the English setter, but the hair color of the English setter is white and black. The only difference between the white, the black, the white and black, and the red setters is in their coat color; there are no significant differences in their mental or temperamental qualities. No one ever asks whether there are mental and temperamental differences between white, black, or brown horses—such a question would seem rather silly. When, however, it comes to man, the prejudice of anyone who has ever made the statement that skin color is associated with mental capacity is accepted as gospel. For such an assumption there is about as much justification as there would be for the assumption that there exist substantial differences between different color varieties of setters. We know this to be false concerning setters only because we have paid more unprejudiced attention to the mental qualities of dogs than we have to those of human beings. But those of us who have paid some attention to the character and form of the behavior of peoples belonging to different varieties of mankind and to different cultures have satisfied ourselves by every scientific means at our disposal that significantly or innately determined mental differences between the varieties of mankind have thus far not been demonstrable. It may be that some such differences do exist, but if they do they have so far successfully eluded every attempt to prove their existence. There is every reason to believe that such mental differences as we observe to exist between the different varieties of man are due principally to factors of a cultural nature and are in no demonstrably significant manner inseparably related to biological factors. We shall presently refer to the nature of the mental differences which are alleged to exist between different ethnic groups.

Whether the varieties of mankind have a common origin or not is strictly a matter which need concern us little, in view of the fact that structurally and functionally, in spite of superficial differences, they are all so much alike. There are few physical traits which are limited to any particular variety. Perhaps it is nearer the truth to say that different varieties show higher frequencies in the possession of certain physical traits than others do. Such differences in the distribution of the frequencies of physical traits in different human groups may mean that at some time in the past individuals of different heredity interbred, and in isolation continued to do so with the result that a new combination of characters became more or less evenly distributed throughout the group. In this way a new variety or ethnic group was produced. The probability that such factors as isolation and hybridization have played a large part in the evolution of most human groups is suggested not only by what we know of human crosses today—particularly the American Negro—and the behavior of other animal groups, but also by the presence in all human beings of by far the most substantial majority of characters most frequently found in any one group. The fundamental genetic kinship of all the ethnic groups of mankind would, therefore, seem to be clear.

Le Gros Clark makes the important point that "From the purely anatomical point of view, there are already available certain elementary observations on the physical anthropology of race which, though well-known to anatomists, are not, I think, widely enough recognized by those who are concerned with the sociological problems of race. At first sight, the contrast in appearance between such extreme types of mankind as the Negroid, Mongoloid and European might suggest fundamental constitutional differences. In fact, however, a close anatomical study seems to show that the physical differences are confined to quite superficial characters. I may best emphasize this by saying that if the body of a Negro were to be deprived of all superficial features such as skin, hair, nose and lips, I do not think that any anatomist could say for certain, in an isolated case, whether he was dealing with the body of a Negro or a European. Naturally, such a test, being limited to the rather crude evidence of gross anatomy, is not by itself to be taken as a final demonstration of the constitutional equivalence of one race with another. Nor does it take account of statistical differences of a relatively minor character. But it does suggest very strongly indeed that the somatic differences of race may after all not be of a very fundamental nature." [20]

With respect to the nature of those physical characters in the frequency distribution of which various groups differ from one another, it needs to be said that not one can be classified as either "higher" or "lower," "superior" or "inferior," in the scale of development. Every normal physical character must be appraised as equally valuable for the respective functions which it is called upon to perform. Skin color is a character concerning the evolution of

---

[20] Le Gros Clark, *Fitting Man to His Environment*, p. 19.

which we know virtually nothing. Whatever its origin, a black skin is undoubtedly a character of adaptive value, for there is some evidence that it enables its possessor to withstand the effects of prolonged exposure to sunlight. It is known that under such conditions the Negro skin is less liable to sunburn and cancer than is the white.[21] Hence, for groups living in areas of intense sunlight a black skin would, in terms of natural selection, in general be superior to a white skin.

By definition all members of the human species belong to the same classificatory and evolutionary rank, and the varieties of the human species, for the most part, merely represent the expression of successful attempts at adaptation to the environment or habitat in which they have been isolated. It is not altogether an accident that we find dark skins associated with regions of high temperatures and intense sunlight and light skins associated with cooler climates and moderate degrees of sunlight. In this same connection, compare the habitat of the white bear with that of the black or brown bear; also, the frequency of black insects in deserts. Gloger's rule states the fact that melanin (black) pigmentation in mammals and birds increases in warm and humid regions, and lighter pigmentation increases in arid regions. Lukin finds that darkly pigmented races of insects are found in regions whose climate is humid, and lightly pigmented races of insects are found in regions with arid climates.[22]

Black skin appears to represent a character of adaptive value which in some groups followed upon the loss of the body covering of hair. Thus, most apes and monkeys which possess an abundant hairy coat have *white* skin beneath the hair. It might, therefore, be assumed that the skin of the earliest men was probably white; but the opposite assumption may be equally true, that is, some groups of the earliest men may have been black. In that case we would have to say, disregarding for the moment all other considerations, that white-skinned peoples have a reduced distribution of pigment in their skin merely because the shift from the birthplace of their ancestors, which there is good reason to believe was Africa south of the Sahara, to the cooler regions of Europe gradually resulted in a decrease in the distribution

[21] Blum, "The Physiological Effects of Sunlight on Man," *Physiological Reviews*, XXV (1945), 524; Blum, "Does the Melanin Pigment of Human Skin Have Adaptive Value?" *Quarterly Review of Biology*, XXXVI (1961), 50–63.
[22] Dobzhansky, "Rules of Geographic Variation," *Science*, XCIX (1944), 127-28; Huxley (ed.), *The New Systematics*, pp. 213–14.

of pigment in their skin, so that in the course of time, by means of selection of genes for low pigmentation, this has become considerably reduced.[23] The pigmentary difference is not one of *kind* but of degree. The same chemical pigments are present in the skins of all human beings (with the exception of albinos, who have no pigment at all), varying only in its diffusion throughout the body rather than in quality.

The principal pigment, melanin, is produced in pigment cells known as melanocytes, by a reaction between the amino acid tyrosine and oxygen. The enzyme tyrosinase in the melanocytes acts on tyrosine to produce and control the speed of production of melanin. Exposure to the ultraviolet rays of sunlight, for example, activates tyrosinase to convert tyrosine into melanin. There are no differences in the number of melanocytes in the different ethnic groups. Differences in pigmentation in populations and in individuals, as also in different parts of the body are due to differences in the dispersion and distribution of melanin particles in the melanocytes. This is in part under genetic, and in part under environmental, control.

To the present day, exposure to the intense sunlight will bring about the production of an increased amount of pigmentation in many whites, so that depending upon the degree of exposure the skin may turn dark—even black. This latter phenomenon will occur more readily in brunets than in blonds, simply because brunets possess a great amount of the substances required for the production of pigment, whereas blonds possess a much lower proportion of these substances.[24]

It should be obvious that black and white skins are, in their own ways, characters of physiological importance for the survival of the

[23] For a further speculative discussion of skin color see Coon, Garn, and Birdsell, *Races*, pp. 51–55; and Blum, *op. cit.;* Thomson, "Relative Efficiency of Pigment and Horny Layer Thickness in Protecting Skin of Europeans and Africans Against Solar Ultraviolet Radiation," *Journal of Physiology,* CXXVII (1955), 236–46.

[24] Edwards and Duntley, "The Pigments and Color of Living Human Skin," *American Journal of Anatomy,* LXV (1939), 1–33. The darkening of white skin under sunlight has, of course, no effect on the genes for white skin. Any permanent change in skin color could only come about by the selection of genes for more pigmentation. See also, Fitzpatrick, Seiji, and McGugan, "Melanin Pigmentation," *New England Journal of Medicine,* CCLXV (1961), 328–32, 374–78, 430–34.

individual. In hot, humid climates those individuals would be most favored who possessed skins sufficiently dark to prevent heat loss at too rapid a rate, and thus avoid heat exhaustion. In cool climates in which the humidity is relatively low, those individuals would be at an advantage—that is, over a considerable period of time—who were characterized by a lesser amount of pigment in the skin. For the white skin, less abundantly supplied with sweat glands than the black, acts as a good insulator against heat and cold.

Albinos, individuals whose skin tissues are completely devoid of any pigment, suffer intensely when exposed to sunlight. Their pigmentless tissues are incapable of making the necessary adjustments to the rays of the sun; in other words, they have no adaptive mechanism to protect them from the effects of solar radiation. In so far as they lack such a mechanism they are biologically unadapted to meet efficiently the demands of their environment and to that extent they are adaptively inferior to those of their fellows who are so adapted. But there is no evidence of any associated mental inferiority in such cases. The Negro is much better adapted to meet the demands of the conditions of intense sunlight and high temperatures to which his ancestors were born than is the white man,[25] just as the white man is better adapted to meet the requirements of the cooler climates of his adopted homelands. Is the one therefore superior or inferior to the other? Is the white man superior to the Negro because he has lost so much of his pigment? Because biologically his organism has not required its presence under the conditions in which he has lived? And is the Negro superior (or inferior) because he is the descendant of ancestors who were able to survive by virtue of the selective value of their darkly pigmented skins? Clearly, there can be no question here of either inferiority or superiority. Both Negro and white man have survived because they and their ancestors were possessed of characters of adaptive value which, under the respective conditions of their differing environments, enabled them to survive. Characters of adaptive value, whatever form they may take, are usually desirable, because from the standpoint of the organism and of the group they enable it to survive under the unremitting action of the processes of natural selection.

Is there any reason, then, for devaluing a person because of the

---

[25] Lewis, *The Biology of the Negro,* pp. 94–96.

color of his skin, that selfsame color which probably enabled the ancestral group that gave him birth to survive the rigors of this world? Of course there is none, and there can be none from any possible point of view. The same is true of hair and eye color.

But, as racists insist, it is not only the color of the skin which counts; what of the Negro's kinky hair, thick lips, lack of general body hair, and so forth? These, surely, are all marks of inferiority? We may well ask: "Marks of inferiority in what sense? In the cultural or in the biological sense?" If the statement is made from the cultural point of view, there can be no argument, for what a community or person considers culturally satisfying in such connections is purely an arbitrary matter of taste, and concerning taste it is notorious there can be no disputing. Even Negroes when educated in Western cultures, as in North America, owing to the cultural norms which are everywhere set before them as standards or values, frequently come to consider that straight hair and white skin are to be preferred to black skin and kinky hair.[26] But if the statement is made in the biological sense as meaning that such Negroid physical traits are marks of biological inferiority, then it can be demonstrated that such a statement stands in complete contradiction to the facts.

The three traits in question, namely, kinky hair, thick lips, and general lack of body hair, are *not* marks of inferiority, but are, unequivocally, in the biological sense, examples of traits which have progressed further in development than have the same physical structures in whites. In these very traits the Negro is from the evolutionary standpoint more advanced than the white, that is, if we take as our criterion of advancement the fact of being furthest removed from such conditions as are exhibited by the existing anthropoid apes, such as the gorilla and chimpanzee. If racists would take the trouble to visit their local zoo and for a moment drop their air of superiority and take a dispassionate look at either one of these apes, they would find that the hair of these creatures is lank, that their lips are thin, and that their bodies are profusely covered with hair. In these characters the white man stands nearer to the apes than does the Negro. Is the white man, then, for this reason, to be judged inferior to the Negro? Surely not.

---

[26] For the preferences of Negroes in these and other respects see Brenman "Urban Lower-Class Negro Girls," *Psychiatry,* VI (1943), 311–12.

We do not know why the Negro's head hair, body hair, and lips have developed as they have or why whites have more nearly retained the primitive condition of these characters.[27] But we can be certain that biologically there is a good functional reason responsible in both cases, which in the system of values involved in biological judgments must be appraised as equally valuable for the respective functions which each is called upon to perform.

It has been suggested that the broad nose of the Negro is adapted to meet the requirements of air breathed at relatively high temperatures, whereas the comparatively long, narrow nose of the white is adapted to breathing air at relatively low temperatures.[28] From the standpoint of aesthetics, a much stronger case could be made out for the Negro's nose than for that of the white. The peninsula of bone, cartilage, and soft tissues which juts out from the face of the white, with its stretched skin, which becomes shiny as soon as the sweat begins to break through its enlarged pores, is really something of an atrocity. At least, any ape would think so. Let us try to imagine, for a moment, such an outgrowth from the middle of one's face. In such a case, we would regard this structure, from our present aesthetic standards, as an unsightly abnormality. But were the nose growing out of the middle of one's forehead the usual thing, we would, of course, find it perfectly acceptable, and even a thing of beauty. Cultural habituation and social standards of beauty are all. We have all grown used to our noses and take them very much for granted,

> He is foolish who supposes
> That one can argue about noses.

All that one can say is that biologically the form of the Negro nose and the form of the white nose are each in their own way perfectly capable of performing the functions to which they appear to be equally well adapted in all environments. That being so, there can be no question of either superiority or inferiority. Whether such characters are due to adaptation, to natural selection, to social selection, or to a combination of such factors is uncertain. What is certain is that such characters do enable individuals possessing them to meet the demands

---

[27] For some interesting conjectures see Coon, Garn, and Birdsell, *Races.*
[28] Thomson and Buxton, "Man's Nasal Index in Relation to Certain Climatic Conditions," *Journal of the Royal Anthropological Institute of Great Britain and Ireland,* LIII (1923), 92–122.

which their environments have made upon them and upon their ancestors. They have adaptive value. And this may be said for most, possibly all, the normal characters of the varieties of man.

There is one character of the human body which has been cited more frequently than any other as a "proof" of the inferiority of the Negro as compared with the white man. This is the size of the brain. The size or volume of the brain is usually estimated from the capacity of the skull in terms of cubic centimeters. The material available upon which to base a discussion of the value of the size of the brain as related to mental capacity is far from satisfactory. We do not possess sufficient series of thoroughly controlled measurements on numerically adequate samples taken upon the brains of skulls of different human groups. The material that is available is of such a nature that it is possible for anyone who sets out with the intention of proving a particular case to prove it in precisely the terms he wishes.[29] But upon the basis of the available facts the scientist can come to only one conclusion, and that is that since there is no demonstrable difference in the structure, gross or microscopic, of the brains of the members of different ethnic groups, and since the variability in the size of the brain is such that there is no demonstrable relationship between cultural and intellectual status and brain size, there is therefore no significance to be attached to brain size as a mark of cultural or intellectual development. Let us briefly consider the facts.

The cranial capacity of paleolithic Neanderthal men was, on the average, 1,550 cc. What an extraordinary situation! So-called "primitive" Neanderthal man, who lived more than 50,000 years ago, had a larger brain than the average white man of today. Strange that this elementary fact has been so consistently overlooked. Are we to assume, then, that Neanderthal man was culturally and intellectually superior to the average modern white man? The Negro has an average cranial capacity of 1,350 cc., 50 cc. less than the white, whereas the modern white has a cranial capacity which is lower than that of these Neanderthal men by about 150 cc. Are we, then, to draw the conclusion from these facts that the modern white is intellectually three times as much or at least as much inferior to Neanderthal man as the Negro is to the white? We believe not.

---

[29] For an excellent discussion of this subject see Lewis, *The Biology of the Negro*, pp. 77–81.

We know that Neanderthal man was hardly as highly developed culturally as the modern white or Negro. But that he possessed the same capacities for cultural and intellectual development as does modern white or Negro seems highly probable. Neanderthal man was neither inferior nor superior to modern man because of his large brain —he was inferior culturally to modern man for the simple reason that the opportunities for cultural development open to him were strictly limited. His brain almost certainly had nothing whatever to do with the comparatively undeveloped state of his culture, just as the brain of the vast majority of modern white men has little to do with the state of development of the Western world today. The brain is essentially the organ which co-ordinates or integrates nervous activities, and to a large extent it performs that co-ordination or integration according to the educative pattern which is offered to it. That pattern is always culturally determined and conditioned. Therefore, it depends to a considerable extent upon the sort of cultural experience to which an individual has been exposed and caused to co-ordinate or integrate within his nervous system, whether he is capable of functioning at the necessary integrative level or not.

The material bases of those structures which are eventually organized to function as mind are to a large extent inherited precisely as are all other structures of the body. This is an assumption, but it seems a perfectly legitimate one to make. The qualification "to a large extent" is introduced for the reason that in man the nervous system continues to develop long after birth and is therefore appreciably influenced by the experience of the individual.[30] There is every reason to believe, as Edinger has pointed out, "that in certain parts of the nervous mechanism new connections can always be established through education."[31] And, as Ranson has put it, "the neurons which make up the nervous system of an adult man are therefore arranged in a system the larger outlines of which follow an hereditary pattern, but many of the details of which have been shaped by the experiences of the individual."[32] It is evident that experience must play a considerable role in the development of the structure and functioning

[30] Kennard and Fulton, "Age and Reorganization of the Central Nervous System," *Journal of the Mount Sinai Hospital,* IX (1942), 594–606.

[31] Edinger, *Vorlesungen über den Bau der nervösen Zentralorgane des Menschen und der Tiere.*

[32] Ranson, *The Anatomy of the Nervous System,* p. 41.

relations of the nervous system, and it is also clear that that aspect of the functioning of the body or nervous system which we know as *mind* is dependent upon the interaction of several factors; these are, primarily: the inherited, *incompletely developed,* structure of the nervous system; and the character of the *external developing* influences.

There can be little doubt that the material bases of mind are inherited in much the same manner as are the other structures of the body. While the organization of the structures of the body is appreciably influenced by external factors, the resulting effects appear to be incomparably fewer and less complex than are those which are capable of being produced through the organization of those nervous structures which function as mind.[33]

While it is possible—though it has never been demonstrated— that in different ethnic groups the nervous system differs in some of its structural characters, it is certain that if such differences exist, they are of the most insignificant kind. Summarizing the findings of scientists, Professor W. E. Le Gros Clark, one of the most distinguished neuroanatomists and physical anthropologists of the day, is quite positive upon this point. He writes that "in spite of statements which have been made to the contrary, there is no macroscopic or microscopic difference by which it is possible for the anatomist to distinguish the brain in single individuals of different races." [34] The measurable mental characters of different human groups strongly suggest that between such groups there exist few, if any, mental differences which can be attributed to the characters of the nervous system alone. Furthermore, the mental differences which occur between human groups would appear to be much less considerable than those found to exist between individuals of the same group. In the light of our present knowledge, the evidence indicates that within the limits of the normal, brain weight, cranial capacity, head size, or the gross structure and form of the brain, bears no relation whatever to the

---

[33] It should be clearly understood that while mind is an aspect of the functioning body it is also a great deal more than that, and that in man it is at least as much a product of culture as of genes. See White, *The Science of Culture;* Cassirer, *An Essay on Man;* Ryle, *The Concept of Mind;* Laslett (ed.), *The Physical Basis of Mind;* Montagu (ed.), *Culture and the Evolution of Man.*

[34] Le Gros Clark, *Fitting Man to His Environment,* p. 19.

characters of the mind, as between individuals of the same or different ethnic groups.[35] As Professor C. Judson Herrick has remarked, "mental capacity cannot be measured in avoirdupois ounces on the scales." Nor is there necessarily any association between certain ethnic group characters and certain kinds of mentality.

Since mental functions are so largely dependent upon experience, upon cultural conditions, it is impossible to make any inferences as to the equivalence or nonequivalence of mental potentialities as between ethnic groups or peoples among whom the cultural conditions are not strictly comparable. In short, no statement concerning the mentality of an individual or a group is of any value unless it is accompanied by a specification of the conditions of the cultural environment in which that mentality has developed. No discussion of "racial" mental characters can be countenanced which neglects full consideration of the associated cultural variables. For it is evident that it is precisely these cultural variables that play the most significant part in producing mental differences between groups. As I have already indicated, it is more than probable that genetically determined mental differences do exist between individuals of the same and different ethnic groups, but there is absolutely no evidence that significant mental differences which may be determined by the genetic characters of the nervous system exist between any two ethnic groups. It is, of course, possible that future researches may reveal that in some ethnic groups there exist differences in the frequency distribution of genes which exercise limiting effects upon some potentialities. It would, however, be very surprising if it were found that such differ-

---

[35] On these matters see Pearson, "Relationship of Intelligence to Size and Shape of the Head and Other Mental and Physical Characters," *Biometrika*, V (1906), 105–46; Pearl, "On the Correlation between Intelligence and the Size of the Head," *Journal of Comparative Neurology and Psychology*, XVI (1906), 189–99; Murdock and Sullivan, "A Contribution to the Study of Mental and Physical Measurements in Normal Children," *American Physical Education Review*, XXVIII (1923), 209–15, 278–88, 328; Reid and Mulligan, "Relation of Cranial Capacity to Intelligence," *Journal of the Royal Anthropological Institute of Great Britain and Ireland*, LIII (1923), 322-32; Paterson, *Physique and Intellect* (1930); Pickering, "Correlation of Brain and Head Measurements and Relation of Brain Shape and Size to Shape and Size of the Head," *American Journal of Physical Anthropology*, XV (1931), 1–52; von Bonin, "On the Size of Man's Brain, as Indicated by Skull Capacity," *Journal of Comparative Neurology*, LIX (1934), 1–28.

ences were anything more than differences in the *frequency* with which such genes occur in such groups, genes which are common to all mankind. The evidence, as we know it, indicates that all human groups possess all the gene potentialities that all other human groups possess, but that there are differences, between groups, in the manner in which such gene potentialities are both distributed and environmentally conditioned. At the present time we know what amounts to absolutely nothing concerning the *gene frequency distribution* of such potentialities in any of the groups of mankind. It is quite possible that we never shall. In any event, the important point is this: While on theoretical grounds we may be interested in the gene frequency distribution of such potentialities in *populations,* we are in actual practice concerned with the expression of the potentialities of the *individual.* As human beings we are not, and should not, be concerned with groups, but with human beings, with persons. "Do not speak to me of mankind," said Goethe, "I know only men." We must judge each man on his own merits, and in making our judgments we must be careful not to attribute to genes what may be, and usually is, for the most part determined by the environment in interaction with the genes.

As we have already said, apparently it is principally, if not entirely, due to differences in cultural experience that individuals and groups differ from one another culturally, and it is for this reason that, where the cultural experience has appreciably differed, cultural achievement is an exceedingly poor measure of the mental value, genetically speaking, of an individual or of a group. For all practical purposes, therefore, and until further evidence to the contrary be forthcoming, we can safely take cultural achievement to represent the expression chiefly of cultural experience, not of biological potentiality.

Professor Otto Klineberg, our leading authority in the field of "racial" or ethnic psychology, after considering the evidence from every standpoint, offers the following important conclusion: "We may state," he writes, "with some degree of assurance that in all probability the range of inherited capacities in two different ethnic groups is just about identical." [36]

---

[36] Klineberg, "Mental Testing of Racial and National Groups," in Corrigan (ed.), *Scientific Aspects of the Race Problem,* p. 284; see also Klineberg, "Race Differences: The Present Position of the Problem," *International Social Science Bulletin* (UNESCO), II (1950), 460–66.

The environmental plasticity of mental characters is so great that when the evidence is all in, it will almost certainly show that the average differences between ethnic groups will be smaller than the amplitude of the differences to be found within each of the ethnic groups themselves.

The brain does not secrete cultural or intellectual power in the same way that the liver secretes bile. One is not born with the ability to think brilliantly. Such an ability can be brought about only by exposure of the brain and nervous system to, and education in, the proper conditions.

Two thousand years before the birth of Christ the people of what is today England were living in an Early Bronze Age phase of cultural development. Long before this period the civilization of the Egyptians, as represented by the Old Kingdom (III–IV dynasties, 2780–2270 B.C.), had reached one of its most splendid periods. As a people the Egyptians had long been in contact with other peoples who had acted upon them as so many cultural fertilizing agents, whereas the Britons had been isolated from the main course of such contacts. Well might the Egyptians at this time have looked upon the Britons as a "primitive people."

Were the brains of the Britons in the Early Bronze Age made of such inferior stuff that they could only assume efficient qualities by the infusion of new genes? Clearly, genes and brain had nothing to do with the matter; on the other hand, the cultural stimulation which came to them increasingly after the Early Bronze Age, and particularly after the Iron Age, when Julius Caesar landed on their shores, had everything to do with the development which eventually culminated in that great cultural efflorescence which has been called the Greece of the modern world.

The English until very recently were the most notoriously unmusical people of our age. Yet in Elizabethan times they were the most musical people in Europe. What had happened? Had the "musical part" of the English brain atrophied? We can be certain that it had not. The cultural and economic development of the English had simply led in a direction away from such interests to other pursuits. Brain has nothing to do with the matter, culture everything.

In short, it is culture which makes "brains"; not brains, culture. If this were not so, then the Amahosa of Africa, who have few cultural opportunities but more brains by size than whites, with 1,490 cc. as compared with 1,400 cc. for European males and 1,300 cc. for females, would be culturally and intellectually superior to whites, as would the Buriats, 1,496 cc.; the Iroquois, 1,519 cc.; the Eskimos, 1,563 cc.; and the Mongols, 1,570 cc.[37] If we are to hold that the Negro is mentally inferior to the white because his brain has, on the average, a volume of 50 cc. less than that of the white, then by the same token we must hold that Amahosa, Eskimos, Mongols, and many other peoples are superior to whites. This we have reason to believe is untrue. There is no evidence that any people is either biologically or mentally superior or inferior to any other people in any way whatever. What we do know is that there exist considerable cultural differences between peoples and that these cultural differences are readily explained upon purely historical grounds, not upon any biological ones.

Differences in brain size have about as much relation to intelligence and cultural achievement as have differences in body size; that is to say, within the limits of normal variation absolutely none, either between groups of individuals or between individuals of the same group. In short, the concept of "race" which holds that the physical differences between peoples are reflections of underlying significant mental differences is a concept which, on the existing evidence, cannot be scientifically substantiated. It is a myth and a delusion.

The average person in our society observes that certain other persons belonging to different ethnic groups possess physical and mental traits which differ from his own. He concludes that these physical and mental traits are somehow linked together, and these traits are inborn, and that they are immutable.[38] Vague notions about a unilinear evolution "from monkey to man" encourage him to believe that such "races" are "lower" in the "scale" of evolution than is the group to which he belongs; that there is a hierarchy of "races." From such a starting point as "prehistoric man" he envisages a continuous progression upward, culminating in the final development of his own "race"

---

[37] For a list of cranial capacities in fossil and living man, as well as in fossil and living apes, see Montagu, *An Introduction to Physical Anthropology*, pp. 458–59.

[38] "We are apt to construct ideal local types which are based on our everyday experience, abstracted from a combination of forms that are most frequently seen in a given locality, and we forget that there are numerous individuals for whom this description does not hold true." Boas, "Race and Progress," *Science*, LXXIV (1931), 1.

or group. Between "prehistoric man" and himself stand, in an intermediate position, all the other peoples of mankind. "Race" is a definite entity to him, and all the intellectual supports for his conception of it are ready at hand. Newspapers, periodicals, books, radio, TV, publicists, politicians, and others tell him much the same story. The significance of "race" for him emotionally is, as we shall soon see, of considerable importance. Therefore, "race" exists. Such is the conception of "race" with which we have to reckon. We have seen that there are no scientific grounds for this conception.

5

Natural Selection and the Mental
Capacities of Mankind

THE BIOLOGICAL HEREDITY of man is transmitted by mechanisms similar to those encountered in other animals as well as in plants. Similarly, there is every reason to believe that the evolutionary factors which led up to the development of man were of much the same nature as those which have been operative in the evolution of other organisms. The evolutionary changes that occurred before the pre-human could become human, as well as those which supervened since the attainment of the human estate, can be described causally only in terms of mutation, selection, genetic drift, and hybridization— common processes throughout the living world. This reasoning, in-disputable in the purely biological context, becomes a fallacy, however, when used, as it often has been, to justify narrow biologism in dealing with human material.

The specific human features of the evolutionary pattern of man cannot be ignored. Man is a unique product of evolution in that he, far more than any other creature, has escaped from the bondage of the physical and biological into the integratively higher and more complex social environment. This remarkable development introduces a third dimension, a new zone of adaptation, in addition to those of the external and internal environments—a dimension or zone of adaptation which many biologists, in considering the evolution of man, tend to neglect. The most important setting of human evolution is the human social environment. This human social environment can influence evolutionary changes only through the media of mutation, natural selection, social selection, genetic drift, and hybridization. Nevertheless, there can be no genuine clarity in our understanding of man's biological nature until the role of the social factor in the development of the human species is understood. A biologist approaching the problem of human evolution must never lose sight of the truth stated by Aristotle more than two thousand years ago: "Man is by nature a political animal."

In the words of R. A. Fisher, "For rational systems of evolution, that is, for theories which make at least the most familiar facts intelligible to the reason, we must turn to those that make progressive adaptation the driving force of the process." It is evident that man by means of his reasoning abilities, by becoming a "political animal," has achieved a mastery of the world's varying environments quite unprecedented in the history of organic evolution. The system of genes which has permitted the development of the specifically human mental capacities has thus become the foundation and the paramount influence in all subsequent evolution of the human stock. An animal becomes adapted to its environment by evolving certain genetically determined physical and behavioral traits; the adaptation of man consists chiefly in developing his inventiveness, a quality to which his physical heredity predisposes him and which his social heredity provides him with the means of realizing. To the degree to which this is so, man is unique. As far as his physical responses to the world are concerned, he is almost wholly emancipated from dependence upon inherited biological dispositions, uniquely improving upon the latter by the process of learning that which his social heredity (culture) makes available to him. Man possesses much more efficient means of achieving immediate or long-term adaptation than any other biological species, namely, through learned responses or novel inventions or improvisations.

In general, two types of biological adaptation in evolution can be distinguished. One is genetic specialization and genetically controlled fixity of traits. The second consists in the ability to respond to a given range of environmental situations by evolving traits favorable in these particular situations; this presupposes genetically controlled plasticity of traits. It is known, for example, that the composition of the blood which is most favorable for life at high altitudes is somewhat different from that which is characteristic at sea level. A species which ranges from sea level to high altitudes on a mountain range may become differentiated into several altitudinal varieties, each having a fixed blood composition favored by natural selection at the particular altitude at which it lives; or a genotype may be selected which permits an individual to respond to changes in the atmospheric pressure by definite alterations in the composition of the blood. It is well known that heredity determines in its possessor not the presence or absence of certain traits but, rather, the responses of the organism to its environment. The responses may be more or less rigidly fixed, so that approximately the same traits develop in all environments in which life is possible. On the other hand, the responses may differ in different environments. Fixity or plasticity of a trait is, therefore, genetically controlled.

Whether the evolutionary adaptation in a given phyletic line will occur chiefly by way of genetic fixity or by way of genetically controlled plasticity of traits will depend on circumstances. In the first place, evolutionary changes are compounded of mutational steps, and consequently the kind of change that takes place is always determined by the composition of the store of mutational variability which happens to be available in the species populations. Secondly, fixity or plasticity of traits is controlled by natural selection. Having a trait fixed by heredity and hence appearing in the development of an individual regardless of environmental variations is, in general, of benefit to organisms whose milieu remains uniform and static except for rare and freakish deviations. Conversely, organisms which inhabit changeable environments are benefited by having their traits plastic and modified by each recurrent configuration of environmental agents in a way most favorable for the carrier of the trait in question.

Comparative anatomy and embryology show that a fairly general trend in organic evolution seems to be from environmental dependence toward fixation of the basic features of the bodily structure and function. The appearance of these structural features in the embryonic development of higher organisms is, in general, more nearly autonomous and independent of the environment than in lower forms. The development becomes "buffered" against environmental and genetic shocks. If, however, the mode of life of a species happens to be such that it is, of necessity, exposed to a wide range of environments, it becomes desirable to vary some structures and functions, in accordance with the circumstances that confront an individual or a strain at a given time and place. Genetic structures which permit adaptive plasticity of traits become, then, obviously advantageous for survival and so are fostered by natural selection.

The social environments that human beings have created everywhere are notable not only for their complexity but also for the rapid changes to which immediate adjustment is demanded. Adjustment occurs chiefly in the mental realm and has little or nothing to do with physical traits. In view of the fact that from the very beginning of human evolution the changes in the human environment have been not only rapid but diverse and manifold, genetic fixation of behavioral traits in man would have been decidedly unfavorable for survival of individuals as well as of the species as a whole. Success of the individual in most human societies has depended and continues to depend upon his ability rapidly to evolve behavior patterns which fit him to the kaleidoscope of the conditions he encounters. He is best off if he submits to some, compromises with some, rebels against others, and escapes from still other situations. Individuals who display a relatively greater fixity of response than their fellows suffer under most forms of human society and tend to fall by the way. Suppleness, plasticity, and, most important of all, ability to profit by experience and education are required. No other species is comparable to man in its capacity to acquire new behavior patterns and discard old ones in consequence of training. Considered socially as well as biologically, man's outstanding capacity is his educability. The survival value of this capacity is manifest, and therefore the possibility of its development through natural selection is evident. Natural selection on the human level favors gene complexes which enable their possessors to adjust their behavior to any condition in the light of previous experience. In short, it favors educability.

The replacement of fixity of behavior by genetically controlled plasticity is not a necessary consequence of all forms of social organization. Attempts to glorify insect societies as examples deserving emulation on the part of man ignore the fact that the behavior of an individual among social insects is remarkable precisely because of the rigidity of its genetic fixation. The perfection of the organized societies of ants, termites, bees, and other insects is indeed wonderful, and the activities of their members may strike an observer forcefully by their objective purposefulness. The purposefulness is retained, however, only in environments in which the species normally lives. The ability of an ant to adjust its activities to situations not encountered in the normal habitats of its species is limited. On the other hand, social organizations on the human level are built on the principle that an individual is able to alter his behavior to fit any situation, whether previously experienced or new.

This difference between human and insect societies is not surprising. Adaptive plasticity of behavior can develop only on the basis of a vastly more complex nervous system than is sufficient for adaptive fixity. The genetic differences between human and insect societies furnish a striking illustration of the two types of evolutionary adaptations—those achieved through genetically controlled plasticity of behavioral traits and those attained through genetic specializations and fixation of behavior.

The genetically controlled plasticity of mental traits is, biologically speaking, the most typical and uniquely human characteristic. It is probable that the survival value of this characteristic in human evolution has been considerable for a long time, as measured in terms of human historical scales. Just when this characteristic first appeared is, of course, conjectural. Here it is of interest to note that the most marked phylogenetic trend in the evolution of man has been the special development of the brain, and that the characteristic human plasticity of mental traits seems to be associated with the exceptionally large brain size. The brain, for example, of the Middle Pleistocene fossil forms of man was, grossly at least, scarcely distinguishable from that of modern man. The average Neanderthaloid brain of the Upper Pleistocene was somewhat larger than that of modern man. More important than the evidence derived from brain size is the testimony of cultural development. The Middle Acheulian handiwork of Swanscombe man of three hundred thousand years ago, the Tayacian handiwork of Fontéchevade man of one hundred and sixty thousand years ago, and the beautiful Mousterian cultural artifacts associated with Neanderthal man of one hundred thousand years ago, indicate the existence of minds of a high order of development.

The cultural evidence suggests that the essentially human organization of the mental capacities emerged early in the evolution of man. However that may be, the possession of the gene system, which conditions educability rather than behavioral fixity, is a common property of all living mankind. In other words, educability is truly a species character of man, Homo sapiens. This does not mean, of course, that the evolutionary process has run its course and that natural selection has introduced no changes in the genetic structure of the human species since the attainment of the human status. Nor is there any implication that no genetic variations in mental equipment exist at our own time level. On the contrary, it seems likely that with the attainment of human status the part of man's genetic system which is related to mental potentialities did not cease to be labile and subject to change.

This brings us face to face with the old problem of the likelihood that significant genetic differences in the mental capacities of the various ethnic groups of mankind exist. The physical and, even more, the social environments of men who live in different countries are quite diversified. Therefore, it has often been argued, natural selection would be expected to differentiate the human species into local groups or races differing in mental traits. Populations of different regions may differ in skin color, head shape, and other bodily characters. Why, then, should they be alike in mental traits?

It will be through investigation rather than speculation that the problem of the possible existence of genetic differences in the mental make-up of human populations of different geographical origins will eventually be settled. Arguments based on analogies are precarious, especially where evolutionary patterns are concerned. If human races differ in structural traits, it does not necessarily follow that they must also differ in mental ones. Ethnic group differences arise chiefly because of the differential action of natural selection on geographically separated populations. In the case of man, however, the structural and mental traits are quite likely to be influenced by selection in different ways.

We are not directly concerned here with the problem of ethnic differentiation of structural traits. Suffice it to say that ethnic differences in such traits as the blood groups may conceivably have been brought about by genetic drift in populations of limited effective size, as well as by selection. Other ethnic traits are genetically too complex and too consistently present in populations of some large territories to be accounted for by genetic drift alone. Differences in skin color, hair form, nose shape, etc., are almost certainly products of natural selection.[1] The lack of reliable knowledge of the adaptive significance

---

[1] For suggestive treatment of this subject see Coon, Garn, and Birdsell, *Races, a Study of the Problems of Race Formation in Man.* See also Dobzhansky, *Mankind Evolving;* Howells (ed.), *Ideas on Human Evolution;* Montagu (ed.), *Culture and the Evolution of Man;* Spuhler (ed.), *The Evolution of Man's Capacity for Culture;* Roe and Simpson (eds.), *Behavior and Evolu-*

of these traits is perhaps the greatest gap in our understanding of the evolutionary biology of man. Nevertheless, it is at least a plausible working hypothesis that these and similar traits have, or at any rate had in the past, differential survival value in the environments of different parts of the world. By contrast, the survival value of a higher development of mental capacities in man is obvious. Furthermore, natural selection seemingly favors such a development everywhere. In the ordinary course of events in almost all societies those persons are likely to be favored who show wisdom, maturity of judgment, and ability to get along with people—qualities which may assume different forms in different cultures. Those are the qualities of the plastic personality, not a single trait but a general condition, and this is the condition which appears to have been at a premium in practically all human societies.

In human societies conditions have been neither rigid nor stable enough to permit the selective breeding of genetic types adapted to different statuses and forms of social organization. Such rigidity and stability do not obtain in any society. On the other hand, the outstanding fact about human societies is that they do change and do so more or less rapidly. The rate of change was possibly comparatively slow in earlier societies, as the rate of change in present-day nonliterate societies. In any event, rapid changes in behavior are demanded of the person at all levels of social organization even when the society is at its most stable. Life at any level of social development in human societies is a pretty complex business, and it is met and handled most efficiently by those who exhibit the greatest capacity for adaptability, plasticity.

It is this very plasticity of his mental traits that confers upon man the unique position which he occupies in the animal kingdom. Its acquisition freed him from the constraint of a limited range of biologically predetermined responses. He became capable of acting in a more or less regulative manner upon his physical environment instead of being largely regulated by it. The process of natural selection in all climes and at all times has favored genotypes which permit greater and greater educability and plasticity of mental traits under the influence of the uniquely social environments to which man has been continuously exposed.

---

tion; Sahlins and Service (eds.), *Evolution and Culture;* Washburn (ed.), *Social Life of Early Man.*

As Muller has pointed out "racial genetic differences ... may well be insignificant in comparison with the individual ones, owing to the lack of any substantial difference in the manner of selection of most of these characters in the major part of the past history of the various human races." Whether or not we are reasonably justified in assuming that there has been little if any significant change in man's mental potentialities during the major part of his past history, this does seem to be reasonably clear, namely, that the effect of natural selection in man has probably been to render genotypic differences in personality traits, in mental traits, in genetic potentialities, as between individuals and particularly as between ethnic groups or "races," relatively unimportant compared to their phenotypic plasticity. Man's genotype is such that it makes it possible for him to develop the widest range of behavioral adjustments and adaptations. Instead of having his responses genetically fixed as in other animal species, man is the species that invents its own responses, and it is out of this unique ability to invent, to improvise, his responses that his cultures develop.

There is every good reason to believe that natural selection has been operative upon traits making for educability in much the same way from the earliest beginnings of man's history, and in all human groups, no matter how long isolated they may have been from one another. It should be obvious that under any and all forms of social organization, as David and Snyder put it, "flexibility of behavioral adjustment to different situations is likely to have had a selective advantage over any tendency toward stereotyped reactions. For it is difficult to conceive of any human social organization in which plasticity of response, as reflected by ability to profit from experience (that is, by intelligence) and by emotional and temperamental resilience, would not be at a premium and therefore favored by natural selection. It therefore seems to us highly improbable that any significant genetic differentiation in respect to particular response patterns, personality types, temperaments, or intellectual capacities among different populations or races has occurred in the history of human evolution." [2]

And that is the conclusion of this chapter; or, to put it more positively, the evidence considered in this chapter points to the conclusion that in the evolution of man natural selection has placed, as it were, a

---

[2] David and Snyder, "Genetic Variability and Human Behavior," in Rohrer and Sherif (eds.), *Social Psychology at the Crossroads*, p. 71.

high premium upon plasticity or educability, that it has done so nondifferentially, and that for these reasons it becomes highly probable that the mental capacities of mankind are everywhere pretty much of a muchness.[3] This does not mean that all men have become exactly alike; such a statement would be demonstrably untrue. Men differ from one another in many traits, and there can be little doubt that mental traits are influenced by many genes, and that as long as this remains the case men will always differ from each other—more so within groups than between groups. What this statement does mean is that the selection pressure to which the human species has been subject since its origin has been nondifferential selection for educability, "i.e., for the capacity to modify one's behavior under the influence of experience and reasoning."[4] This seems to have had the effect of bringing all human groups up to pretty much the same mental level.

Finally, it is becoming increasingly clear that intelligence, from the genetic standpoint, is not so much a product of major genes, that is, of single genes producing a large effect, but rather of polygenes, that is, of many genes each of which produces a small individual quantitative effect. This being the case it is highly improbable that differences in intelligence could have been brought about in the small, separated populations of man by genetic drift. This would require the assumption of so many correlated changes in positive-acting or negative-acting genes as to render such an effect quite out of the question.[5]

---

[3] Dobzhansky and Montagu, "Natural Selection and the Mental Capacities of Mankind," *Science*, CV (1947), 587–90.

[4] Dobzhansky, "The Genetic Nature of Differences among Men," in S. Persons (ed.), *Evolutionary Thought in America*, p. 154.

[5] Fuller, *Nature and Nurture*, pp. 27–28.

6

"Race" and Society

NO ACTIVITY OF MAN, whether it be the making of a book, the contraction of a muscle, the manufacture of a brick, or the expression of an idea, can be fully understood without a knowledge of the history of that activity in so far as it has been socially determined. For, obviously, any neglect to take into consideration the relations of the social framework can only lead to an incomplete and defective understanding of such events. It should be clear that man develops in and through an environment that is social as well as physical. There is, perhaps, no subject and no event of which this is more conspicuously true than of that tendentious and reverberative word "race." I say "event," because in a definite sense it would be preferable to speak of "race" as an "event" rather than as a word. Apart from the cells of a dead lexicographer's brain or the taxonomist's judgment, "race" in reality hardly ever functions as a word, but almost always as an event. In our society—and it is within the universe of our society that I am speaking—"race" is not merely a word which one utters but it is also an event which one experiences. The word itself merely represents a series of sounds which usually serve as a stimulus to set in motion a host of feelings and thoughts which, together, form an emotional experience; this, for most people, is what "race" is.[1] It is of the greatest importance that this fact be clearly understood, and in this chapter an attempt will be made, among other things, to inquire into the development of those psychological factors which tend to make this event possible. That such

---

[1] For an interesting discussion of the meaning of the word along these lines see Hayakawa, "Race and Words," *Common Sense*, XII (1934), 231–35.

psychological factors exist is indisputably clear, but these factors are not so well known as they deserve to be.

"Race," in our society, is not a term which clearly and dispassionately defines certain real conditions which can be demonstrated to exist, but, as I have already said, the word acts more as a stimulus which touches off a series of emotional charges that usually bear as much relation to the facts as bees do to bonnets. Feelings and thoughts concerning such a concept as "race" are real enough, and so, it may be pointed out, are feelings and thoughts concerning the existence of unicorns, pixies, goblins, satyrs, ghosts, and Aryans. Endowing a feeling or a thought about something with a name and thereby imputing to that something a real existence is one of the oldest occupations of mankind. Man forces on nature the limitations of his own mind and identifies his view of reality with reality itself. Pixies, ghosts, satyrs, and Aryans, and the popular conception of "race" represent real enough notions, but they have their origin in erroneous interpretations of simple facts. Error, imagination, emotion, and rationalization are among the chief components of these notions. Facts, it should always be remembered, do *not* speak for themselves, but invariably through an interpreter. The word "fact" (*facere*) originally meant a thing made; we still make our own "facts," but fail to realize how much of ourselves we put into them or how much others have put into them. This is especially unfortunate in a century in which, as Ignazio Silone has pointed out, words have been so much perverted from their natural purpose of putting man in touch with man as they are today.[2] No matter if words and beliefs are false, if men define them as real, they are real in their consequences. Nothing, indeed, can be so real as the unreal.

It is not here my purpose to show that concepts denoted by such a term as "ghost" or "race" do not, in the sense in which they are commonly used and understood, correspond to anything scientifically demonstrable as having a real existence. Madame de Staël once remarked, "I do not believe in ghosts, but I am afraid of them." Rationally convinced of the nonexistence of ghosts, Madame de Staël nonetheless reacted irrationally and emotionally to the notion of ghosts for all the world as if they had a real existence. Most of us are familiar with such reactions. It is evident that in her early childhood

---

[2] Silone, *Bread and Wine*, p. 158.

Madame de Staël had been emotionally conditioned to believe in the existence of ghosts to such an extent that as an adult she was quite unable to throw off the effects of that conditioning. This is what occurs, in most cases, with regard to "race." Even though they may know it is nothing but a "ghost," most persons continue to be haunted by it. As Mussolini put it in his preracist days, "Race! It is a feeling, not a reality." [3]

Indeed, where matters of "race" are concerned feelings are likely to be involved. The fault, however, lies not so much in the emotional involvement, but in the refusal to recognize that involvement for what it is, and to exercise some measure of rational control over it.

There can be little doubt of the fact that in many parts of the world children are early emotionally conditioned to a belief in the existence of "race" differences.[4] In many parts of Europe, for example, where the larger number of troubles of state and person have traditionally been attributed to the Jews, such attributions can hardly have failed to escape the attention of most children. Indeed, they usually become aware quite early in their lives that hostility toward Jews is a socially sanctioned, even required, form of behavior. Such children would grow up to accept the existence of imputed "race" differences as real and would act upon such beliefs almost automatically. But just as Madame de Staël became intellectually convinced that ghosts do not exist in spite of the acknowledged strength of the emotion attached to the idea, so, too, it is quite possible to produce an intellectual appreciation of the nature of their error among those who have been emotionally conditioned to accept the mythology of "race" as real.

---

[3] In the spring of 1932, during his conversations with Emil Ludwig, Mussolini declared: "Of course there are no pure races left; not even the Jews have kept their blood unmingled. Successful crossings have often promoted the energy and beauty of a nation. Race! It is a feeling, not a reality; ninety-five percent, at least, is a feeling. Nothing will ever make me believe that biologically pure races can be shown to exist today. . . . No such doctrine will ever find wide acceptance here in Italy. . . . National pride has no need of the delirium of race." Ludwig, *Talks with Mussolini*, pp. 69–70. In 1939, under the influence of his Axis partner, Hitler, he completely reversed himself and introduced racist measures of great severity. See Agronsky, "Racism in Italy," *Foreign Affairs*, XVII (1939), 391–401.

[4] On this subject see Lasker, *Race Attitudes in Children;* Goodman, *Race Awareness in Young Children;* Trager and Yarrow, *They Learn What They Live;* Clark, *Prejudice and Your Child*.

Indeed, nearly all of us have been to some extent so emotionally conditioned, yet many of us have been more or less able to emancipate ourselves from the effects of such conditioning by becoming acquainted with the facts relating to these matters. But with many others it cannot be as simple as that, for the roots of their prejudices go much deeper—as we shall soon see. But for those whose prejudices are more superficial an adequate discussion of the facts should suffice. Hence, one of the first requirements necessary for the production in the individual of an intelligent understanding of "race" problems must be the existence of a readily available body of adequately correlated scientific facts relating to every aspect of the "race" problem for use in the education or re-education of the individual. Moreover, these facts must be used, and they must be made available in a form for use. In this field science and knowledge are valueless unless they can be applied in a practical way to increase human happiness. The dispassionate scientific collection and analysis of facts are activities of the first importance, but the end of such activities should not rest with their publication in learned journals. The ultimate purpose of these scientific activities must be recognized as having been defeated unless the most pertinent results are disseminated in such a manner as to increase the understanding of these matters in every human being, until correct understanding is translated into sound conduct.[5]

All who at present appear to be hopelessly confused upon the subject of "race" are not beyond redemption. Methods can be developed by means of which many persons who now superficially harbor myths and delusions concerning "race" may be reached and re-educated. Through the press, periodicals, popular lectures, books, the film, the radio, television, the church, and many similar agencies innumerable misguided persons can be reawakened to their true relation to their fellow men. With respect to those who are more pervasively infected with the virus of racism, I am not so sure.

But more important than these is the growing generation. Through the lower and upper grade schools the most significant work can be done in clarifying the minds of individuals concerning the facts relating to the varieties of man and in educating them in the proper mental attitudes.[6] Let us teach geography, but instead of presenting

---

[5] This is a task which has been undertaken by UNESCO. See Appendix A, pp. 361–71.

[6] Excellent volumes along these lines published for the Bureau for Intercul-

the subject in a dry-as-dust manner, let us humanize its teaching and furnish its field with the living peoples who inhabit the earth.[7] Let us teach our children what we know about the peoples of the earth, and about their respective values for one another and for civilization as a whole. Let us emphasize their likenesses and create interest in their differences, differences which enrich the common heritage of humanity and make the world the richly variegated experience it can be. Let us teach appreciation of the other person's point of view, the more so since, if it is unlike our own, it will require more sympathetic appreciation if it is to be understood.

Relations between other human beings and ourselves form the most important of all the experiences and situations of our lives. Nevertheless, in our society human beings are permitted to enter into such relations without being equipped with the most elementary understanding of what they mean.[8] No attempt is made to supply them with the facts relating to "race" as demonstrated by science. On the contrary, they are supplied with the kind of information which makes fertile ground for the development of "race" prejudices.[9]

Prejudices early acquired are notoriously difficult to eradicate. What must be done is to see to it that, instead of such prejudices, the growing personalities in our schools are taught the facts which anthropological and psychological science has made available. Our children

---

tural Education by Harper & Brothers, New York, are the following: Vickery and Cole, *Intercultural Education in American Schools;* Powdermaker, *Probing Our Prejudices;* Brown, *They See for Themselves;* Brameld, *Minority Problems in the Public Schools;* Brown, *Race Relations in a Democracy;* Van Til, *et al., Democracy Demands It;* Trager and Yarrow, *They Learn What They Live.* See also Watson, *Action for Unity;* Curriculum Office, Philadelphia Public Schools, *Open-Mindedness Can Be Taught;* Clark, *Prejudice and Your Child;* Lillian Smith, *Now Is the Time;* Dean and Rosen, *A Manual of Intergroup Relations;* Martin and Westie, "The Tolerant Personality," *American Sociological Review,* XXIV (1959), 521–28; Sherif and Sherif, *Groups in Harmony and Tension.*

[7] See, for example, the admirable book by Russell and Kniffen, *Culture Worlds;* Mead, *Peoples and Places;* Montagu, *Man: His First Million Years;* Montagu, *The Science of Man.*

[8] See Montagu, *On Being Human;* Montagu, *The Direction of Human Development;* Montagu, *Education and Human Relations.*

[9] See Baker, "Do We Teach Racial Intolerance?" *Historical Outlook,* XXIV (1933), 86–89; Radke and Trager, "Children's Perceptions of the Social Roles of Negroes and Whites," *Journal of Psychology,* XXIX (1950), 1–33.

must be taught that a certain form of nose or a certain skin color is in both the physical and the human scale of values neither better nor worse than any other; that the accents of different people, their manners, their facial appearance, their expression—like the clothes they wear—are not necessarily altogether biologically determined; that they are, indeed, to a much larger extent than is customarily supposed, determined by cultural factors.[10] They must be taught that there is nothing in such characters which is inherently objectionable. For it should be obvious that, though some of us may not be particularly attracted to people who exhibit a certain type of physiognomy, the cause of our dislike lies not in their physiognomy but in the values, the culturally determined ideas, in our own minds which have taught us to react in this way to the perception of such physiognomies. The causes of such dislikes must be looked for in the cultural background of one's intellectual being, not in the shape of the nose or the color of the skin of our neighbors. Physical differences are merely the pegs upon which culturally generated hostilities are made to hang, ending with the smug and empty conviction that a superior "race" is one that you look like and an inferior "race" is one that you don't look like. Here, then, is a most important field in which a great and valuable pioneer work remains to be done. Academic discussions will not carry us far. We must be willing to roll up our sleeves and set to work on this immense and pressingly important problem in human relations, until it is solved.[11]

Community projects for teaching sympathetic understanding of other peoples and ethnic groups, such as that inaugurated in 1939 in Springfield, Massachusetts,[12] have demonstrated to what an extent "race" prejudice can be handled. Treated like any other disease, "race" prejudice can be prevented where it has not yet become endemic and eliminated where it has. Each community should make itself responsible for ridding itself of a disease which makes for so much social wastage and distress. Each community should see to it that it thinks and acts, in its own cooperative interests, in the light of the soundest

---

[10] La Barre, "The Cultural Basis of Emotions and Gestures," *Journal of Personality,* XVI (1947), 49–68; Silberman and Spice, *Colour and Class in Six Liverpool Schools.*

[11] See footnote 6, this chapter; also Mudgett, *Democracy for All.* See also the *Teaching Biologist,* IX (1939), 17–47.

[12] See Appendix E for an account of the Springfield Plan.

modern knowledge and the best human practice. Where there is a desire for just action it will be achieved, and where there is more than a hope of clarity, confusion will yield. Our communities often have departments of sanitation, departments of roadways, why not a department of human relations?

One of the first points to be grasped before much progress in this subject can be made is that, so far as human beings and as far as society and social development are concerned, "race" is not a biological problem at all; furthermore, that it does not even present any socially relevant biological problems. "Race" is a term for a problem which is created by special types of social conditions and by such types of social conditions alone. In terms of social relations so-called "race problems" are, in the modern world, essentially of the nature of caste problems.

"RACE" AND CASTE

We must recognize the fact that in our own society the "race problem" is essentially a problem of social relations and that it is, therefore, fundamentally a social problem. In the social context of America, to take an example with which we are all familiar, what is usually referred to as a "race" or "racial" group in reality constitutes a caste. Thus, Negroes, Jews, Japanese, and Indians are to varying degrees, and in different regions, treated very much, by the dominant white groups, as if they were members of specific castes.

A caste may briefly be defined as a specific, socially limited status group, or more fully as an hereditary and endogamous group, occupying a position of superior or inferior rank or social esteem in comparison with other such groups. The functions of the limiting factors of caste are, in effect, primarily to create barriers against sexual relations between members of the "superior" caste and those of the "inferior" castes and, secondarily, to regulate the social status, privileges, and social mobility of the members of the "inferior" castes.

A class differs from a caste in that a greater degree of social mobility is, in all respects, permitted between the members of the upper and the lower social classes than is permitted between castes. The caste is static, the class dynamic.

As Cooley, Angell, and Carr have pointed out, "the presence of caste is revealed by two crucial attitudes: (1) a sentiment against intermarriage; (2) the practice of judging individuals on the basis of their group membership rather than their individual merits."[13] When we speak of the "race problem" in America, what we really mean is the caste system and the problems which that caste system creates in America.[14] To recognize this fact is to recognize and to effect a clarification and a change in conceptual approach to a problem upon which, perhaps more than any other in our time, clear thinking and accurate concepts are an urgent necessity.

Humphrey has suggested that "the term race should be discarded entirely in the cultural reference, and the more appropriate term caste employed in its stead."[15] This is a worthy suggestion. There can be no cultural races; there can only be cultural castes. But when Humphrey adds that "the term race should be retained in its biologic context as a taxonomic category for the delineation of types of mankind," we must, as the lawyers say, put in a demurrer, for the term "race," as we have seen, is embarrassed, and it is a question whether as a taxonomic category referring to man it is not unrescuably compromised. Even geneticists today tend to avoid its use. As Kalmus points out, "A very important term which was originally used in systematics is 'race.' Nowadays, however, its use is avoided as far as possible in genetics. . . . The term used by modern geneticists to take the place of race is strain, which has a more precise meaning; it is applied to forms which differ from the commonly wild type by one or several precisely defined hereditary characters which usually breed true."[16] In the latest and most exhaustive dictionary of biology thus far published the term "race" is altogether omitted,[17] while in the most recent

---

[13] Cooley, Angell, and Carr, *Introductory Sociology*, p. 287. See Sorokin, "What Is a Social Class?" *Journal of Legal and Political Sociology*, IV (1946), 15–28.

[14] The same is true for most other areas of the world. See: Hutton, *Caste in India*; Beaglehole, "Race, Caste and Class," *Journal of the Polynesian Society*, LXII (1943), 1–11; Humphrey, "American Race and Caste," *Psychiatry*, IV (1941), 159–60; Montagu, "Race, Caste and Scientific Method," *Psychiatry*, IV (1941), 337–38; Dollard, *Caste and Class in a Southern Town*; Warner and Davis, "A Comparative Study of American Caste," in Thompson (ed.), *Race Relations and the Race Problem*, pp. 219–45; Davis, Gardner, and Gardner, *Deep South: A Social Anthropological Study of Caste and Class*; Pope, *The Kingdom Beyond Caste*.

[15] Humphrey, "American Race and Caste," *Psychiatry*, IV (1941), 159–60.

[16] Kalmus, *Genetics*, pp. 45–46.

[17] Abercombie, Hickman, and Johnson, *A Dictionary of Biology*.

authoritative work on evolution the author points out that such terms as " 'race,' 'variety,' and 'form' are used so loosely and in so many senses that it is advisable to avoid using them as infraspecific categories." [18]

Let us consider a little further what the meaning of this term "race," in the social sense, really is. In countries such as England, France, Germany, and Spain, in which class distinctions are well marked and there exist no significantly large ethnic groups other than the dominant national population, "race" prejudice is replaced by class prejudice. In fact, there is scarcely any difference between the two phenomena. Almost every condition encountered in the one is to be found in the other, even down to the imputed biological differences. In his beautiful novel, *Bread and Wine,* Ignazio Silone, writing of his native Abruzzi in Italy, describes the social identification of "class" with "race." He writes: "Don Paolo was surprised to observe the rôle that mustaches, beards, and hair still played in differentiating the professional class from the peasants and the landlords. He realized also why the various classes were indicated in dialect by the word 'race'—the 'race' of husbandmen, the 'race' of 'artists' (artisans), the 'race' of landowners. The son of a petty landowner who studies, and therefore inevitably becomes a state or municipal employee, promptly tries to obliterate the fact that he comes of the 'race' of husbandmen by brushing his hair in the style of his new station." [19]

The upper classes make much of "breeding," of "good family" or "birth" or "ancestry," and will not, generally, marry out of their "class" or "quality." [20] To marry out of one's class is to lose "caste," or status not only socially but also, it is considered, biologically, for such a person's children can belong only to the class and caste of the "inferior" parent. There are, of course, many exceptions, but this is the general rule. This rule tends to be more strictly applied to women

---

[18] Carter, *Animal Evolution*, p. 163. See also Calman, *The Classification of Animals*, p. 14. Also Appendix B, the present volume, p. 372; Dover, "The Classification of Man," *Current Science*, XXI (1952), 209–13.

[19] Silone, *Bread and Wine*, p. 151.

[20] For some pithy remarks on this subject see Hogben, "Race and Prejudice," in his *Dangerous Thoughts*, pp. 45–58. "There is of course a parochial distinction between *Rassenhygiene* and its sister cult in Britain. In Germany the Jew is the scapegoat. In Britain the entire working class is the menace" (p. 51). To the same effect see Tawney, *Equality*.

than to men. The upper-class male generally elevates the woman he chooses to marry to his own class; the lower-class male generally reduces his wife and children to his own class. In the Western world the biology and stratification of the classes are patrilineally determined; that is to say, they operate through, and in favor of, the male line. This is not the case where ethnic crossing is concerned, and it constitutes one of the few differences between the workings of class and "race" prejudice. Thus, for example, should an upper-class white male marry a Negroid female, the offspring will, in the United States at least, be relegated to the mother's caste, and not to that of the father.

The mechanism of this "caste" form of race prejudice is clearly seen at work in England. During the last two decades there has been an appreciable increase in the colored population of England, principally owing to the immigration of West Indians, and a concomitant appearance of "race prejudice" where formerly it was nonexistent. But as Banton[21] and others[22] have pointed out, the English form of "race" discrimination, is not really "race prejudice," but an expression of the desire to avoid losing caste in one's own group by behaving as an equal to those who are for one reason or another regarded as of lower status. Since "class" is largely determined by the people with whom one associates, and since a dark skin color, in England, is largely identified with subject peoples, association with persons of color detracts from one's social standing. Banton in his study found that by far the majority of Britons felt sympathetically towards colored people, but the problem of caste bothered them. In a recent study of colonial students in London, Carey found that London landladies preferred white to colored lodgers mainly because of their fears about what other people might think. One boardinghouse landlady remarked: "Of course, I don't take blacks; I'm sorry for the darkies, that I am, but I know what the neighbours would say: 'Look at Mrs. So-and-So! She really has come down in the world.' "[23]

This kind of discrimination must be distinguished from "race prejudice." It is not based on emotional or irrational prejudgments or

---

[21] Banton, "Beware of Strangers!" *The Listener*, 3 April 1958, pp. 565–67.

[22] Little, *Negroes in Britain;* Richmond, *The Colour Problem;* Banton, *White and Coloured;* Freedman (ed.), *A Minority in Britain;* Collins, *Coloured Minorities in Britain; Idem,* "The Status of Coloured People in Britain," *Phylon,* XVIII, (1957), 82–87.

[23] Carey, *Colonial Students.* See especially Patterson, *Dark Strangers.*

on hostility, but represents a response to social situations, defined by considerations of social status. There can be little doubt that elsewhere in the world such factors enter into much that is called "race prejudice."

In the United States Westie has shown that the occupational status of the Negro is a significant determinant of the response that whites make to a particular Negro.[24] And as Liston Pope has put it, "The mill worker, with nobody else to 'look down on,' regards himself as eminently superior to the Negro. The colored man represents his last outpost against social oblivion."[25] A study, by Dr. William T. Liu, mainly of Catholics who had emigrated to Tallahassee, Florida, from other regions, principally the North, revealed that moral values, though important, did not decisively determine these persons' attitudes toward segregation. Residential stability and subjective identification with the Southern community seem to have been the critical factors.[26]

Blumer draws attention to the fact that the collective process through which a group position is formed, vis-à-vis other groups, is a potent factor in the genesis of "race prejudice." "Race prejudice becomes entrenched and tenacious to the extent the prevailing social order is rooted in the sense of social position."[27] The process of group definition produces an abstract image of the subordinate groups, which spreads out far beyond the boundaries of contacts with individual members of such groups, and transcending any experience with them. The reaction or response to all members of such subordinate groups is not in terms of experience of them, but in terms of the abstract image of the group that has been built up of them, and into which they are made to fit.

Amongst the strongest supporters of the view that the upper classes are not only socially but biologically superior to the lower classes are those who have themselves recently migrated into the ranks of the upper classes from the ranks of the lower classes. Success in life is

[24] Westie, "Negro-White Status Differentials and Social Distance," *American Sociological Review*, XVII (1952), 550–58.

[25] Pope, *Millhands and Preachers*, p. 69.

[26] Liu, "The Community Reference System, Religiosity, and Race Attitudes," *Social Forces*, XXXIX (1961), 324–28.

[27] Blumer, "Race Prejudice as a Sense of Group Position," in Masuoka and Valien (eds.), *Race Relations*, pp. 217–27.

held to be not so much a matter of social opportunity as of biological quality. Such views are, of course, rationalizations, but once made they help to determine the attitudes not only of the upper but also of the lower classes. Indeed, as Polanyi has pointed out, the poorer classes of England a century ago were the detribalized, degraded natives of their time.[28] And, as Johnson has stated, the arguments used to justify the practice of child serfdom in England were identical with those used to justify the slave trade.[29]

It should be fairly evident that in societies in which there is an extreme division of men into classes whose interests are necessarily opposed and in which the means of earning a living, the economic system, is organized upon an unequal or extremely competitive basis, there will be abundant opportunities for class or "race" antagonisms. This is a matter with which we shall deal in the next chapter.

The point I wish to bring out here is that "race" prejudice is merely a special case of class prejudice, a prejudice that will be developed, under certain conditions, where different ethnic groups are thrown together in significant numbers.[30] In the absence of such conditions or in the absence of a variety of ethnic groups the prejudices of the upper classes against all members of the lower classes and their conduct toward the members of such classes will, in almost every respect, take the form which is usually associated with "race" prejudice. Wherever classes exist there exists class prejudice. In socially stratified class societies the shift from class prejudice to "race" prejudice is easily achieved and, in fact, amounts to little more than a change of names, for the "race" against which prejudice is now especially directed is but another class or caste, even though it may be regarded as something substantially different.

Race and class prejudices are simply particular kinds of the group phenomenon of which national prejudices, religious prejudices, sex

---

[28] Polanyi, *The Great Transformation*, p. 290.

[29] Johnson, "Race Relations and Social Change," in Thompson (ed.), *Race Relations and the Race Problem*, p. 274.

[30] For an account of the absence of "race" problems among ethnic groups of the same populations see Gillin, " 'Race' Relations without Conflict: A Guatemalan Town," *American Journal of Sociology*, LIII (1948), 337–43; Redfield, "Culture Contact without Conflict," *American Anthropologist*, XLI (1939), 514–17; Redfield, "Race and Class in Yucatan," in *Cooperation in Research*, pp. 511–32.

prejudices, and the like are other kinds. As MacCrone points out, "We must not think of race prejudices as if they were a unique kind of group or social attitude; instead we must think of them in their proper context as simply one of a class of group or cultural phenomena, all of which are dependent upon the same kind of conditions, display the same basic characteristics, and serve the same functions." [31]

In the case of the American Negro it is necessary to understand that the original difference in his status was one of caste, not of biology. It was only later that the allegedly biological differences were attached to the difference in caste. An African or American Negro would be enslaved by virtue of the fact that he was considered to belong to the infidel slave class, *not* biologically but socially. American Indians were not usually enslaved, because they had established themselves as a class that did not adapt itself to slavery. White men, however, could be bought and sold if they belonged to the class born to servitude, the lowest class. The status of the Negro could be recognized at once by the color of his skin, which was a great convenience, but nothing more than that. It was only afterward that the obvious physical differences were utilized to reinforce the strength of the arguments in favor of the necessity of continuing the depressed social status of the Negro.

Thus, in the case of peoples showing any physical differences which distinguished them from the dominant class or caste, the mechanism of exclusion works both ways: one may oppose such peoples on the ground of their social inferiority and one may oppose them on the ground of their biological inferiority, the physical differences being taken to signify the latter. One may then proceed to adopt the view that such peoples are socially inferior because they are physically or biologically inferior, and since the physical or biological difference is constant, the social difference will always remain so. In this way one may not only have one's cake but one may also cut it into thin slices and eat it too. Imperialism, itself a racist idea, extended this conception of human relations to all peoples.[32]

Looking back now upon the history of the nineteenth century, it seems fairly clear that the drive to find differences in the "races" of mankind grew out of, among other things, the general social climate of the day. A natural stratification of the "races" mirrored the social

---

[31] MacCrone, *Group Conflicts and Race Prejudice*, p. 7.
[32] Curtin, "The Origins of the 'White Man's Burden,'" *The Listener*, LXVI (1961), 412–15.

stratification of the classes, and in the light of the baleful doctrine of "the survival of the fittest" sanctioned and justified the exploitation and oppression of both.

Most authorities at the present time entertain no doubts as to the meaninglessness of the older anthropological conception of "race." They do not consider that any of the existing concepts of "race" correspond to any reality whatever; the general opinion is that these concepts are usually nothing more than poor substitutes for thought. But they do consider that the persistence of the term and the concept has been responsible for much confused thinking and, what is worse, has rendered possible much confused and confusing action resulting in the most tragic consequences for millions of human beings. "Race" has, indeed, become a fratricidal word.

> ... And what if all-avenging Providence,
> Strong and retributive, should make us know
> The meaning of our words, force us to feel
> The desolation and the agony
> Of our fierce doings?
>
> —S. T. COLERIDGE[33]

It is for these reasons, because the term, as it were, has been compromised, that a number of us, as biologists, have recently urged that the term "race" be altogether dropped from the vocabulary. If we do no more than indicate our demotion of the term, this in itself will serve as a contribution to clear thinking, precisely as the banishment of the term "instinct" from psychological thought forty years ago has had a most beneficial effect upon the development of the science of psychology. Not that there has been a loss of contact with what science means by "race," for many scientists are themselves far from clear as to what they mean when they use the term. On the other hand, many scientists who have concerned themselves with the problem have contributed to its confusion. "Verbal habits," remark Ogden and Richards, "overpower the sense of actuality even in the best of philosophers." And as Korzybski has stated, "because of the great semantic influence of the structure of language on the masses of mankind, leading, as it does, through lack of better understanding and *evaluation* to *speculation on terms,* it seems advisable to abandon completely terms which imply to the *many* the suggested elemental-

---

[33] From "Fears in Solitude," 1798.

ism, although these terms are used in a proper non-elementalistic way by the few." [34]

Huxley has suggested that "it would be highly desirable if we could banish the question-begging term 'race' from all discussions of human affairs and substitute the noncommittal phrase 'ethnic group.' That would be a first step toward rational consideration of the problem at issue." [35]

Since Huxley does not venture a definition of an "ethnic group," the definition I have already proposed may be repeated: An ethnic group represents one of a number of populations, which together comprise the species *Homo sapiens,* but individually maintain their differences, physical and cultural, by means of isolating mechanisms such as geographic and social barriers. These differences will vary as the power of the geographic and social barriers vary. Where these barriers are of low power, neighboring ethnic groups will intergrade or hybridize with one another. Where these barriers are of high power, such ethnic groups will tend to remain distinct from each other or replace each other geographically or ecologically.

From this definition or description of an ethnic group it will be seen that the problem of ethnic variation is in part a geographic problem involving the physical mobility of populations and the consequences resulting therefrom. Thus, the problem of ethnic variation falls definitely within the purview of the student of the social life of man.

One of the most important advantages of the term "ethnic group" [36] is that it eliminates all question-begging emphases on physical factors or differences and leaves that question completely open, while the emphasis is now shifted to the fact—though it is not restricted to it—that man is predominantly a cultural creature. The change in emphasis seems to me highly desirable. It does not exclude the consideration of the possible significance of physical characters, but it leaves the question of the latter open for further dispassionate analysis, omitting any suggestion that the physical factors are determined, fixed, or definable,

---

[34] Korzybski, *Science and Sanity,* p. 31.

[35] Huxley, "The Concept of Race," in *Man Stands Alone,* p. 126.

[36] The term "ethnic" is derived from the Greek ἔθνος, *ethnos,* meaning a number of people living together, a company, a body of men. In the *Iliad* Homer variously uses the word to mean a band of comrades, a tribe, a group. Pindar uses it in the sense of a family, tribe, nation, or people.

or that they are in any way connected with mental or cultural factors. This is not to replace one term by another, but constitutes a positive shift in emphasis based upon a fundamental difference in point of view. It is the point of view of the person who is desirous of taking a mature, responsible view of the words he uses and who is anxious to avoid the consequence of thinking in "fuzzy" terms.

If, then, we can eliminate the outmoded concept of "race" by presenting the advantages of the concept of "ethnic group," we shall have secured a real clarification and change in conceptual approach to a problem whose importance requires no emphasis here. The sociologist will then be able to proceed with the study of the problem of caste, intra- and intersocially, with the clear consciousness of the fact that, as far as he is concerned, the problem is entirely a social problem and that for him, at any rate, it has no biological relevance at all, but that, in so far as it is necessary for him to take cognizance of the biological evidence, the old concept of "race" has no more scientific justification for use in the field of human biology than it has in the field of human sociology. Since the matter of terminology is of great importance in the future development of clear thinking upon this subject, I shall consider in Appendix B the arguments for and against the phrase "ethnic group."

Were we to pay attention to the realities of the situation in the cultural reference, the term "race" would be entirely discarded and the term "caste" would be employed in its stead; while the term "race" would, in popular parlance, be replaced by the term "ethnic group" in the biologic or social context with reference to man.

7

Biological and Social Factors

THE PROBLEM of the origin and development of different physical types is part of the larger problem of discovering how we all come to be the way we are; that, too, is a social problem, and only arbitrarily and in a limited technical sense is it a biological problem. Man is outstandingly the one animal species in which "biological" development has, from the earliest times, been substantially influenced by the operation of social factors—and this, ever increasingly, continues to be the case. The biological development of man cannot be considered apart from his social development, for man is a domesticated, a self-domesticated, animal,[1] and domestication is a social or cultural process by means of which biological changes are produced in animals. Such changes, to some extent, represent the socially preferred expression of genetic rearrangements of characters common to the whole of mankind. The chief agencies in the production of such changes are social,

---

[1] Upon this important subject see the following: Hahn, *Die Haustiere;* Klatt, "Mendelismus, Domestikation und Kraniologie," *Archiv für Anthropologie,* N. S., XVIII (1921), 225–50; Friedenthal, "Die Sonderstellung des Menschen in der Natur," in *Wege zum Wissen,* VIII (1925); Fischer, "Rasse und Rassenentstehung beim Menschen," *Wege zum Wissen,* LXII (1927), 1–137; Laufer, "Methods in the Study of Domestications," *Scientific Monthly,* XXV (1927), 251–55; Herskovits, "Social Selection and the Formation of Human Types," *Human Biology,* I (1929), 250–62; Renard, *Life and Work in Prehistoric Times;* Boas, *The Mind of Primitive Man,* pp. 74–98; Boas (ed.), *General Anthropology,* p. 108; Fortuyn, "The Origin of Human Races," *Science,* XC (1939), 352–53; Montagu, "The Socio-Biology of Man," *Scientific Monthly,* L (1940), 483–90; Haldane, "The Argument from Animals to Men," in Montagu (ed.), *Culture and the Evolution of Man,* pp. 65–83; Washburn (ed.), *Social Life of Early Man;* Spuhler (ed.), *The Evolution of Man's Capacity for Culture.*

133

but the scientific study of such social agencies has only just begun. Thus far, the emphasis has for the most part been upon the biological aspect of such changes, while there has been an almost complete failure to recognize their socially induced origin.[2]

The biological aspects of the subject are important, but only in so far as they render possible an understanding of the physiological and genetic mechanisms underlying the actual process of change. R. A. Fisher has remarked: "While genetic knowledge is essential for the clarity it introduces into the subject, the causes of the evolutionary changes in progress can only be resolved by an appeal to sociological, and even historical facts. These should at least be sufficiently available to reveal the more powerful agencies at work in the modification of mankind." [3] When the mechanism of these physiological and genetic changes is understood, it is then fully realized that "race" is a term which refers to a process representing a series of genetically active temporary conditions, always in process of change. It then becomes clear that the stage at which one catches this process depends upon the segment of time which one arbitrarily delimits from the space-time continuum in which the process is occurring. Neither "races" of men nor "races" of lower animals are immutable; they seem to become so, but then only conceptually, when an anthropologist or a taxonomist follows the traditional practice of pinning his specimens down for study and classification. It is erroneous to conceive of any animal group, particularly human groups, as static and immutable. It is an error to do so in the case of man in particular, because the facts of prehistory and those of more recent times indicate that new varieties of man have been and are being synthesized very rapidly. In this process social factors play an important role. Upon recognizing this fact we must further recognize that in our own society the problem of "race" is essentially a problem of caste and class relations and that it is, of course, fundamentally a social problem.

In our own society, explanations of the "race" problem have been offered in terms of economic forces, social stratification, biological differences, or all three. Such explanations have never been altogether convincing. The causes motivating human behavior are complex, and human behavior is hardly ever to be explained in terms of single proc-

---

[2] Montagu, op. cit.; Washburn, op. cit.
[3] Fisher, The Genetical Theory of Natural Selection, p. 174.

esses, which in themselves are complicated enough, such as the economic, the biological, or the purely sociological. In all cases, in order to understand the nature of any event it is necessary to discover and to relate all the conditions entering into its production. In other words, what is required is a specification of all the necessary conditions which together form the sufficient cause of the event into whose nature we are inquiring.

While it may be true, for instance, that certain conditions arising out of our present economic organization of society are responsible for maintaining and exacerbating the "problem of race," it is by no means certain that a reorganization of our economic system would automatically result in a solution of that problem, although it is probable that it would help. It is quite conceivable that "race" problems may exist under ideal economic conditions. These problems, indeed, are far from simple, and it is therefore necessary to approach them by the use of such methods as are calculated to clarify them. It would obviously be an egregious error to approach the study of "race" from the standpoint of the economic determinant alone, precisely as it would be an error to approach the study from the viewpoint solely of biology or of sociology.

This brings us to what I consider to be an extremely important methodological aspect of the whole problem. It is the matter of the person who discusses the subject of "race." Hitherto, practically anyone with the ability to develop a hoarse throat, with arrogance in place of erudition, has been able to set himself up as an authority on "race." We need only recall the names of Gobineau, Stoddard, Houston Stewart Chamberlain, Madison Grant, Adolf Hitler, and their like,[4] to discover that the principal equipment necessary to qualify one as an authority on "race" consists in a well-rounded ignorance, a considerable amount of viciousness, and an unshakable confidence. To listen to such "tangled oracles which ignorantly guide" is to suffer a positive increase in one's ignorance. With the passing of the above-mentioned individuals the nuisance is not abated, for there are always others who are ready to take their place.[5] In the universe of science the situation, though incomparably better, is not by any means—as we have already seen—all that could be desired. Until very recently

---

[4] See Lowenthal and Guterman, *Prophets of Deceit.*

[5] Cook, *The Segregationists;* Epstein and Forster, *The Troublemakers.*

little progress had been made in the scientific study of "race." This had been chiefly due to the fact that the subject had been dealt with in a piecemeal manner and by specialists with an insufficient grasp of the complexities of the subject. Thus, psychologists failed to take into account the sociological and biological factors (if only to dismiss the latter as of no significance); while sociologists have in the past failed to give adequate consideration to the psychological and anthropological factors. Finally, and worst of all, the physical anthropologists restricted their studies almost entirely to the morphological aspects of the subject. The complexity of the problem is today recognized by most students, and thanks to the increasing volume and quality of their work, we today see that problem much more clearly than we did a decade ago. Nevertheless, we still need more students who will combine the best qualities of the psychologist, the sociologist, the biologist, and both the cultural and physical anthropologist.[6]

Racism as an ideological phenomenon has its origins and being in social and political forces. Its motivations are never the discovery of what *is,* of the facts, but of what, according to its proponents, ought to be. And what ought to be is determined by the political and social necessities of the moment. These will vary at different times and in different places, but in general these necessities are interpreted to mean that the differences which characterize various "races" determine a hierarchy of values. These values are always distinguished in terms of "superiority" and "inferiority." The recognition of these values then determines the manner in which the "superior" must conduct themselves in relation to the "inferior," and vice versa. The racist is not interested in the scientific facts, except to the extent to which, in some special form, they may serve his purposes. Because he is not interested in the facts, but in an ideology, it is quite impossible to demonstrate the fallacy of his views to the racist. Any attempt to reason with racists on the basis of the facts is rather more than a

---

[6] For an analysis of the problem of prejudice and discrimination, and a program of investigation and strategy, see MacIver, *The More Perfect Union;* also, Young, "Techniques of Race Relations," *Proceedings of the American Philosophical Society,* XCI (1947), 150–61; Allport, "Controlling Group Prejudice," *Annals, American Academy of Political and Social Science,* CCXVIV (1946), 1–240; *Idem, The Nature of Prejudice* and *Personality and the Social Encounter;* Gittler (ed.), *Understanding Minority Groups;* Mason, *An Essay on Racial Tension;* Rose (ed.), *Race Prejudice and Discrimination.*

waste of time. Anyone who has had experience of these persons will know how unspeakably vicious they can be. The whole history of racism testifies to that fact. But while racists can be ignored, racism cannot.

As Manning Nash has pointed out, the skeletal form of any racial ideology may be stated in six propositions, as (1) The attempt to flout natural law by man-made edicts about race relations, (2) The races differ in their capacities to embrace the complexities of civilization, (3) The level of cultural achievement of races indicates their relative innate capacities, (4) Left on their own, inferior races tear down a cultural heritage, (5) The fight against racial equality is the fight for truth in the interests of all mankind, and (6) Those who favor equality are undesirables.[7]

The scientist is put in the position of having to make available the facts, for the benefit of those who may wish to judge the evidence for themselves. But, again, it needs to be said that the rights of man are not dependent upon the facts of science or the assertions of racists or of any other kind of statement. Those rights rest squarely and firmly upon an ethical principle, the principle that by virtue of a man's humanity he has the right to the fullest development of his potentialities, the right to fulfill himself. No man or group has the right to stand in the way of another's development. This is an evil. It is a social evil, and it is only by social means that it will ever be corrected.

"Race," it should always be remembered is a human grouping which is culturally defined in a given society. "Race prejudice" is a system of reciprocal relations of stereotyping, discrimination, and segregation existing between human groupings which are considered as "races." [8]

Since, as I have already pointed out, facts do not speak for themselves, but are at the mercy of whoever chooses to give them a meaning, it is obviously of the first importance that the meaning which they shall receive be given them by those who have made themselves thoroughly acquainted with those facts. As Henry A. Wallace has said: "For the combating of 'racism' before it sinks its poison

---

[7] Nash, "Race and the Ideology of Race," *Current Anthropology,* III (1962), 285–88; Zanden, "The Ideology of White Supremacy," *Journal of the History of Ideas,* XX (1959), 385–402.

[8] Van Den Berghe, "The Dynamics of Racial Prejudice: An Ideal-Type Dichotomy," *Social Forces,* XXXVII (1958), 138–41.

fangs deep in our body politic, the scientist has both a special motive and a special responsibility. His motive comes from the fact that when personal liberty disappears scientific liberty also disappears. His responsibility comes from the fact that only he can give the people the truth. Only he can clean out the falsities which have been masquerading under the name of science in our colleges, our high schools and our public prints. Only he can show how groundless are the claims that one race, one nation, or one class has any God-given right to rule." [9]

In the modern world, racial problems, as I have already said, are essentially social problems. But no student of human society can ever hope to assist in the solution of these problems without acquiring an adequate understanding of what the biologist, the psychologist, and the psychoanalyst can alone supply, namely, an appreciation of the nature of the fundamental facts of physical and mental development. Obviously, what we need is more human ecologists, liaison officers between the sciences of man. [10]

THE ECONOMIC FACTOR AND THE FACTOR
OF SOCIAL STRATIFICATION

Our society is a socially stratified one, and social stratification in our society is determined principally by the manner in which our society is economically structured. It is usually possible to migrate from one social stratum or class to another only by means of the economic process. By the acquisition of economic power one rises in the social hierarchy; by the loss of economic power one falls. Groups and persons who are denied effective participation in the economic process clearly cannot rise above the lower social strata, while the only way to exclude groups and persons who have not been denied an effective participation in the economic process from rising and maintaining

[9] Wallace, *The Genetic Basis for Democracy*, p. 7. See also Wallace, "Racial Theories and the Genetic Basis for Democracy," *Science*, LXXXIX (1939), 140–43.

[10] Montagu, "A Cursory Examination of the Relations between Physical and Social Anthropology," *American Journal of Physical Anthropology*, XXVI (1940), 41–61; Montagu, "Physical Anthropology and Anatomy," *American Journal of Physical Anthropology*, XXVIII (1941), 261–71; Gillin (ed.), *For a Science of Social Man;* Montagu, *Man in Process;* Montagu, *The Biosocial Nature of Man.*

their places socially is to erect barriers against them, to deprive them, in various ways, of their economic rights. We need hardly go farther back than our own time for the evidence with which to prove the truth of this statement. In those parts of Europe which were under Nazi domination in World War II such barriers were deliberately created in the form of a mythological "racial" dogma which was imposed upon whole peoples—a dogma which, in operation as a barrier, deprived all those who were not mythical "Aryans" of the right to earn a living and to keep even the little which they had. No more telling or painful example than this could be cited of the blatant economic motivation underlying the creation and practice of this mythology which leads so effectively to the social and economic disfranchisement of helpless groups.

In the United States there are several ready examples which may be cited as illustrating the relationship between the economic factor and the presence of racial barriers. Along the Pacific coast, where the Japanese and Chinese constituted an appreciable competitive group, there was considerable "race" prejudice against them. With the increase in the number of Filipinos entering the United States within recent years, despite the heroic resistance of their compatriots against the Japanese in the Philippines during World War II and their loyalty to the United States, racial prejudices were rapidly transferred to them.[11] Along the Atlantic coast, where the numbers of these ethnic groups are comparatively small and they cannot possibly be conceived to constitute economic competitors, there has been relatively little prejudice against them, apart from that which was generated by war conditions. Similarly, in California, when American Indians were

---

[11] "Unwanted Heroes," *New Republic,* CVI (1942), 655; McWilliams, *Brothers under the Skin.* It is sad to have to record the fact that in the third week of September, 1944, the Fourth Filipino Inter-Community convention held at New City, California, adopted as two of its objectives "the abolition of discriminatory legislation against Filipinos" and "permanent post-war exile of all Japanese from California" (reported in the *Pacific Citizen,* Salt Lake City, Utah, September 23, 1944, 3–4). The Filipinos apparently regarded the Japanese as serious economic competitors, and desired to eliminate their "competition" by this means. In a period of high feeling there was also the motive of jumping on the bandwagon of the most vocal California "patriots." In addition we may perceive here the mechanism of response to frustrations of low status position in the scapegoating of another (even if temporarily) low status group. See Miner, *Timbuctoo,* p. 254.

numerous there was a great deal of prejudice against them. In the Middle West, where Indians are relatively few and under "control," there is little prejudice against them. In the East a trace of Indian ancestry has some prestige value, for Indians are so rare that they are almost worth their weight in genes. In areas such as the South, where the social status of the Negro is changing and he emerges as an economic competitor, the prejudices against the large population of Negroes constitute a serious problem. In the North, where the economic situation is much better, the Negro has always enjoyed a much greater degree of social and economic freedom, limited as that social and economic freedom has always been. In England, when there were few Negroes or Indians, there was little active prejudice against these peoples. In localities, however, in which there exists a concentration of such a distinct ethnic group the usual racial prejudices are encountered.[12] In the days when Englishmen went out to the "colonies," they soon learned that the native peoples "threatened" their own interests and those of their own people, and thus frequently developed the usual "racial" prejudices. Today, with the immigration into England of thousands of colored people Englishmen no longer have to go abroad to develop "race prejudice." [13]

Sir Arthur Richmond, who as a young man went out to serve under Lord Milner in South Africa in 1901, recounts how without being aware of it "race" prejudice crept up on him. He writes, "Before the Boer war no Kaffir had been allowed to walk on the side-walk in a town. He had to walk in the roadway. I had not particularly noticed that they always, women as well as men, walked in the middle of the road when, one day, a Kaffir came towards me striding along the side-walk of the principal street in Pretoria. Instantly I felt a surge of indignation. I had not before been conscious of any colour prejudice; I hardly knew of the rule forbidding the use of the side-walk to black men, yet subtly and unconsciously I had been infected with the accepted view that blacks must not be allowed any kind of equality with whites. I was horrified by my automatic reaction, and its immediate effect was to make me feel intense sympathy for the black man and to realize how conscious I had to be of the difficulties

---

[12] Little, *Negroes in Britain;* Banton, *White and Coloured;* Richmond, "Racial Relations in England," *Midwest Journal,* III (1951), 1–13; Richmond, *The Colour Problem*; Patterson, *Dark Strangers.*
[13] See pp. 126–27 ante.

inherent in the relationship between the black man and the white." [14]

Without in the least underestimating the important role which economic factors play in the creation of "race" prejudice in Western society generally, it may be observed that there is no absolutely necessary or sufficient relationship between economic conditions and "racial" problems. Just as it is possible to conceive of difficult racial problems existing under ideal economic conditions, so it is quite possible to conceive of perfect ethnic relations and mutual appreciation under the most difficult economic conditions.

So far as the individual is concerned, "race" prejudice is by no means a necessary concomitant of economic anxieties. For example, Bettelheim and Janowitz in a study of a group of World War II veterans found that there were quite a number who, in spite of a doubtful economic future, were sufficiently well integrated to be able to control any hostilities they may have had without the need to discharge them upon some scapegoat. [15] These were men who were secure in their personalities, who had been given emotional security in their childhood. Fundamentally, the problem is one of personality structure—and whatever it is that may contribute to that structure is an essential part of the problem; it is of no use dealing with the one without the other. Economic conditions may, of course, produce substantive changes in the personality. When children are brought up in families in which the economic conditions are satisfactory, the children are likely to be emotionally more secure than in families in which the economic conditions have been poor. But whatever the economic conditions in the family, if the child is made to feel secure, he will not need to indulge in irrational discharges of hostility against the members of an outgroup. The problem, then, is fundamentally not one of economics, though improving economic conditions will help. The problem is really one of emotional integration and security, a problem of parent-child relationships, a problem of human relations. [16]

The fact is that in our own society the regrettable discovery has been made that by utilizing the physical and cultural differences which exist between groups and individuals, it is a relatively simple

[14] Richmond, "Memories of South Africa," *The Listener*, LX (1958), 736–39.
[15] Bettelheim and Janowitz, *Dynamics of Prejudice*, pp. 169–86.
[16] Clark, *Prejudice and Your Child;* Montagu, *On Being Human;* Montagu, *The Direction of Human Development;* Davidson, *Personality and Economic Background.*

matter to disguise the motives and evade the consequences of one's own conduct by attributing existing and potential evils to the conduct of some other group or to utilize those differences for the most ignoble political purposes. In this way, by setting groups of people against one another, attention is diverted from the real sources of evil. The discovery is, in fact, an old one. As a device for moving people it is extremely well grounded in that it caters to a deep-seated tendency which many persons have acquired during their early conditioning to find a scapegoat outside themselves upon which to blame their troubles or release their aggressive, frustrated feelings. Tertullian, for example, in pagan Rome was fully aware of the fact that the persecution of the Christian minority was merely being used as a device to sidetrack the attention of the people from the real causes of corruption within the Roman state. Says Tertullian, "If the Tiber rose to the walls of the city, if the inundation of the Nile failed to give the fields enough water, if the heavens did not send rain, if an earthquake occurred, if famine threatened, if pestilence raged, the cry resounded: 'Throw the Christians to the lions!' " In this manner the Roman populace was provided, as later peoples have been, with a socially sanctioned outlet for their pent-up feelings. And that is the important point to grasp about the nature of "race" prejudice, namely, that it is a socially sanctioned and socially learned attitude. It is a ready-made and culturally accepted outlet for various forms of hostility and feelings of frustration.

In the South, "race" hatred has long been kept alive and fanned to white heat at the instigation of unscrupulous industrialists and politicians, ever ready to capitalize on baseless popular superstitions, prejudices, and beliefs, because there is no issue more useful than "race" as a political platform for securing votes. Tell the poor whites, and others not so poor, that their status is due to, and continually threatened by, the competition of the Negroes, and they will vote for anything to which such an issue is tied in promised favor of themselves.[17]

---

[17] "There are millions of white and black men in the South, and their children, on blighted farms and in the slums, who live a more bearable life because of what the Roosevelt administration made possible. But these are the poor and the ignorant, and their race hate, kept alive for years just as Governor Dixon and the Alabama capitalists are keeping it alive now, makes them vulnerable. Of these millions of people whom the New Deal aided, the Negroes cannot

The granting of statehood to the territories of Alaska and Hawaii had been opposed and blocked since 1916, largely by Southern Democrats who feared that the potentially incoming four Senate votes would bring about the advancement of civil rights. These territories are now full states within the Union. The fears of the Southern Democrats appear to have been groundless.

The case is exactly the same in the Union of South Africa, where race discrimination is part of the order of things and a comparatively small white population[18] is attempting to protect its economic and social privileges against any incursions which might be made upon it by the large colored and Asiatic population, immigrants, and Jews. The percentage representation of the various groups of the South African population is as follows: Africans, 76.7; Europeans, 20.7; and Asiatics, 2.5. The Jews form only 4.75 percent of the total population, and they have from the first proved themselves loyal and able citizens of the Union. What, then, is the reason for the prejudice against the Jews? Is it the fear of economic competition? In view of their small representation this cannot be the whole story. The fact, again, is that, while they themselves do not constitute an economic problem, the prejudice against them is utilized and, indeed, inspired by politicians and other interested parties for economic purposes. In a sympathetic and penetrating study of the Union, Lewis Sowden returns an answer to the question "Why prejudice against the Jews?" He writes: "Simply this, that South Africa, like most other countries, has its Jewish problem kept alive by politicians for purposes of personal or party aggrandisement. The Nationalists used it in 1930

---

vote; most of the whites who can have been poisoned by the propaganda of the reactionaries into a belief that the President and Mrs. Roosevelt are trying to wipe out all racial barriers under the war emergency; the Dixons are now in the saddle; they seem to be able to foist on the disfranchised masses anything they want to; and once more the white man's fear of the Negro has made it possible. It is no mystery why the South's congressmen, elected by a small and privileged proportion of its population fight so hard to defeat an anti-poll-tax bill; and it is no mystery, come to think of it, why reactionary Northern members, their blood brothers, by one subterfuge and another let them get away with it." Sancton, "Trouble in Dixie," *New Republic,* CVIII (1943), 51.

[18] The composition of the population of South Africa is as follows: African Negroes, 9,700,000; half-castes and other colored, 1,400,000; Asiatics, 450,000; and Europeans, 3,011,000.

to strengthen their hold on the country and to embarrass General Smuts's opposition. Their Quota Act [aimed against the Jews] had the full support of their own people and many sympathisers among the other parties. General Smuts's men could not effectively oppose it for fear of being accused as 'pro-Jewish,' fatal, of course, for any politician." [19]

In May, 1948, the Nationalist Party of Dr. Malan was returned to power in South Africa on a straight racist ticket. "The election was mainly fought on the propaganda slogan: 'Vote for a White South Africa.' All the emphasis was on the 'Black Menace.' " [20]

At a conference of Protestant theologians held early in 1954 in South Africa the question of apartheid as a policy of permanent political separation of Negroes and whites was discussed. Is apartheid untrue to the teachings of Christ? The South African Anglican bishops replied, "No." The leaders of the Dutch Reformed Church, whose members have vast material and political interests at stake, answered that cooperation between Negroes and whites was sinful. Equal rights for all men, it was held, is a perversion of true Christian doctrine. "It is a misinterpretation of Scripture and therefore a defiance of the will of God."

"We know" stated these Reformed theologians, "God the Creator in Scripture as Hammabdil, as the Maker of Separations. To create a cosmos God separated things; light from darkness,[21] waters above the firmament, dry land from the sea. From the very beginning it was the intention of the Lord that mankind should live in separate nations. In his awful self-conceit man wished to frustrate this intention. . . . Therefore attempts at unification, the equalitarian idea, and a revival of the Babylonian spirit." [22]

---

[19] Sowden, *The Union of South Africa*, p. 216. See also Burger, *The Black Man's Burden;* Russell, *Colour, Race and Empire;* Gibbs, *Twilight in South Africa;* Adamastor, *White Man Boss;* Sachs, *Black Anger;* "South Africa," *Time,* LIX (1952), 32–38; "America and the Challenge of Africa," *Saturday Review,* XXXVI (1953), 9–29; Van Rensburg, *Guilty Land: The History of Apartheid;* Horrell, *A Survey of Race Relations in South Africa;* Phillips, *The Tragedy of Apartheid;* Ritner, *The Death of Africa;* Lowenstein, *Brutal Mandate;* Kuper, Watts, and Davies, *Durban: A Study in Racial Ecology.*

[20] Robertson, "Racism Comes to Power in South Africa," *Commentary,* VI (1948), 428.

[21] "Light from darkness," of course, means "white from black."

[22] *Round Table Magazine,* April, 1954.

A year prior to this meeting of theologians Prime Minister Malan declared that "the color question is the greatest and most urgent matter on which the election must hinge," and in April, 1953, Malan's Nationalist party received an overwhelming majority at the polls.[23]

In South Africa there is a serious poor white land problem. Sachs states that "About a quarter of the Afrikaner farmers do not own the land they work and there has set in among them the kind of spiritual degeneration described in Erskine Caldwell's *Tobacco Road*. Hitlerism gave them a new hope, as it did to the *'Lumpen'* in the Berlin tenement houses. The slogan, 'The Jews are our misfortune,' proved an acceptable and satisfyingly simple explanation of their misery and want." [24]

The outcome of racism in South Africa has been tragically stated by Professor P. V. Pistorius of the University of Pretoria: "We see our doom inevitably approaching, but we are powerless to avert it. And it is a doom of our own making. . . . He who creates a tribal god will perish by the tribal gods of others. He who worships his own group and regards even injustice as good if it is thought to be in the interest of his group, will perish by the injustices perpetrated by other groups." [25]

In a study of race relations between Negroes and whites in Liverpool, England, Richmond has shown that under conditions of economic stress, the coincidence of the three factors, insecurity, visibility, and stereotype, will help to produce a predominating attitude of prejudice and hostility among the members of the "in-group" toward the members of the "out-group." The intensity of expression of this attitude will vary according to any changes in one or other of the three predisposing factors. The more highly visible the "out-group" the more derogatory are the stereotypes, or the greater the degree of insecurity felt among the members of the "in-group," the greater will be the tension.[26]

It should be fairly evident that "race" prejudice is easily generated

---

[23] Z. K. Matthews, "The Black Man's Outlook," *Saturday Review*, XXXVI (May 2, 1953), 13–14, 51–52.

[24] Sachs, "South Africa: Life on a Volcano," *Commentary*, IX (1950), 536. For a full account of race problems in South Africa see Hellman and Abra-

[25] Quoted in Paton, *Church and Race in South Africa*.

[25] Quoted in Paton, *Church and Race in South Africa*.

[26] Richmond, "Economic Insecurity and Stereotypes as Factors in Colour Prejudice," *Sociological Review*, XLII (1950), 147–70.

in the societies of the Western world, because those societies are socially and economically so structured as to be continually productive of frustrations in the individual, from childhood on; these, in turn, produce an aggressiveness, a hostility, for which the individual must find expression in some way. But the aggressiveness for which the individual must secure release is not entirely produced by economic factors. It should also be clear that the frustrative situations called into being by economic and social factors, while producing some aggressiveness in the individual, do not in themselves and need not necessarily lead to "race" prejudice. That the aggressiveness produced by such factors may lead to "race" prejudice is largely to be explained by the fact that "race" prejudice constitutes a socially sanctioned and encouraged or socially directed means of releasing aggressiveness. The aggressiveness may in part be produced by socioeconomic factors, but the form of the response which that aggressiveness takes is not necessarily linked with such factors. Alternative responses are available, but "race" prejudice is among the easiest and the psychologically most satisfying.

Merton has effectively described the frustrative situation which exists in Western societies. He writes: "It is only when a system of cultural values extols, virtually above all else, certain *common* symbols of success *for the population at large,* while its social structure rigorously restricts or completely eliminates access to approved modes of acquiring these symbols *for a considerable part of the same population,* that antisocial behavior ensues on a considerable scale. In other words, our egalitarian ideology denies by implication the existence of noncompeting groups and individuals in the pursuit of pecuniary success. The same body of success-symbols is held to be desirable for all. These goals are held to *transcend class lines,* not to be bound by them, yet the actual social organization is such that there exist class differentials in the accessibility of these *common* success-symbols. Frustration and thwarted aspiration lead to the search for avenues of escape from a culturally induced intolerable situation; or unrelieved ambition may eventuate in illicit attempts to acquire the dominant values. The American stress on pecuniary success and ambitiousness for all thus invites exaggerated anxieties, hostilities, neuroses and antisocial behavior." [27]

---

[27] Merton, "Social Structure and Anomie," *American Sociological Review,* III (1938), 680. See also McDill, "Anomie, Authoritarianism, Prejudice, and Socio-

The avenue of escape from such frustrative conditions is almost always the same, through aggressiveness. The object to which that aggressiveness may attach itself is culturally determined by what is rendered culturally available.[28] "Race, from an objective point of view, represents a cultural misunderstanding of certain facts, but from the point of view of the psyche of the person (which is far from objective), it presents a most satisfactory solution of a particular problem, affording, as it does, both a convenient and a suitable release object for aggressiveness. It should, however, be clearly understood that the misunderstanding is psychological or cultural in origin, not economic. The conception of "race" is a psychological or cultural artifact and does not in itself lead to "race" prejudice. What leads to "race" prejudice is the cultural manipulation of those psychophysical energies which, in most persons, overtly find expression in some form of aggressiveness, no matter what the underlying motivation of that manipulation may be. Economic factors represent but one group of conditions—and these are of the greatest importance—by means of which such aggressiveness may be called forth under conditions and in situations in which it may be easily attached to "race." Economic factors, in Western society, are certainly among the most important of the factors leading to situations in which "race" prejudice may be caused to develop. But their dependence upon cultural factors for the direction they can be made to give to individual aggressiveness is proved by the fact that the aggressiveness arising under those same economic conditions can also be directed toward the production of good-fellowship and mutual aid between different ethnic and social groups. Such fellowship and cooperation between different groups have been repeatedly witnessed in times of war, when, for example, an alien nation has become the socially sanctioned release-object for one's aggressiveness. In peacetime the repair of some natural disaster, affecting the lives of all, frequently produces the same effect, by providing a wholesome outlet for such aggressiveness. As Freud remarked in this connection, "It is one of the few noble and gratifying spectacles that men can offer, when in the face of an elemental catastrophe they awake from their muddle and confusion, forget all their internal

---

Economic Status: An Attempt at Clarification," *Social Forces*, XXXIX (1961), 239–45.

[28] For a development of the frustration-aggression hypothesis, see Dollard *et al.*, *Frustration and Aggression*.

difficulties and animosities, and remember the great common task, the preservation of mankind against the supremacy of nature." [29] The attack upon some social problem requiring solution is in every way a far more satisfactory outlet for aggression than an attack upon other human beings. Clearly, then, it is what is culturally offered as the most suitable object for the release of these aggressive tendencies that is the primarily important fact, the economic factor is only of secondary importance. As Dollard has put it, "Race prejudice seems, then, but a footnote to the wider consideration of the circumstances under which aggression may be expressed within a society." [30] It is only under special kinds of conditions that worry, fear, and insecurity may be made to add up to "race" prejudice. Economic conditions are culturally utilizable, for good or for evil purposes, as each culture, or segment thereof, sees fit. If in some cultures the aggressiveness which arises under such conditions is made to discharge itself in hostile behavior toward some group, that can hardly be said to be due to economic conditions, but must clearly be held to be due to those factors which render possible the cultural manipulation of the situation to which such conditions give rise. In short, economic factors may provide some of the conditions in which "race" hostility may be generated but, unless those conditions are directed into channels leading to "race" hostility, there will be no "race" hostility, and the aggressiveness which must be released will have to find some other outlet.

Under prosperous economic conditions, when the individual's feeling of security is at an optimum level, emotions are not apt to be aroused as easily in the form of anxiety as they are under conditions productive of anxiety.

The history of prejudice against the Japanese in California affords an excellent case study of the complexity of the factors involved. Here it would be an easy matter for the economic determinist to show that economic factors are chiefly responsible for that prejudice, but he would not be entirely correct. A study of the history of the prejudice against the Japanese in California proves that a large number of independent factors are involved.

In the first place, Japanese immigration into California unfortu-

[29] Freud, *The Future of an Illusion*, p. 27.
[30] Dollard, "Hostility and Fear in Social Life," *Social Forces*, XVII (1938), 15–26.

nately coincided with the rise of Japan as a great power with territorial ambitions, hence Japanese immigrants came to be regarded as "the spearhead of Japanese invasion." Corrupt politicians, anxious to divert public attention from their own malpractices, and newspapers, supporting the latter or for their own particular purposes, have continually emphasized the danger that California might develop a "race problem" even worse than the color problem in the South. The continual emphasis on the inevitability of war with Japan, the fact that the Japanese present perceptible physical and cultural differences, their hard-won, but warmly resented, expansion into fields of commerce in which they have become "competitors" where whites formerly held the field exclusively, are important factors, among others, which together have been responsible for the development of "race" prejudice against the Japanese in California.[31]

The aggressive intentions of the Japanese government and fear of the development of another "color problem," two issues almost daily drummed into the ears of Californians, would alone have been sufficient to produce an acute case of "race" prejudice. Add to these the other factors already mentioned, and many others not mentioned, and it becomes clear that any explanation in terms of a single factor does violence to the facts.

Many Californians disliked the Japanese, not because they constituted an economic threat but because they had been taught to believe that the Japanese were opposed to all that good Californians and good Americans stood for. This belief made it possible for the federal government to avail itself of racial discrimination as an instrument of national policy following the attack on Pearl Harbor. In the spring of 1942 approximately 110,000 Japanese and Japanese-Americans were forcibly and illegally evacuated from the area of the Western Defense Command, and interned in concentration camps.[32] This, in spite of

---

[31] For an able analysis of the problem in California see McWilliams, *Brothers under the Skin*, pp. 147–75, and the same author's *Prejudice—the Japanese-Americans: Symbol of Racial Intolerance*.

[32] For an objective account of conditions in these camps as experienced by an internee see Okubo, *Citizen 13660*. The detailed story of the Japanese-American evacuation is authoritatively told in Grodzins' *Americans Betrayed*. The socio-economic consequences are dealt with by Bloom and Riemer in their book *Removal and Return;* the social and psychological consequences by Thomas and Nishimoto, *The Spoilage,* and Leighton, *The Governing of Men.*

the fact that to this date not one single act of espionage or sabotage has been traced to any person of Japanese descent either in Hawaii or on the mainland.[33] In spite of this fully established fact, attested by such persons as Secretary of War Henry L. Stimson, Chief of the Federal Bureau of Investigation J. Edgar Hoover, and others, a public opinion survey conducted in 1946 revealed that two-thirds of the American public believed Japanese-Americans had been guilty of such acts.[34]

Following the conclusion of World War II some Californians violently opposed the return of loyal American citizens of Japanese ancestry to their former homes in California. Scheming politicians declared that were they permitted to do so every Japanese seen on the streets would be killed, thus artfully inciting the public to riot and murder. What were the motives of these politicians? Obviously, what they have always been: to keep the "race" issue alive so that they might fully exploit it for their own and their friends' economic advantage.

The California Alien Land Law which rendered Japanese-Americans ineligible to own agricultural land and the California law barring Japanese from the fishing industry were clearly economically motivated, even though both were patently unconstitutional and in direct violation of the Fourteenth Amendment, and in 1950 were so declared by the Supreme Court of California.

The details may vary where the members of different groups are involved and in different regions, but the general pattern of racism is the same wherever found and under whatever high-sounding name

---

[33] In November, 1946, the Privy Council of the government of England, the British Empire's highest court of appeals, upheld Canadian legislation forcing the deportation of citizens and resident aliens of Japanese ancestry. In short, the representatives of the British Empire ruled that a person's citizenship in one of its dominions may be revoked and that person exiled for no other reason than "race." Against this may be set the achievement of the voters of Saskatchewan, Canada, who, on May 1, 1947, made it a punishable offense by law for anyone to infringe the right of any person "to obtain and retain employment; engage in business; own and occupy property; have access to public places, hotels, theatres, restaurants; to membership in professional and trade organizations; education and enrollment in schools and universities." Saskatchewan is the only Canadian province which has a Cooperative Commonwealth Federation government.

[34] "Survey of the National Opinion Research Center of the University of Denver," *Pacific Citizen*, XXI (August 31, 1946), 3.

it may be disguised. Not one factor, but a complex of factors, is generally involved. Nevertheless, when this has been said and all the necessary conditions entering into the cause of "race" prejudice have been specified, it remains certain that one of the most important factors involved in those conditions is the economic factor. Our economic system, with all the frictions, frustrations, misery, and war which it brings, is a basic cause of racism and "race" situations. These, together, supply the motivation and a good deal of the aggressiveness expressed in "race" prejudice. "Race" prejudice is a socially sanctioned and socially channelized means of relieving aggressive tensions, because in our society there exist powerful groups of men who believe that in their own interest and in order to maintain their power or increase it they must maintain divisions between men. It is the domestic application of the formula "Divide and rule." What more simple than to produce such divisions between members of different ethnic groups within our society? They are "aliens," "foreigners," "the white man's burden," "the rising tide of color," "the yellow peril," "niggers," "the international Jew," "wops," "Greeks," "the lesser breeds without the law," and so on. In an economic organization of society which is always characterized by the presence of one crisis or another, with its attendant unemployment in the industries involved, the aggrieved part of the population is easily led to believe that if there were fewer people to be employed there would be employment and adequate wages for all. "Race" antagonism under such conditions is easily generated.

As Reuter has put it, "In the human as in the subhuman realm, the geographic distribution, the physical differences, the varying modes of life, and the mental traits and characteristics are, in large measure, the impersonally determined end results of the competitive struggle to live. Men live where they can secure the means to life, and they develop the physical, mental, and social characters that enable them to live in the area." [35]

One of the most serious "end results of the competitive struggle to live" in our society is "race" prejudice. It has been emphasized that the economic factor is not the sole condition involved in the causation of "race" antagonism; it is one of the conditions which make easy the

---

[35] Reuter, "Competition and the Racial Division of Labor," in Thompson (ed.), *Race Relations and the Race Problem*, p. 49.

development of "race" prejudice, but it is not the only condition. It should, however, be quite clear that in our society the economic factor is a dominant condition in the causation of such antagonisms, a necessary condition without which—whatever we may be able to *conceive* to the contrary—such antagonisms would be much less likely to occur. Like good doctors, therefore, if we would prevent the disease we must eliminate or modify the principal condition or conditions which make it possible. In other words, we must eliminate the condition of economic duress under which so many human beings are unjustly forced to live today.[36] By so doing we will have removed one of the most important culture-media in which the virus of "race" prejudice so readily grows; such other conditions as remain can then be dealt with efficiently. This is something to understand and to work for.

---

[36] For a discussion of the facts and also for the necessary recommendations see Bettelheim and Janowitz, *Dynamics of Prejudice,* pp. 174 *et seq.;* MacIver, *The More Perfect Union;* MacIver (ed.), *Unity and Difference in American Life;* Rose and Rose, *America Divided;* Spitz, *Patterns of Anti-Democratic Thought;* Saenger, *The Social Psychology of Prejudice;* Lind (ed.), *Race Relations in World Perspective;* Bigelow (ed.), *Cultural Groups and Human Relations;* Sherif and Sherif, *Groups in Harmony and Tension;* Cole and Cole, *Minorities and the American Promise;* Smith, *Now Is the Time;* Mason, *Common Sense About Race;* Marrow, *Changing Patterns of Prejudice;* Conant (ed.), *Race Issues on the World Scene;* Abernethy (ed.), *The Idea of Equality;* Ramsey, *Christian Ethics and the Sit-In.*

8

Psychological Factors

A T THIS STAGE of our discussion I wish to focus attention upon the
general factor which is too frequently overlooked in discussions
of the "race" problem. This is the factor of the normal psychological
and psychophysical traits of the person—traits which are utilized in
the generation of "racial" enmities and which have already been
touched upon in the preceding chapter.

The one thing clear concerning "racial" hostility and prejudice is
the ease with which persons are led to exhibit it. There are few persons
in our society who have not, at one time or another, exhibited "race"
prejudice. It would seem clear that most persons are capable of being
brought to a state of mind in which they are glad of the opportunity
of freely releasing their feelings against some group or person representing such a group. When society as a whole sanctions such provo-
cations against any group, the free exercise of "racial" intolerance is
enjoyed as a happy release for feelings which are ever ready to find
expression. It is in the nature of such feelings—the character of which
we shall presently discuss—that they can be suitably directed against
some person or particular group of persons, and it is for this reason
that they can be so easily directed to the support and maintenance of
"race" prejudices. The person exhibits "race" prejudice because it
affords him a means of easing certain tensions within himself; because
his tensions are reduced when he is most freely able to discharge those
tensions. As far as the person is concerned, the prejudice itself is
unimportant, it merely provides the channel through which his feelings are allowed necessary expression. Such feelings should, and for
the sake of the health of the person must, find expression. As I have
already said, feelings will attach themselves to the most suitable object

offered—whatever it may be. Such feelings are *not* feelings of "race" prejudice or any other kind of prejudice; and they are not inborn. On the contrary, such feelings are to a large extent generated during the early childhood development of almost every person. There can, however, be little doubt that the elementary forms of these affective states in their undifferentiated condition are physiologically determined.[1] The manner in which such feelings are generated has been discussed in great detail by the psychoanalysts and others. I shall here briefly review the process involved in these dynamisms.

The aggressiveness which adults exhibit in the form of "race" hatred would appear to have universally the same origin. That is to say, the aggressiveness, not the "race" hatred, has the same origin universally and that aggressiveness is merely arbitrarily directed, in some societies, against certain groups. Under other conditions, this same aggressiveness could be directed against numerous different objects, either real or imagined. The object against which aggressiveness is directed is determined by particular conditions, and these we shall later briefly consider. If in "racial" intolerance and prejudice a certain amount of aggressiveness is always displayed, we must ask and answer two questions: (1) where does this aggressiveness originate and (2) why is it exhibited?

Briefly, a considerable amount of the aggressiveness which adults exhibit is originally produced during childhood by parents, nurses, teachers, or whoever else participates in the process of socializing the child. By depriving the infant, and later the child, of many of the means of satisfaction which it seeks—the nipple, the mother's body, uncontrolled freedom to excrete and to suck, the freedom to cry at will, to stay up as late as one wishes, to do the thousand and one things that are forbidden—expected satisfactions are thwarted and frustration upon frustration is piled up within the child. Such frustrations lead to resentment, to fear, to hatred, and to aggressiveness.

---

[1] Fremont-Smith, "The Physiological Basis of Aggression," *Child Study,* XV (1938), 1–8, and "The Influence of Emotional Factors upon Physiological and Pathological Processes," *Bulletin of the New York Academy of Medicine,* XV (1939), 560–69; Jost, "Some Physiological Changes during Frustration," *Child Development,* XII (1941), 9–15; De Fleur and Westie, "The Interpretation of Interracial Situations," *Social Forces,* XXXVIII (1959), 17–23, who found that autonomic physiological responses below the threshold of awareness indicated the degree of involvement.

In childhood this aggressiveness or resentment is displayed in "bad temper" and in general "naughtiness." Such conduct almost invariably results in further frustration—in punishment. At this stage of his development the child finds himself in a state of severe conflict. He must either control the expression of his aggressiveness or else suffer the punishment and the loss of love which his aggressiveness provokes. Such conflicts are usually resolved by excluding the painful situation from consciousness and direct motor expression—in short, by the repression of one's aggressive energies. These are rarely completely repressed, but only in so far as they permit a resolution of the original conflict situation, and the further the original derivatives of what was primarily repressed become removed from the latter, the more freely do these energies gain access to consciousness and the more available for use do they become.[2] The evidence renders it overwhelmingly clear that these energies are never to any extent destroyed or exhausted. As a part of the total organism, they must, in one way or another, find expression, and the ways in which they can find expression are innumerable. "Race" hatred and prejudice merely represent familiar patterns of the manner in which aggressiveness may express itself.[3]

Fear of those who have frustrated one in childhood and anxiety concerning the outcome of the situation thus produced lead to the repression of aggression against the original frustraters and thereby to the *conditioning* of an emotional association between certain kinds of frustrative or fear situations and aggressive feelings. As a result of such conditioning, any object even remotely suggesting such fear or frustrative situations provokes the aggressive behavior with which such fears and frustrations have become associated.

The aggressiveness, more or less common to all human beings, is not a cause of "race" prejudice, but merely represents a motive force or affective energy which can be attached, among other things, to the notion that other groups or "races" are hateful and may thus serve to keep such ideas supplied with the emotional force necessary to keep them going. Under such conditions "race" becomes important,

---

[2] Adorno *et al., The Authoritarian Personality.*
[3] For interesting treatments of this view see Dollard *et al., Frustrations and Aggression,* and Durbin and Bowlby, *Personal Aggressiveness and War;* Bender, *Aggression, Hostility, and Anxiety in Children;* Jackson, *Aggression and Its Interpretation;* Lewin, *Resolving Social Conflicts;* Maier, *Frustration;* Scott, *Aggression;* Buss, *The Psychology of Aggression.*

not as a biological description or ethnic classification but as a means of expressing an unconscious conflict.

Since the infliction of mental, and even physical, pain, as well as the frustration and depreciation of others, is involved in the process of "race" prejudice, and since much of the aggressiveness of the individual owes its existence to early experiences of a similar sort, it is perhaps not difficult to understand why it is that most persons are so ready to participate in the exercise of "race" prejudice. By so doing they are able to find an object for their aggressiveness which most satisfactorily permits the free expression of aggressiveness by means almost identically resembling those which in childhood were indulged in against them. In this way is the individual enabled, as an adult, to pay off—quite unconsciously—an old score of childhood frustration. The later appreciable frustrations suffered in adolescence and adult life naturally add to the store and complexity of aggressiveness, and require no discussion here. At this point reference should be made to such important psychological mechanisms as "displacement," which defines the process whereby aggression is displaced from one object to another, and "projection," the process of attributing to others feelings and impulses originating in ourselves which have been refused conscious recognition.

When the release of aggression toward certain objects or agents is socially interdicted or otherwise made difficult, as in the case of parents, teachers, or employers, aggressiveness may then be displaced toward some more accessible target. The government, Negroes, Jews, Catholics, bankers, et cetera, will conveniently serve as such targets, and where such displacement of aggression occurs the object of it becomes the scapegoat. Collective displacement of this sort is a well-known phenomenon. Both on the individual and on the group level forbidden thoughts and aggressions are by its means turned into socially acceptable activities. Man in search of a target readily utilizes social tension for the displacement of individual tension.[4] Since the displacement occurs from that which is forbidden to that which is not, it would be a psychologically sound procedure to make the socially acceptable in this case socially unacceptable in demonstrable form such as by legal fiat. For the displacers displace because they are,

---

[4] Hartmann, Kris, and Lowenstein, "Notes on the Theory of Aggression," *The Psychoanalytic Study of the Child*, III/IV (1949), 9–36.

among other things, great respecters of authority, and will displace their aggression only where it is socially permissible.

This analysis is fully supported by several recent clinical studies which were instituted in order to discover what kind of persons adopt and become active carriers of anti-Semitic ideas, why they so readily become "scapegoat-addicts," and what function, if any, anti-Semitism serves in their personality structure.[5]

A group of approximately 100 state university students, 76 of them women, provided the material for this study. Subjects giving evidence of a high degree of anti-Semitism were classified as "high extremes," those showing the contrary tendency were classified as "low extremes," and those with in-between attitudes, as "intermediate."

The high extremes were conservative in their attitudes, automatically tending to support the status quo; they were generally Republicans, although they showed few signs of having developed an organized social-political outlook; and there was a tendency to hold their own ethnic or social group in high esteem, to keep it unmixed and pure, and to reject everything that differed from it. The fathers' income was higher than that of the fathers of the average intermediate or low-extreme subjects, and the appearance of the high-extreme girls was in the best middle-class tradition of good grooming (almost all subjects were members of the middle class), very different from that of the low-extreme girls. On the surface these anti-Semitic girls appeared composed and untroubled. They seemed to have little familiarity with their inner lives, but were characterized rather by a generally externalized orientation. They were sensitive to any encroachment from the outside. On the surface they showed an uncritical devotion and obedience to their parents, and to authority in general. They were mostly interested in social standing, and in making an appropriate marriage.

The low extremes, on all these points, contrasted strongly with the high extremes, being nondescript in appearance, less at ease socially, possessed of varied interests, quite willing to talk about themselves and their situations, and able to make critical appraisals of their parents.

Examination of the results of tests and interviews revealed the fact

---

[5] Frenkel-Brunswik and Sanford, "Some Personality Factors in Anti-Semitism," *Journal of Psychology*, XX (1945), 271–91.

that the high extremes were markedly characterized by unconscious aggressive drives of a destructive nature, the repression of basic impulses, ambivalent attitudes of love and hate toward their parents, basic insecurity. Both sexes in the high-extreme group tended to be intellectually underproductive, somewhat lower in intelligence, and lacking in creative imagination. They were less interested in human beings as individuals, and tended to be more hypochondriacal. "The analysis of the content of their responses suggests that the adoption of an aggressive attitude towards outgroups may stem from frustrations received (mainly at the hands of the mother-figure) in childhood"— frustrations which appeared to have produced definite inferiority feelings.

The rigidity with which the high-extreme girl adhered to her conventional values or stereotypes of behavior and the anxiety which she exhibited in the presence of opposite tendencies afforded the clue to the sources of her behavior. Insecurity was the condition with which such girls were struggling. "The fear of losing status is associated with the fear that they will be tempted to release their inhibited tendencies in the way they believe Jews and proletarians do." Anti-Semitism thus helps them to maintain their identification with the middle class and to ward off anxiety.

"Thus," the authors of this valuable study go on to say, "it is not so much middle class values themselves that we would call into question, but rather the rigidity with which they are adhered to. And in the individual case this appears to be the result of the manner in which they have been put across. The mischief is done when those trends which are taboo according to the class standards become repressed, and hence, no longer susceptible to modification or control. This is most likely to happen when parents are too concerned and too insistent with respect to their positive aims for the child and too threatening and coercive with respect to the 'bad' things. The child is thus taught to view behavior in terms of black and white, 'good' and 'evil'; and the 'evil' is made to appear so terrible that he cannot think of it as something in himself which needs to be modified or controlled, but as something that exists in other 'bad' people and needs to be stamped out completely." [6]

Parent-child relationships clearly need to undergo a substantial

---

[6] *Ibid.*, p. 289.

change in the direction of greater understanding and sympathy on the part of parents, in the dropping of "either-or" attitudes, for disjunctive commands give rise to disjunctive personalities. As Frenkel-Brunswik and Sanford say, if the kind of repression which they have uncovered in their high-extreme girls, and its consequences, is to be prevented, "there must be less fear of impulses on the part of parents. The parental attitude toward children must be more tolerant and permissive. Parents must learn that 'bad' impulses can be modified and controlled and that it is of crucial importance to invite the child's participation in these processes." [7] Parents must learn how to give their children the maximum degree of security consonant with the ideal of a socially fully integrated personality. Parents must develop a greater interest in the significance of the whole socialization process. In this task teachers must play almost as large a part as parents.[8]

Ackerman and Jahoda have made available the results of a study calculated to reveal the dynamic basis of anti-Semitic attitudes in a number of persons who have experienced psychoanalytic therapy. The material was collected from some 30 accredited psychoanalysts, and the conclusions both enlarge and confirm those of Frenkel-Brunswik and Sanford as well as those of other investigators.

Two extreme categories of anti-Semitic types were theoretically set up by the authors. The one is the anti-Semite whose attitude seems to be one of superficial conformity to the values, in this respect, of the dominant group; the other is the anti-Semite whose hostility derives from some definite disorder in his own personality structure to which his anti-Semitism has a specific relation. All the cases encountered fell between the two extremes, presenting both elements in varying proportions.

All the patients suffered from anxiety. They were insecure in their group membership. They had a basic feeling of rejection by the world, a feeling of not belonging. They failed to form safe and secure personal attachments. They felt a continuous apprehension of injury to their integrity as individuals. They frequently suffered from an exaggerated sense of vulnerability. They did not seem able to derive support from their own identity as persons. Because of their insecurity, their confused and unstable image of themselves, they lacked direction

---

[7] *Ibid.*, p. 290. See also Bettelheim and Janowitz, *Dynamics of Prejudice*, p. 170.

[8] See Adorno *et al.*, *The Authoritarian Personality*.

and made erratic shifts in their group associations. Fundamentally they were weak, immature, passive, dependent, with the desire to control unrealized in the normal channels of constructive action. They endeavored to deny to consciousness the image of themselves as inferior and crippled. "Overtly they have the urge to conform but unconsciously they resent the compulsory submission and react with destructive rebellion. At the unconscious level they have no hope of being able to repair their damaged identity as persons; basically they accept it as irreversible. However, this basic despair is concealed from consciousness, where they behave in exactly the opposite manner. The core of these character traits is the weak identity, the immaturity, the unconscious passivity, the intense sense of vulnerability to social injury —all of which are denied in consciousness where they are replaced by aggression." [9]

In relation to such a syndrome anti-Semitism plays a functionally well-defined role. It is a defense against self-hate, a displacement of the self-destroying trends of the character structure described. At the psychic level anti-Semitism assumes the function of a profound though irrational effort to restore the crippled self, and at the social level it constitutes a pattern producing secondary emotional gain. Were the anti-Semite to permit his internal conflict, between what he *is* unconsciously and what he thinks of himself as being consciously, to proceed to its logical conclusion, he would find the consequences unbearable. And so he escapes the dilemma by preoccupation with external events, thus achieving a spurious relief from tensions and the bogus satisfaction of being a member of a powerful, united group, an ingroup in whose program of action he can join. Nevertheless, the central conflict continues with unabated intensity.

To summarize: the prejudice pattern is created through the mobilization of the following series of mechanisms: (*a*) by denial of anxiety and substitution of aggression, (*b*) by an effort to reinforce affiliation with dominant social groups, (*c*) by the elaboration of a variety of reaction formations and compensatory emotional drives, and (*d*) by renunciation of parts of the person's image of self and the concomitant substitution of a borrowed identity. Associated with this there is a suppression and repression of anxiety-ridden impulses. "Having submissively renounced parts of their own individuality they feel deep

---

[9] Ackerman and Jahoda, "Toward a Dynamic Interpretation of Anti-Semitic Attitudes," *American Journal of Orthopsychiatry*, XVIII (1948), 168.

resentment against any one who does not do likewise. They demand that other people should conform to the same restrictions. The demand for conformity is thus a result of partial self-renunciation. The person who is forced to renounce his real self as the price of social acceptance is doubly sensitive to others who do not conform. Here lies the root of the excessive reaction to difference which characterizes our anti-Semitic patients. Every sign of non-conformity in another person is, as it were, an unwelcome reminder of the painful sacrifice that the prejudiced person has made by renouncing part of his self in the vain hope of achieving group identification. The fear of the 'different' is hence not in proportion to the extent of objective, measurable differences; rather it grows in proportion to the implied ego threat, in other words, to the degree to which the difference symbolizes the fruitless suppression of the self. All prejudiced people insist on conformity to the extent of trying to destroy the non-conformist. Since conformity denotes surrender of the individuality, a person who is 'different' symbolizes non-surrender, and therefore, an individual who is strong, mature, independent, superior, able to stand up against others with his differences. The prejudiced person cannot bear the implied comparison. Because of the inherent weakness of his own self-image, the 'different' person represents a potential menace to his own integrity as an individual or whatever there is left of it. The inevitable response is to attack the menace, the person who symbolizes the difference." [10]

The elaborated and inconsistent picture of the stereotype Jew forms a perfect projective screen for the anti-Semite's irreconcilable impulses. The Jew is at once successful and low class; capitalist and communist; clannish and an intruder into other people's society; highly moral and spiritual and given to low forms of behavior such as greed, sharp business practices, and dirt; magically omnipotent and omniscient, and incredibly helpless and defenseless and therefore readily destroyed.

What any individual projects upon the Jew invariably represents unacceptable components of the self or components envied in others, at least unacceptable on the conscious level though unconsciously such attributes form an active part of the person's psychic drives.[11] Hence,

[10] *Ibid.*, p. 171.
[11] Ackerman, "Anti-Semitic Motivation in a Psychopathic Personality," *Psychoanalytic Review*, XXXIV (1947), 76–101.

the object which is consciously rejected, the Jew, may, at the unconscious level, be represented by a strong identification with him. This identification, because of the symbolic aspect of the Jew's weakness, his crippled, defenseless position, cannot be admitted, because to do so would be to endanger the person's ego and social position. It is therefore denied and in its place there is substituted an identification with the attacker, in order to avoid being victimized and also to draw strength through identification. "Thus the Jew at one and the same time stands for the weakness or strength of the self; for conscience, for those parts of the person which blame and accuse the weakness of the self, and also for those primitive appetites and aggressions which must be denied as the price of social acceptance." [12]

It may be objected that inferences based on data obtained from patients who have been psychoanalytically treated cannot be justly applied to the analysis of the behavior of normal persons. To this objection several replies may be made. First, it is doubtful whether normal persons are ever anti-Semitic in the disordered sense here described, and since a large proportion of persons give evidence of disordered character structure it is likely that the observations made and the conclusions drawn from them are valid for a great segment of the population of anti-Semites. Second, the inability to pay the fees of a psychoanalyst is no mark of normality; and, third, in any event the study of the pathological is still one of the best ways of learning to understand the nature of the pathological, and anti-Semitism is a pathological disorder of persons and of societies.

Anti-Semitism is, of course, only one form of group prejudice, as is "race" prejudice in general.[13] Other kinds of group prejudice, such as religious prejudices, national prejudices, sex prejudices, class preju-

---

[12] Ackerman and Jahoda, "Toward a Dynamic Interpretation of Anti-Semitic Attitudes," *American Journal of Orthopsychiatry*, XVIII (1948), 173.

[13] For the material on anti-Semitism see Ackerman and Jahoda, "The Dynamic Basis of Anti-Semitic Attitudes," *Psychoanalytic Quarterly*, XVII (1948), 240-60; Ackerman and Jahoda, *Anti-Semitism and Emotional Disorder;* Massing, *Rehearsal for Destruction;* Adorno *et al., The Authoritarian Personality;* Bettelheim and Janowitz, *Dynamics of Prejudice;* Lowenthal and Guterman, *Prophets of Deceit;* Graeber and Britt (eds.), *Jews in a Gentile World;* Sachar, *Sufferance Is the Badge;* Samuel, *The Great Hatred;* Livingston, *Must Men Hate?;* McWilliams, *A Mask for Privilege;* Tenenbaum, *Why Men Hate;* Simmel (ed.), *Anti-Semitism: A Social Disease;* McDonagh, "Status Levels of American Jews," *Sociology and Social Research*, XXXII (1948), 944-53;

dices, and the like, as has already been pointed out, are merely special forms of the same general phenomenon of group prejudice. As soon as one becomes aware of group membership and identifies oneself with that group the ground is laid for the development of group prejudice in some particular form. The prejudice may be of the most benign kind and socially not make for the least disharmony. On the other hand, it may develop under certain conditions in so disoperatively strong a manner as to threaten the very existence of the society in which it appears. This happens to be the case in the United States as well as in some other lands. Awareness of this fact, together with our understanding of the psychodynamics of the development of such forms of behavior, suggests the immediate necessity of reconsidering our processes of socializing children in relation to the health of the social structure as a whole. "Race" prejudice is at its strongest where social maturity is at its weakest.

The teaching of the facts about "race" or "race" prejudice will not be adequate to solve the problem. The roots of prejudice are woven into the very psychic structure of the person, and unless we attend to the soil from which they draw nourishment it will not help either the resulting plant or ourselves if we attempt to cure its sickness by lopping off the ailing leaves. The soil in which "race" prejudice grows is the social experience to which the developing person is exposed, and it is to this that we must attend if we are ever to be delivered from the sickness which is "race." As Bettelheim and Janowitz put it, "It seems reasonable to assume that as long as anxiety and insecurity persist as a root of intolerance, the effort to dispel stereotyped thinking or feelings of ethnic hostility by rational propaganda is at best a half-measure. On an individual level only greater personal integration combined with social and economic security seems to offer hope for better inter-ethnic relations." [14] These authors point out that on the social level a change of climate is necessary. Their subjects who accepted social controls and were more tolerant of other minorities were

---

Parkes, *The Jewish Problem in the Modern World;* Parkes, *An Enemy of the People: Antisemitism;* Finkelstein (ed.), *The Jews;* Sartre, "Portrait of the Anti-Semite," *Partisan Review,* XIII (1946), 163–78; Epstein and Forster, *Some of My Best Friends . . . ;* Hay, *Europe and the Jews;* Trachtenberg, *The Devil and the Jews.*

[14] Bettelheim and Janowitz, "Prejudice," *Scientific American,* CLXXXIII (1950), 13.

also less tolerant of the Negro, because discrimination against Negroes is more commonly condoned, both publicly and privately. They suggest, therefore, that this should lead, among other things, to additional efforts to change social practices in ways that will tangibly demonstrate that ethnic discrimination is contrary to the mores of society.

MacCrone, in a valuable study of the psychology and psychopathology of "race" prejudice in South Africa, has written that "the extra-individual conflicts between the two racial groups are but the intra-individual conflicts within the mind writ large, and until the latter are removed, reduced, or modified, they must continue to exercise their baleful influence upon the race relations and the race contacts of white and black." [15]

It is these intra-individual conflicts, the psychological factor, the deep, early conditioned motive forces represented by the aggressiveness which is produced in so many human beings and is continually being augmented by the frustrations of adolescent and adult life, that must receive more attention than they have in the past. It is this aggressiveness which renders so easily possible the usual emotional and irrational development of "race" prejudice. A rational society must reckon with this factor, for since a certain amount of frustration is inevitable, and even desirable, in the development of the person and a certain amount of aggressiveness is inevitably produced by some social controls, and by some even considered a necessary part of the equipment of most human beings,[16] the task of an intelligent society is clear. Society must provide outlets for the aggressiveness of the person which will result in benefits both to him, and through him, to society. Outlets for aggression which result in social friction and in the destruction of good relations between human beings must be avoided. Frustrations in the early and subsequent development of the person must be reduced to a minimum, and aggressiveness always directed toward ends of constructive value. Indeed, as the writers of The Authoritarian Personality conclude, all that is really necessary is that children be genuinely loved and treated as human beings.[17]

The findings revealed in the studies of The Authoritarian Personality have been challenged as probably not applying to all classes

---

[15] MacCrone, Race Attitudes in South Africa, p. 310.
[16] See Freud on this subject, Appendix I.
[17] Adorno et al., The Authoritarian Personality, p. 975.

of society. The subjects of that study were largely middle class. The findings and conclusions as a whole, however, have been supported by the independent studies of other investigators.[18] A study by Mc-Cord, McCord, and Howard, based on interviews, in 1948, with 48 males aged 20 years of lower class origin revealed that the apparently tolerant did not differ from the bigoted members of this small sample.[19] As Allport[20] and others have pointed out, not all prejudice is necessarily related to the personality as a whole, some prejudices are conformative or mildly ethnocentric. And as McDill has shown, in a study of 146 female and 120 male white non-Jewish adults in Nashville, Tennessee, anomie and authoritarian influences are equally important in accounting for intolerant attitudes toward minority groups.[21] The McCords and Howard incline to the belief that prejudice in the lower classes is based on a generally stereotyped culture, which is not related to specific personality needs or to unique familial environments. Prejudice in the lower classes appears to be the result of adult rather than childhood experiences, according to these investigators.

If this hypothesis is correct, and it would certainly appear to be so in many cases, then improvement in economic and educational opportunities and other social conditions would offer some hope of reducing the quantum of bigotry.

Koenig and King, in a study of students on a coeducational campus in the Southwest, found that "Cognitively simple persons tend to overlook nuances and to classify experience into a few, inclusive categories. Unable to perceive the behaviors of others accurately, they project their own characteristics (including attitudes) onto others. This tendency is related to stereotyping and to intolerance or preju-

---

[18] Harris, Gough, and Martin, "Children's Ethnic Attitudes: II, Relationships to Parental Beliefs Concerning Child Training," *Child Development*, XXI (1950), 169–81; Frenkel-Brunswik, "Patterns of Social and Cognitive Outlook in Children and Parents," *American Journal of Orthopsychiatry*, XXI (1951), 543–58; Ackerman and Jahoda, *Anti-Semitism and Emotional Disorder*.

[19] McCord, McCord, and Howard, "Early Familial Experiences and Bigotry," *American Sociological Review*, XXV (1960), 717–22.

[20] Allport, *The Nature of Prejudice*, pp. 395, 408.

[21] McDill, "Anomie, Authoritarianism, Prejudice, and Socio-Economic Status: An Attempt at Clarification," *Social Forces*, XXXIX (1961), 239–45.

dice." [22] Such findings have been many times independently made by other investigators.

Martin, in a study designed to determine whether some of the findings of *The Authoritarian Personality* would also obtain in a randomly selected adult sample drawn from a balanced urban community, Indianapolis, secured results which confirmed the California studies strikingly. The study involved visits to 668 households and preliminary interviews with 429 persons. The final study was reduced to 41 tolerant and 49 prejudiced individuals. Martin has described his findings in the strongly prejudiced and strongly tolerant syndromes so well, they will be given here at some length.

In general, the strongly prejudiced person presents the following pattern or syndrome of traits and characteristics: he tends to be quite ethnocentric; he makes sharp distinctions between his in-groups and out-groups; he is a "social reductionist," in that his reference groups reflect an *exclusive* rather than an *inclusive* emphasis; he is unlikely to identify with "humanity," but prefers more exclusive levels of identification; he thrives on selective membership with himself on the "inside." Such an attitude provides a sustaining and compensating mechanism for psychological and social insecurity. Although typically obscure himself, he borrows prestige from his "race," nation, etc.

The prejudiced person tends to be suspicious, distrustful and extrapunitive. He attributes ulterior motives to Negroes and other outgroup members. The "Negro problem" is due to Negroes, and if their lot is not to their liking then it is because they are at fault. He is afraid of contact with minority group members, and foresees dire consequences of intergroup interaction. Segregation is the politicalsocial policy he urges and defends because he "knows" that Negroes and whites cannot live peacefully together.

He views the world as an arena of conflict, involving power struggles and competition among individuals and groups. Other people are not to be trusted in general, because everyone is seeking to maximize his own advantage at the expense of others. He prides himself on his "realism" and tends to regard "idealistic" people as naive and even dangerous, and he favors the "practical" over the "theoretical."

The strongly prejudiced person seeks certainty through the use of dichotomized absolutes. He does not think in relative terms; he keeps

[22] Koenig and King, "Cognitive Simplicity and Prejudice," *Social Forces*, XL (1962), 220–22.

his fear of doubt repressed by the dogmatism he substitutes for it. He therefore views Negroes and whites as being essentially and markedly different; a person is either good or evil, and a statement is either true or false.

The strongly prejudiced person favors obedience and submission to authority. This trait is congruent with his zeal for definiteness and his basic distrust of the impulses and motives of other people. He prefers order, discipline, and conformity in the social environment. He is likely to be conservative in his social attitudes and interests, and is often a vigorous supporter, at the verbal level, of conventional morality. He is moralistic, but distinctly unsentimental. Such a person evidently represses much and engages in considerable projection, particularly in connection with the matter of conventional moral norms and their violation.

The strongly prejudiced person also tends to be poorly endowed with imagination, humanitarianism, creativeness, and compassion. He tends to be fatalistic; he is pessimistic about the scientific study of human behavior. Superstition has a considerable appeal to him, as do the magical, the mystical, and the mysterious.

Compared to the tolerant type he tends to be more emotional and less rational, and he is more moralistic rather than ethical (in terms of the connotations of these two words). The strongly prejudiced individual is typically non-intellectual and frequently anti-intellectual; he is very often dogmatic in expression and angers easily when he meets with disagreement. He is likely to interpret intellectual disagreement as a personal affront.

In religion the bigot subscribes to the more fundamentalistic, dogmatic, irrational, and authoritarian doctrines and beliefs. He is less likely to concur with ideals and values relating to brotherhood, basic humanity, and unselfish deeds. He is opposed to "modernism," and would appear to resent having to donate money to his religious group.

In terms of social characteristics, the prejudiced person has less formal education, a lower occupational level, and perhaps a smaller circle of friends than the tolerant type, even though the latter may often have a lower income.

In general the very tolerant, or relatively unprejudiced person presents the following pattern or syndrome of traits and characteristics: His tolerance tends to be general with respect to people; perhaps the only exception is his intolerance of persons who are bigoted. A conspicuous trait is his trust of other people. The tolerant person is inclined to look for the best in people; he gives them the "benefit of the doubt." He tends to judge individuals *as individuals,* and rejects the practice of group stereotyping. He expects other people to be friendly, fair, and cooperative, and he is likely to suspend his judgment of others beyond the first impression.

The tolerant person apparently feels reasonably secure, or at least he is not prone to exaggerate actual threats from other people. He may be neurotic but he is rarely paranoid. He is inclined to be rational, humanitarian, liberal in social attitudes, and intropunitive.

The tolerant person is also characterized by a high degree of empathic ability, and is much more likely to be sympathetic and compassionate than the strongly prejudiced person. He is "sensitive" as distinct from being "tough"; he is opposed to cruelty, violence, and harsh discipline where the strongly prejudiced person would be likely to condone it. Whereas the bigoted male is often ultra-masculine (to the point of having almost no compassion), the tolerant male seemingly has no obsessive need to "prove" his masculinity, at least he is seldom "swaggering and arrogant" in his maleness.

The tolerant type is able to perceive variation accurately and realistically; thus he is less impelled to resort to stereotyping and dogmatism. He apparently realizes and recognizes that each individual is unique (though not radically different from other persons), and that good and evil, shortness and tallness, darkness and lightness, stupidity and intelligence, are all relative concepts. He has no obsessive fear of being mistaken or wrong, he is willing to admit his own shortcomings and weaknesses.

The tolerant personality is not a highly rigid one. He is more likely to be witty and have a highly developed sense of humor than the bigot. For example, the tolerant person is capable of engaging in self-ridicule, whereas the image of a grim and rigidly serious expression is more plausibly associated with the bigot.

The tolerant person is typically interested in and optimistic about the improvement of human society. He is likely to stress cooperation as against competition in achieving human progress. He is often idealistic and utopian, and interested in intellectual matters. Likewise, the tolerant person values creative activities and is not so prone to stress the "practical" over the "theoretical." The tolerant type is much less of a "social reductionist." It is "humanity" that interests him. Being a member of an "exclusive" group has a weak appeal for him.

The unprejudiced person tends to be "kindhearted," if not "softhearted"; he is typically in sympathy with the underdog, and is not characterized by the "threat-competition orientation" so evident in highly intolerant people. This is readily observable in the religious values and beliefs of tolerants; there is an emphasis upon brotherhood, humanitarianism, charity, reason, and tolerance of personal deviation. Similarly, he is likely to be altruistic and somewhat sentimental, and be more appreciative of the aesthetic, as compared to the strongly prejudiced person.

Such a personality is more concerned with *serving* than *leading;* is likely to be relatively autonomous; does not have a strong need for dominance; is rarely ever obsessively conformist; and dislikes both subordination and superordination of any appreciable degree. He tends to view his social interaction and social relationships as possibilities for expression, mutual assistance, affective response, etc., rather than as opportunities for exploitation and manipulation.

Socially speaking, the relatively unprejudiced person is almost certain to have more formal education than the highly intolerant person, and his occupational status is usually higher. Although it is not borne out by the reports of the subjects in this study, the investigators are of the opinion that the tolerant type usually experiences a childhood family environment characterized by an absence of harsh discipline and authoritarian parental control.

The child-rearing attitudes of the strongly prejudiced subjects certainly suggest that authoritarian discipline is actually applied by such parents, and one would assume that their offspring would show the effects of this conditioning in their intergroup attitudes. It is surmised that the tolerant person would usually come from a more relaxed, secure, and lenient home environment, and would experience more affection and less rejection and hostility from parents than the highly intolerant person.[23]

Thus, it will be seen that the Indianapolis study in every way supports the findings of the California authoritarian-personality study.

[23] Martin, "Tolerant and Prejudiced Personality Syndromes," *Journal of Intergroup Relations,* II (1961), 171–75.

"RACE" PREJUDICE AND CLASSIFIED HOSTILITIES

"Race" prejudice in many cases may be regarded as one of a number of *classified hostilities* that are not a result of an immediate interpersonal relationship, but which arise out of the person's need to fit his hostility into the dynamic framework of his personality structure, altogether apart from the presence of a direct and immediate stimulus situation.

In one very significant sense "race" prejudice arises from the individual's failure to make use of his own potentialities, particularly his powers to relate himself to other beings, to establish human ties. The failure to establish human ties on the basis of the integrity of the individuality of the self allows only one alternative—the adoption of attitudes which seek to justify to himself this failure. "Race" prejudice or the adoption of classified hostilities is one of the methods of trying to satisfy or complete the constellation of needs springing from this failure.

If the constellation of needs in itself arises from a failure to make use of one's powers to love, then there can be no satisfactory solution of the problem in any real sense. For the solution, as offered by rationalizing that there is no basis in reality to love, only succeeds in further stifling this potentiality.

Man is born a social being who can reach his fullest development only through interaction with his fellows. The denial at any point of this social bond between man and man brings with it disintegration. A major symptom of this denial is "race" prejudice. What is observed in this connection is not the failure to develop into that which the individual, the person, in the utmost sense, potentially is, but rather the failure to carry on the process of development. "Race" prejudice functions primarily as a barrier to the further development of the person.

What is the alternative to holding these prejudices or rationalizations? What does it mean to the person to give up these rationalizations? In brief, what is the danger which the person must face if he were to give up these prejudices? That there is a danger is apparent, otherwise men would not cling to ideas, however early formed and strongly held, that can be demonstrated to be factually false.

All the evidence of research and inquiry indicates that the danger seems to lie in the fact that if rationalizations are perceived for what they are and abandoned, the individual faces the necessity of taking his own life seriously, and the necessity of forming meaningful human relations on the basis of his personal integrity is challenged. He must give up the primary dependent ties. He is forced to see himself as an individual entity, and not as a part of another person either in the capacity of master or subject, ruler or ruled. He must be willing to bear the pain of isolation that is concomitant with mature independence.[24] He must recognize his actual position in the universe, feel his aloneness, and at the same time his power to overcome this through love on the basis of his own integrity.

The inability to give up the primary ties is crucial—the ties to the nurturing authority. Often men rationalize that they have given up what could be called their incestuous ties, when a closer examination will reveal that what they have done has been to transfer these ties to a more acceptable object. An interesting fact here is that when group affiliations are of this nature, i.e., a source of power for the person ("I am a member of this strong group"), we find that accompanying this group attachment is a complementary feeling of out-group hostility. That is to say, the stronger and more permanent the person's attachment to the particular group the stronger does his out-group hostility tend to be.

This particular consequence of group allegiances is one of the services the group performs for the person. If the group functions primarily as a *transferred source* of strength for the person, a place of worship of power, this consequence will almost always follow. If, on the other hand, the group serves a cooperative function, if the individual on the basis of his integrity can lend support to efforts that cannot be accomplished on a personal basis, then the consequence of out-group hostility is not a necessary result of such group relationships.

It is evident that this problem can be manipulated in part by manipulation of the groups. In working with boys' clubs and children's groups, some of the hostility which is the side effect of in-group allegiance can be eliminated by reducing the strength of the in-group allegiance. This can be done by making the groups less permanent

---

[24] For a penetrating discussion of this, see Dostoevski, *The Brothers Karamazov*, Chapter V, Book V.

and the membership more flexible.[25] However, it is further clear that it is not the group as such which generates the out-group hostility, but rather the private and personal use to which the group is put by the persons constituting it.

In a sense what develops is a vicious circle. If the group in some (usually disguised) way serves the person as a primary source of strength, a place where he can transplant his umbilical cord, where he can deny his individuality, then it becomes progressively necessary for him to develop the power of the group, but not his own strength. Since the group is a direct source of security, and since he cannot bear to have his security threatened, then progressively more and more effort must be supplied to this source of strength. But what happens is that the person only more firmly binds himself to the nourishing mother. More and more it becomes clear to him that it is his position in the group that is of importance, and not his position in terms of his responsibility to himself. The greater the crippling of his own individualization, the greater the need to cripple it until at last we find men ready blindly to negate their own lives or even life in general in their efforts to protect and revere this source of strength.

The in-group has certain characteristics, too; it must be just that, an in-group. Its membership must be restricted and of relative permanency. For if its membership should be accessible to all mankind (in actuality, not pretense), and if that goal were reached, this group could no longer serve as a source of strength. This kind of strength involves "power over" and there would no longer be any scapegoat to exercise this "power over."

In contrast to this vicious circle is the kind of group relationship where the effort is supplied to achieving "power of"—power of thought, power of understanding, power of growth. The person's relation to the group is one where his individuality is affirmed by his particular contribution to the group effort. Though the group here is also a source of power for the individual, it is a power that affirms life and his own identity. It is an affirmative strength that does not seek the negation of life itself, but rather the enhancement and growth

---

[25] Lewin, *Resolving Conflicts;* Sherif and Sherif, *Groups in Harmony and Tension;* Spicer (ed.), *Human Problems in Technological Change;* Argyris, *Personality and Organization;* Maier, *Principles of Human Relations.*

of those conditions which lead to the fullest development of the person's unique identity.[26]

The satisfactions yielded by and the epidemiology of hostility are interconnected phenomena. Thorne has investigated the epidemiology of hostility through family studies. He has drawn attention to the contagious quality of hostility, its tendency toward chain reactions, and its extreme potency when the recipient is in an inescapable position. A further result of such hostilities is the building up of mutually suspicious and paranoid attitudes.[27]

ATTITUDES OF MIND

The problem of "race" in our society is social, and not biological in any but a vague technical sense.[28] Fairness toward other groups of persons or a person is a matter of simple human decency; and decency is an attitude of mind, for the most part culturally conditioned. Whether ethnic groups or castes are biologically equal is an utterly irrelevant consideration where fair-mindedness is concerned. Whatever differences exist between peoples and however they may have been determined, the willingness to understand those differences and to act upon them sympathetically ought to increase in proportion to the magnitude of the differences which are believed to exist between

---

[26] I have a feeling that I am not altogether the author of the words or ideas in this section on classified hostilities. My notes, made long ago, indicate no outside source. If I have used someone else's ideas or words without individual acknowledgment, I hope this brief note will serve both as explanation and apology.

[27] Thorne, "The Attitudinal Pathoses," *Journal of Clinical Psychology,* V (1949), 1–21; *Idem,* "The Frustration-Anger-Hostility States: A New Diagnostic Classification," *Journal of Clinical Psychology,* IX (1953), 334–39. See also Buss, *The Psychology of Aggression;* Siegal, "The Relationship of Hostility to Authoritarianism," *Journal of Abnormal and Social Psychology,* LII (1956), 368–72; Hokanson, "The Effects of Guilt Arousal and Severity of Discipline on Adult Aggressive Behavior," *Journal of Clinical Psychology,* XVII (1961), 29–32.

[28] This statement has been interpreted to mean that race in the biological sense in man has no existence. Much more is meant here than that, namely that, in so far as social action is concerned, the *biological facts about population differences* do not constitute the *social problem* of "race." It is the *social attitude* toward "race" that constitutes the problem.

ourselves and others. As Professor E. G. Conklin has so well put it: "To the naturalist the differences between human races, subraces, and individuals are small indeed as compared with their manifold resemblances. Biology and the Bible agree that 'God hath made of one blood all nations of men.' Our common traits and origin and fate, our common hopes and fears, joys and sorrows, would call forth our common sympathy with all mankind, if it were not for the lessons of hate which have been cultivated and instilled by selfish and unscrupulous persons and social groups. These racial antagonisms are not the results of inexorable nature, nor of inherited instincts, but of deliberate education and cultivation." [29]

The plea for fairness in dealing with ethnic groups not our own is usually phrased in terms of "tolerance." But if we are to make progress in ethnic relations, it is desirable to recognize that tolerance is not good enough, for tolerance defines an attitude which constitutes a somewhat reluctant admission of the necessity of enduring that which we must bear, the presence of those whom we do not like. A New York high-school girl put the whole matter in a nutshell. "Tolerance," she said, "is when you put up with certain people but you don't like to have them around anyhow." That, it is to be feared, is the general nature of tolerance, the hand-washing indifference of the "superior" person who patronizingly condescends to endure the coexistence of "inferior" beings on condition that they keep their "proper" distance. Tolerance is the attitude of mind of those who consider themselves not only different but superior. It implies an attitude toward different ethnic or minority groups, not of understanding, not of acceptance, not of recognition of human equality, but of recognition of differences which one must suffer—generally, not too gladly. We must be more than tolerant; we must be fair.

Tolerance is the best one can hope from bigots; fairness is the attitude of mind we look for in decent, humane people. By fairness, where ethnic relations are concerned, is meant the attitude of mind which takes it for granted, there being no actual evidence to the contrary, that for all their individual differences no human being is really superior to another by virtue of his group affiliation, and that, given the necessary opportunities, it is probable that the average person of any one group is capable of doing at least as well as the average in-

---

[29] Conklin, "What Is Man?" Rice Institute Pamphlet, XXVIII (1941), 163.

dividual of the culturally most advanced group. It is more than merely being willing to concede that the *others* are not inferior to *us;* it is readiness to accept the verdict that *we* are not superior to the *others.* One is not called upon to be magnanimous, still less is one called upon to condemn or condone, but one is called upon to attempt to be fair—to understand and then to act upon that understanding.[30] Until such an attitude of mind becomes part of the equipment of every person, no amount of instruction in the facts concerning the biology of "race" will ever succeed in eliminating "race" prejudices.

"Race" prejudice is ultimately merely the effect of an incompletely developed personality—a personality, that is, which has not learned any of the simple fundamental facts concerning its nature or of the nature of other human beings, for to understand others it is first necessary to understand oneself. Such a personality is still utilizing the infantile method of beating the object which it imagines has in some way been the cause of its frustration; it is a personality which is still shifting the blame onto someone else for its errors and boasting that "my father is bigger than yours." It is a personality that contrasts sharply with the mature personality which tries to understand and does not seek to wash its hands of its fellows by condemning or condoning their conduct and thus dismissing them from its mind. The mature personality does not automatically resort to the infliction of punishment because he has been frustrated, but he attempts to understand the cause of his frustration and then, in the light of that understanding, so to act that such frustrations will not again be produced. He does not try to escape the exercise of understanding by emotionally letting off steam. He accepts responsibility for his own acts and is moved by the injustice of the acts of others to attempt to remedy the conditions which give rise to them. He understands that no one's father is really bigger than anyone else's father, and that to act in a superior manner is merely a childish way of asserting one's desire to feel important, to feel that one amounts to something. He realizes that, on the other hand, the desire to feel that one belongs with all mankind and not above or below any group, to feel that one is of them and belongs with them, is the most satisfying and efficient way

---

[30] This is what Oscar Wilde meant when he stated that "it is only by the cultivation of the habit of intellectual criticism that we shall be able to rise superior to race prejudices." "The True Function and Value of Criticism," *Nineteenth Century,* XXVIII (1890), 123–47.

of living and thinking. He not only insists upon the right of everyone to be different, but rejoices in most of those differences and is not unsympathetically indifferent to those which he may dislike. He understands that if people are characterized by likenesses and differences, it is no argument against the likenesses to dwell on the differences, or that difference in any way implies inequality. He realizes that diversity is not only the salt of life but also the true basis of collective achievement, and he does everything in his power to further the purposes of that collective achievement.[31]

True culture has been defined as the ability to appreciate the other fellow. While this particular ability has many sources, it is generally derived from varied, sympathetic, and understanding contacts between people who differ from each other in several respects.[32]

If "race" prejudice is ever to be eliminated, society must assume the task of educating the individual—not so much in the facts of "race" as in the processes which lead to the development of a completely integrated human being. The solution here, as in so much else, lies in education; education for humanity first and with regard to the facts afterward. For of what use are facts unless they are intelligently understood and humanely used?

Suppose for a moment that significant differences did exist between different peoples which rendered one, in general, superior to the other; a reasonably developed human being would hardly consider such differences sufficient reason for withholding opportunities for social and cultural development from such groups. On the contrary, he would be the more anxious to provide them with such opportunities. Undeveloped personalities operate in the opposite manner and, creating most of the differences they condemn, proceed to in-

---

[31] For a valuable discussion of this aspect of the subject see Davidson, "The Anatomy of Prejudice," *Common Ground,* I (1941), 3–12; and Huxley, *Man Stands Alone;* see also, Myers, *Are Men Equal?;* Abernethy (ed.), *The Idea of Equality;* Tawney, *Equality;* Thompson, *Equality;* Bryson *et al.* (eds.), *Aspects of Human Equality.*

[32] Taft, "Cultural Opportunities through Race Contacts," *Journal of Negro History,* XIV (1929), 19; Williams, Jr., *The Reduction of Intergroup Tensions,* pp. 69–73; Lewin, *Resolving Social Conflicts;* Bryson *et al.* (eds.), *Approaches to Group Understanding;* Stegner, *One Nation;* Marrow, *Living Without Hate;* MacIver (ed.), *Unity and Difference in American Life;* Johnson (ed.), *Foundations of Democracy;* Handlin, *Race and Nationality in American Life.*

tensify those differences by making it more and more difficult for the groups thus treated to avoid or overcome them.

Fromm writes: "The implicit assumption underlying much reactionary thinking is that equality presupposes absence of difference between persons or social groups. Since obviously such differences exist with regard to practically everything that matters in life, their conclusion is that there can be no equality. When the liberals conversely are moved to deny the fact of great differences in mental and physical gifts and favorable or unfavorable accidental personality conditions, they only help their adversaries to appear right in the eyes of the common man. The concept of equality as it has developed in Judaeo-Christian and in modern progressive tradition means that all men are equal in such basic human capacities as those making for the enjoyment of freedom and happiness. It means, furthermore, that as a political consequence of this basic equality no man shall be made the means to the ends of another group. Each man is a universe for himself and is only his own purpose. His goal is the realization of his being, including those very peculiarities which are characteristic of him and which make him different from others. Thus, equality is the basis for the full development of difference, and it results in the development of individuality." [33]

It is or should be axiomatic that the natural inequality of endowment which exists between all human beings does not render equality of opportunity a contemptible principle.

There exist no really separative or divisive biological differences between the major, or ethnic, groups of mankind; there are differences only between persons. In every group there will be found a large range of differences in the native endowment of its members, some individuals are naturally inferior to others in the realizable potentials of intelligence, in vigor, or in beauty. Such differences may, by some, be made the pretext for heaping contumely and humiliation upon those who are less fortunately endowed than their fellows; but it would be scarcely human to do so, and less than decent.

The form of the mind and body are so dependent upon social conditions that when the latter are unequal for different groups, little or no inference can be made as to the mental and physical potentialities of these groups. As the great American anthropologist Alfred Louis

---

[33] Fromm, "Sex and Character," *Psychiatry*, VI (1943), 23.

Kroeber wrote many years ago, "Most ethnologists, at any rate, are convinced that the overwhelming mass of historical and miscalled racial facts that are now attributed to obscure organic causes or at most are in dispute, will ultimately be viewed by everyone as social and as best intelligible in their social relations."[34]

"Race" prejudice is a pigment of the imagination. It begins in the minds of men, but it doesn't end there. Until we have succeeded in producing emotionally secure, mature human beings, instead of emotionally insecure, immature human beings, until we have succeeded, by means of the proper educational methods,[35] in producing that cultivation of mind which renders nothing that is human alien to it, the "race" problem will never be completely solved. The means by which that problem may to some extent be ameliorated have already been indicated, and will be further discussed in the last chapter.

There is one more aspect of the psychology of "race" prejudice to which I should like to draw attention, that is, the process of rationalization, the process of finding reasons to justify emotionally held, essentially irrational beliefs, and the construction of one's "logic" to fit one's rationalizations.

We saw in Chapter 1 by what means "race" prejudice originally came into existence in the United States, that is, in large part as the stratagem by means of which the proslavery party attempted to meet the arguments of the abolitionists that the slaves were men and brothers and should be free. The upholders of slavery avidly sought for reasons with which to justify their interest in maintaining that institution, and they brought those reasons forward in force and from all sorts of sources, including the Bible. But no matter from what source they drew their reasons, they were nothing but the most patent rationalizations.

Since "race" prejudice invariably rests on false premises, for the most part of emotional origin, it is not surprising to find that it is practically always rationalized. As Professor W. O. Brown points out:

[34] Kroeber, "The Superorganic," *American Anthropologist*, XIX (1917), 163–213.
[35] See Montagu, *On Being Human;* Montagu, *The Direction of Human Development;* Miller, *The Community of Man;* Frank, *Nature and Human Nature;* Ulich, *The Human Career;* Waddington, *The Ethical Animal;* Eiseley, *The Firmament of Time;* Highet, *Man's Unconquerable Mind.*

"The rationalization is a moral defense. And the rationalizer is a moralist. The rationalization, in the nature of the case, secures the believer in his illusion of moral integrity. The morality of the rationalization is perhaps intensified by the fact that it represents an effort to make that which is frequently vicious, sordid, and inhumane rational, idealistic, and humane. The semi-awareness of the real nature of the attitude being rationalized intensifies the solemnity with which the rationalization is formulated. Securing moral values the rationalization naturally partakes of a moral quality. This fact explains, in part, perhaps, the deadly seriousness of the devotee of the rationalization. Its value lies in the fact that it removes the moral stigma attached to race prejudice, elevating this prejudice into a justified reaction." [36]

Practically every one of the arguments used by the racists to prove the inferiority of this or that "race" was not so long ago used by the antifeminists to prove the inferiority of that "lower race," the female of the species. In the case of these sexual prejudices one generation has sufficed to show how completely unfounded they were.[37] It need not take longer to do the same for "race" prejudice. Since this subject provides an instructive and pertinently parallel case history, we shall devote the next chapter to its discussion.

The rationalization is not, of course, regarded as the expression of prejudice, but rather as an explanation of one's behavior—the reason for it. Few rationalizers are aware of the fact that their reasons are simply devices for concealing the real sources of their antipathies, many of which may be quite unconscious.[38] They fail to understand that thought is a means both of concealing and of revealing feelings and that a conviction in the rationality of one's conduct may signify little more than a supreme ability at self-deception. As Professor Brown remarks, "the rationalization is not regarded as cloaking antagonism, but is regarded as a serious interpretation of conduct. No good rationalizer believes that he is prejudiced." Hence, the stronger the reasons we hold for any belief the more advisable it is

---

[36] Brown, "Rationalization of Race Prejudice," *International Journal of Ethics,* LXIII (1933), 305.

[37] Montagu, *The Natural Superiority of Women.*

[38] Alexander, "Antipathy and Social Behavior," *American Journal of Sociology,* LI (1946), 288–92.

to inquire into the soundness of the supports upon which such beliefs rest. This is especially true when the beliefs are as strongly held as they are in connection with "race" prejudice.

The prejudiced individual, constellating ahead of experience, is usually a conformist who worships institutions. He fashions an island of security for himself and clings to it. Any exceptions to his views or beliefs are regarded by him as nonrepresentative and dismissible, for they do not conform to his encrusted system of expectations. What is more, they make him uncomfortable and anxious. They must therefore be suppressed. As Oliver Wendell Holmes remarked, "The mind of a bigot may be compared to the pupil of the eye; the more light you pour on it the more it contracts."

When men have no moral justification for their beliefs or their conduct, they will invent one. Intelligence and humanity call for a tentative attitude, "for an attitude subject to change, 'good for this day only': prejudice is lack of plasticity. A tentative attitude decreases prejudice, for it replaces absolute with relative values . . . breadth of understanding decreases prejudice." [39]

> Through the distorting glass of Prejudice
> All nature seems awry, and but its own
> Wide-warped creations straight; but Reason's eye
> Beholds in every line of nature—truth,
> Immortal truth, and sees a God in all.

---

[39] Wallis, "Some Phases of the Psychology of Prejudice," *Journal of Abnormal and Social Psychology,* XXIV (1930), 426.

9

Antifeminism and Race Prejudice: A Parallel

IN CONNECTION WITH the modern form of race prejudice it is of
interest to recall that almost every one of the arguments used by
the racists to "prove" the inferiority of one or another so-called "race"
was not so long ago used by the antifeminists to "prove" the inferiority
of the female as compared with the male. In the case of these sexual
prejudices one generation has been sufficient in which to discover how
completely spurious and erroneous virtually every one of these arguments and assertions was.

In the nineteenth century it was fairly generally believed that
women were inferior creatures. Was it not a fact that women had
smaller brains than men? Was it not apparent to everyone that their
intelligence was lower, that they were essentially creatures of emotion
rather than of reason—volatile swooning natures whose powers of
concentration were severely limited and whose creative abilities were
restricted almost entirely to knitting and childbirth? For hundreds of
years women had played musical instruments and painted, but to
how many great female musicians and painters could one point?
Where were the great women poets and novelists? Women had
practically no executive ability, were quite unable to manage the
domestic finances, and, as for competing with men in the business or
professional world, such an idea was utterly preposterous, for women
were held to possess neither the necessary intelligence nor the equally
unattainable stamina. Man's place was out in the world earning a
living; woman's place was definitely in the home.

The second decade of the twentieth century, substantially assisted
by World War I, saw the beginning of the dissolution of most of these
prejudices, following the assumption by large numbers of women of

occupations formerly considered exclusively masculine. Women, it had reluctantly to be admitted, did at least as good a job in most of these occupations as men and, it was even whispered by some, there were many things which they did a great deal better. Woman's invasion of industry and her entrance into business has on all fronts proceeded apace. Social and political inequalities have been to a large extent reduced if not entirely eliminated, and women are everywhere in the Western world increasingly being accorded equal rights with men. A certain amount of prejudice still remains and probably always will, but it is nothing compared to what it was at the beginning of the century.

In the eighteenth century men claimed that no woman had produced anything worth while in literature, with the possible exception of Sappho. Since they had failed to do so up to that time, it was a fair assumption that they would never do so. But within the first half of the nineteenth century feminine writers of genius commenced the assault upon the literary citadel and took it by storm: Jane Austen, Mrs. Elizabeth Gaskell, Charlotte Brontë (Currer Bell), George Eliot, George Sand,[1] and Elizabeth Barrett Browning. In more recent times have appeared such distinguished writers as Emily Dickinson, Mary Webb, Virginia Woolf, Edith Wharton, Willa Cather, Edna St. Vincent Millay, Sigrid Undset, Selma Lagerlöf, and Pearl Buck. Nobody any longer doubts that women can write and that what they have to say is worth listening to. But arguments are still heard to the effect that relatively few women have achieved greatness in most of the fields in which men have excelled.

There has been only one great woman scientist, it is said—Mme. Curie. But how many women, it may be asked, have enjoyed the same opportunities as men to become great scientists? What chance does a woman stand to obtain even an instructorship in any of the departments of science in our colleges? I believe that it does not exceed the chance of 1 in 100. The pattern of the antifeminist argument is identical with that of the racist argument. Deny a particular group equality of opportunity and then assert that because that group has not achieved as much as the groups enjoying complete freedom of opportunity it is obviously inferior and can never do as well.

---

[1] Let it not pass unnoticed that these three writers deliberately assumed masculine names in order to avoid the prejudiced judgments which a knowledge of their sex would have elicited.

It is a thought worth pondering whether there may not be some relation between the slackening of prejudices against women and the increase in the intensity of prejudices against ethnic and minority groups; that is, whether a certain amount of displaced aggression is not involved here. Man, it would seem, must have a scapegoat, and for his purposes any distinguishable group will do against which the exhibition of aggression or prejudice is socially sanctioned. It is a likely hypothesis that much of the deep-seated aggression which was at one time canalized in an antifeminist direction today serves to swell the tide of that which expresses itself in race prejudice.

However this may be, the parallel between antifeminism and race prejudice is striking. The same underlying motives appear to be at work, namely, fear, jealousy, feelings of insecurity, fear of economic competition, guilt feelings, and the like. Many of the leaders of the feminist movement in the nineteenth-century United States clearly understood the similarity of the motives at work in antifeminism and race discrimination and associated themselves with the antislavery movement.[2] Very similar devices have been utilized in order to keep women, on the one hand, and "races," on the other, in subjection. In each case, barriers were created. For centuries it was socially quite impossible for women to enter into activities which were regarded as exclusively the prerogative of the male. It was taken for granted that women could never succeed in such occupations. Women have now broken down many of those barriers and shown that they can do at least as well as men in most occupations previously regarded as "masculine."

Modern race prejudice has erected barriers against almost all ethnic groups other than the group of which one is oneself a member. These barriers are calculated to limit and restrict the social participation of such groups and to prevent their ascent in the social scale. By means of these barriers they are set off from the dominant group as members of an inferior caste. But such barriers are removable. As Sidney Olivier wrote in 1923:[3]

> The colored races all over the world are now thinking and aiming exactly as our women have done. The presumption that they are incapable of succeeding is no stronger than the presumption against

---

[2] See, for example, Harper, *The Life and Works of Susan B. Anthony.*
[3] Olivier, "Colour Prejudice," *Contemporary Review,* CXXIV (1923), 457.

women was confidently asserted to be two generations ago. Their intellectual leaders are no more convinced than were the women's leaders of the impossibility of their aims. They are trying, they are going to go on trying, to undeceive us.

We know that to gain even so much as a hearing women had to fight every inch of the way. Ridiculed, maligned, opposed at almost every turn, and even imprisoned, the leaders of the women's movement realized that they would actually be forced to fight—and fight they did. More than any other group it was the militant suffragettes who forced the issue of women's rights and brought that issue to a vote. They pitched no battles, although there were a few clashes with the police, but they insisted on making themselves heard—until they succeeded.

The leaders of groups upon whom the egregious epithet "minority" has come to be visited would do well to take a leaf out of the suffragettes' book. In the year 1963 they finally did.

The Creative Power of "Race" Mixture

ONE OF THE MOST strongly entrenched popular superstitions is the belief that interbreeding or crossing between "races," miscalled "miscegenation," [1] results in inferior offspring and that the greater number of such crossings lead to degeneration of the stock. The commonly employed stereotype has it that the half-caste inherits all the bad and none of the good qualities of the parental stocks. These bad qualities the half-breed is said to transmit to his offspring, so that there is produced a gradual but definite mental and physical deterioration within the group, finally resulting in complete infertility. Not only has the dying out of peoples been attributed to this cause, but it has also been held responsible for "the chronic unrest of eastern Europe, the so-called 'eastern question' " being, it is alleged, "only the ferment of mixed bloods of widely unlike type." [2] It is perhaps unnecessary to add that it was the official Nazi view that race mixture was responsible for the decay of the great civilizations of the past, [3] and it is the stock-in-trade of contemporary racists.

Another view of the dangers of "race" mixture was expressed by the late Madison Grant. According to him, the native American of colonial stock "will not bring children into the world to compete . . . with the Slovak, the Italian, the Syrian, and the Jew. The native American is too proud to mix socially with them, and is gradually

---

[1] For a discussion of the origin and misuse of this term, see Appendix F, pp. 400–01.

[2] Widney, *Mankind: Racial Values and the Racial Prospects*, I, p. 167.

[3] See, for example, Rosenberg, *Der Mythus des 20. Jahrhunderts*, pp. 85–86; Chandler, *Rosenberg's Nazi Myth*, p. 71.

withdrawing from the scene, abandoning to these aliens the land which he conquered and developed." [4]

Here we perceive that it is the fear of "race" mixture, of "race" contamination, and a sense of pride in the "purity" of one's own stock which, according to Madison Grant, is leading to the disappearance of that Old American stock in the United States.

As is the case with most of the evils which have been attributed to so-called "miscegenation," or "race" mixture, there is not a particle of truth in any of these statements. Such facts as they may have reference to are in practically every case due to purely social factors. The colonial stock from which Madison Grant's long-headed, blond, blue-eyed native American is supposed to have descended was far from being the homogeneous "Nordic" stock which he and Henry Fairfield Osborn, who wrote the preface to Grant's book, imagined. It was left to one of those scorned lowly "Slovaks" of tainted ancestry, who had come to these shores as a poor immigrant boy, the distinguished American physical anthropologist Aleš Hrdlička, to show that the colonial stock was a very mixed lot indeed. The evidence indicates that only a few of them could have been blonds and that, for what the cephalic index is worth, the round-headed were distinctly more numerous than the long-headed. [5]

We have already encountered a Greek professor of anthropology, John Koumaris, stating that since "children of mixed parents belong to no race" existing races must preserve their "own 'fluid constancy' by avoiding mixture with foreign elements." [6] To belong to no "race" is apparently stigmatic.

The fact that half-castes often impress those who are not disposed to judge them sympathetically as mentally and morally inferior to their parental stocks is, in many cases, to be explained by the fact that such hybrids are often acceptable neither to the mother's group, on the one hand, nor to the father's group, on the other. That, indeed, is the precise significance implied in the term "half-caste." In most instances the half-caste finds it extremely difficult to adjust to conditions which are themselves the cause of maladjustment in others. Generally it is his lot to live under conditions of the most depressing

---

[4] Grant, *The Passing of the Great Race,* 1st ed., pp. 80–81.

[5] Hrdlička, *The Old Americans,* p. 54.

[6] Koumaris, "On the Morphological Variety of Modern Greeks," *Man,* XLVIII (1948), 127.

kind and to occupy an anomalous and ambiguous position in society.[7] As Castle has written: "Since there are no biological obstacles to crossing between the most diverse human races, when such crossing does occur, it is in disregard of social conventions, race pride and race prejudice. Naturally therefore it occurs between antisocial and outcast specimens of the respective races, or else between conquerors and slaves. The social status of the children is thus bound to be low, their educational opportunities poor, their moral background bad. . . . Does the half-breed, in any community of the world in which he is numerous, have an equal chance to make a man of himself, as compared with the sons of the dominant race? I think not. Can we then fairly consider him racially inferior just because his racial attainments are less? Attainments imply opportunities as well as abilities." [8]

Those who deliver themselves of unfavorable judgments concerning "race-crossing" are usually merely expressing their prejudices. Within the environment which encloses the half-caste we are dealing with a conspicuous example of the action of socially depressing factors, not with the effects of biological ones. The truth seems to be that far from being deleterious to the resulting offspring and the generations following them, interbreeding between different ethnic groups is from the biological and every other standpoint highly advantageous to mankind.

Just as the fertilizing effects of the contact and mixing of cultures lead to the growth and development of the older forms of culture and the creation of new ones within it, so, too, does the interbreeding of different ethnic groups lead to the growth and development of the physical stock of mankind. It is through the agency of interbreeding that nature, in the form of man's genetic system, shows its creative power. Not so long ago, when it was the custom to personify nature and to speak somewhat metaphysically of "her" as the purposive mother of us all, we should have said that crossing is one of nature's principal devices for the uninterrupted production of ever new and more vigorous types of life.

---

[7] For a discussion of the half-caste in our society, see Dover, *Half-Caste;* also Stonequist, *The Marginal Man: A Study in Personality and Culture Conflict;* Reinemann, "The Mulatto Children in Germany," *Mental Hygiene,* XXVII (1953), 365–76.

[8] Castle, "Biological and Social Consequences of Race Crossing," *American Journal of Physical Anthropology,* IX (1926), 147.

Hybridization is one of the most fundamental processes of evolution. Hybridization of plants in nature is a continuous phenomenon; in lower animals it is also continually proceeding; while in man it is an age-old process which was unquestionably operative among his protohuman ancestors.[9] Indeed, if there were any truth in the suggestion that hybridization results in degeneration or decadence, man should have died out long ago or else sunk to the level of a deformed idiot, for he is one of the most highly hybridized creatures on earth. The advantages of hybridization over any other process in developing new human types should be obvious. Evolution by mutation, for example, is a slow and incalculable process compared with evolution by hybridization. Furthermore, far from causing any existing stocks to die out, the infusion of new genes into old stocks may have been the means which has not only saved them from extinction but also served to revitalize them.

Populations consisting of inbred family lines need not be genetically any better or worse than populations which are not mixed, but if, on the whole, we compare the advantages of inbreeding with those of outbreeding, the advantages are chiefly with the latter. Inbreeding is not in itself a bad thing, and under certain conditions may be favorable for the production of speedy evolutionary changes, but there is always a danger of degenerative effects arising from the emergence of concealed deleterious recessive genes. In outbreeding, on the other hand, since the chances of rare deleterious genes coming together are lowered, this danger is reduced to a minimum or altogether eliminated. In general, outbreeding serves to increase physical vigor and vitality. Depending upon the size of the population inbreeding in small populations tends to produce a relative homogeneity of characters; outbreeding, on the other hand, tends to produce a heterogeneity of characters and to increase variability.

The phenomenon of increased vigor following upon hybridization has been long recognized by biologists and is known as *heterosis*, or hybrid vigor.[10] By "hybrid vigor" is meant the phenomenon frequently

---

[9] Darwin was probably the first biologist to suggest that it was the bringing together of dissimilar germinal substances rather than the mere act of crossing, which produced an increase in size and vigor in hybrid plants and animals. See Darwin, *Variation of Animals and Plants under Domestication.*

[10] As early as 1859 Darwin wrote: "Hence it seems that, on the one hand, slight changes in the condition of life benefit all organic beings, and on the

observed as a result of the crossing of the members of two distinct inbred lines derived from different species, varieties, or groups, in which the hybrid, that is, the offspring resulting from the union of a sperm and an egg which differ in one or more genes, exceeds both parents in size, fecundity, resistance, or other adaptive qualities.[11]

From this definition it will be perceived that all possible matings between human beings must result in hybrids, since all potential human matings, whether they occur in the same or in different ethnic groups, are necessarily between individuals who differ from one another in many more than one gene. In practice, however, the term "hybrid" is used to refer to the offspring of two individuals who differ from each other in their genetic constitution for one or more distinctive characters or qualities. The essential difference between these two conceptions of a hybrid is an important one; we shall return to it upon a later page. In what follows we shall abide by the latter conception of a hybrid because it is the sense in which the term is most commonly used.

Evidence of hybrid vigor in man is difficult to obtain because the gene differences between human ethnic groups for the majority of traits are not sufficiently marked. For the same reason we would not expect, and do not find, any degeneration, disharmonies, or infertilities in so-called "race crosses." Inbred plants and animals, on the other hand, constitute highly homozygous strains, often characterized by different chromosome numbers and other genetic differences, which frequently produce genetic disharmonies in the offspring. But this is not the case in man, for the varieties of man are characterized by a high degree of heterozygosity. Heterozygotes are characterized, on the whole, by greater stores of both genotypic and phenotypic plasticity and variability. It has been suggested that hybrid vigor, in the form of benefits which accrue to the offspring and eventually to the group as a result of crossing, occurs because each parent supplies dominant

---

other hand, that slight crosses, that is, crosses between the males and females of the same species, which have been subjected to slightly different conditions, or which have slightly varied give vigour and fertility to the offspring." *The Origin of Species,* Chapter IX.

[11] Genetically this is stated as follows: each inbred line is homozygous or nearly so for its genes or certain ones, but each *different* inbred line is homozygous for different alleles of many genes, with consequent heterozygosity in the F_1s between them.

genes for which the other parent may be recessive. As Scheinfeld has put it, "Suppose some desirable trait ... were dependent for its production on a four-gene combination, 'A-B-C-D.' If, then, only two of the genes, 'A' and 'B,' were common in one racial stock, while the genes 'C' and 'D' were common in the other stock, crossbreeding would bring together the required four genes and prove advantageous. Similarly, where two racial stocks each carry combinations of harmful genes not found in the other stock, intermarriage would reduce the incidence of these combinations and the defects resulting from them." [12] Everyone is acquainted with the offspring of one or more varieties of ethnic intermarriage. Such offspring show the physical characters, as it were, blended of their parental stocks.

The new types which emerge in this way generally exhibit something more than merely the blended sum of the properties of the parental types. That is, they show some characters and qualities which are in their way somewhat novel, characters not originally possessed by, although potentially present in, the groups from which the parents have been derived. We have here the emergence of novelty, the emergents of hybrid syntheses.

Penrose has brought forward excellent evidence to show that hybrid vigor is not exhibited by metrical overdominance in such traits as stature, weight, limb length, and the like, but by changes in fertility connected with subtle mechanisms such as potential resistance to disease. He points out that genes responsible for immunity to infection, if they are dominant or intermediate in their effects, are likely to bestow considerable advantages upon the hybrid. Bridges, for example, tells us that in Tierra del Fuego it was the unmixed natives who succumbed to measles, whereas the hybrids were able to resist the disease.[13] In some cases it is possible that the responsible protective factor was not simply genetic but also immunological, for the conceptus of a woman can actually acquire measles *in utero* without either of the parents necessarily manifesting the disease. Such a child would be born with a lasting immunity.[14] The probabilities are high, however, that hybrid vigor was the responsible factor among the hybrids of Tierra del Fuego. A clear example of the mechanism at work is sickle-cell anemia, which, in the homozygous state, is exhibited in

[12] Scheinfeld, *The New You and Heredity,* 516.
[13] Bridges, *Uttermost Part of the Earth,* p. 520.
[14] Montagu, *Prenatal Influences,* p. 287.

an absence of normal hemoglobin and a resulting severe anemia, which is frequently fatal. Hybridization with normal hemoglobin carriers would result in an obviously immediate advantage, since none of the offspring would suffer from sickle-cell anemia even though they carried the gene for it, and their hemoglobin was not altogether normal. Homozygotes are very susceptible to subtertian malaria, whereas heterozygotes have a strong natural immunity to the disease.[15] Yet one racist writer has seen fit to cite sickle-cell anemia as an example of the disadvantages of "race" mixture! [16]

Penrose has also brought forward convincing evidence that levels of intelligence are prevented from declining because of the more or less continuous process of hybridization within the same ethnic group. Both the differences in fertility and in intelligence as well as in resistance to disease may be due to the slight heterotic effects of many individual genes which in combination serve to produce the improvement.[17]

As might have been expected among mixed populations characterized by a relatively greater heterozygosity than less mixed populations, the hybrids show a highly significantly lower incidence of congenital malformations. Thus, as Murphy has shown for American Negroes in Philadelphia, the malformation rate is 5.7 per 1,000 white babies born, as compared with 3.2 per 1,000 Negro babies born.[18] The significantly lower malformation rate among American Negroes may reflect the influence of a heterotic process, the result of admixture with whites.

The heterotic factor is almost certainly reflected in the findings of Saldanha on the genetic effects of immigration into a rural community some eighty-five miles northwest of São Paulo, Brazil. The population of Capivari consists of some 89 per cent whites, 2 per cent mulattoes, and 9 per cent Negroes. Some 6,742 individuals were examined for, among other things, seven congenital abnormalities. The percentage of abnormalities in the descendants of Brazilians was 5.0, in descendants of Italians 3.3, in the descendants of other nationalities 6.9, and in the descendants of admixture between Brazilians and

---

[15] Montagu, *An Introduction to Physical Anthropology*, 3rd ed., pp. 372–77.
[16] Gates, "Disadvantages of Race Mixture," *Nature*, CLXX (1952), 896.
[17] Penrose, "Evidence of Heterosis in Man," *Proceedings of the Royal Society*, B, CXLIV (1955), 203–13.
[18] Murphy, *Congenital Malformations*, 2d ed., p. 15.

Italians there was only a single instance of abnormality, or 0.6 per cent. In the latter case the individual exhibited Down's syndrome (mongolism), probably a function of maternal age. This strikingly low incidence of congenital malformations in the hybrid group constitutes striking testimony to the beneficial effects of hybridization.[19]

In hybridization the inbreeding rate is reduced, and as a consequence the availability or possible conjunction of rare recessive traits is reduced, while at the same time the increase in heterozygote frequency of new combinations of genes, serves both to reduce the frequency of abnormalities and increase the frequency of heterotic traits. King has suggested that the heterotic effect of hybridization is probably due to the increase in the frequency of non-identical genes.[20]

It is, indeed, a sad commentary upon the present condition of Western man that when it is a matter of supporting his prejudices he will distort the facts concerning hybridization so that laws are caused to be instituted making it an offense against the state.[21] But when it comes to making a financial profit out of the scientifically established facts he will employ geneticists to discover the best means of producing hybrid vigor in order to increase the yield of some commercially exploitable plant or animal product. Should, however, such a geneticist translate his scientific knowledge to the increase of his own happiness and the well-being of his future offspring, by marrying a woman of another color or ethnic group, the probability is that he will be promptly discharged by his employer.[22]

Utilizing the knowledge of hybrid vigor, animal geneticists have succeeded in producing offspring that for particular desired characters are in every way superior to the parental stock, while plant geneticists have succeeded, by the same means, in producing enormous increases in sugar cane, corn, fruits, vegetables, and other economically important foodstuffs.[23] Such hybrids are not inferior to their parents, but

---

[19] Saldanha, "The Genetic Effects of Immigration in a Rural Community of São Paulo, Brazil," *Acta Geneticae Medicae et Gemellologiae*, XI (1962), 158–224.

[20] King, "Inbreeding, Heterosis and Information Theory," *American Naturalist*, XCV (1962), 345–64.

[21] See Appendix G, pp. 402–24.

[22] This has actually occurred in the case of one of the world's leading plant geneticists.

[23] Crocker, "Botany of the Future," *Science*, LXXXVIII (1938), 391.

exhibit qualities far superior to those possessed by either of the parental stocks. They are so far from being weakly that they will frequently show, as in the case of certain kinds of maize, an increase in yield between 150 and 200 per cent. They are usually larger, stronger, fitter, and better in almost every way than their ancestral parental stocks.

As a rule hybridization takes place only between the members of the same species, although interspecific crosses and even intergeneric crosses do occasionally occur.[24] The best-known example of an interspecific cross is the mule, which is the hybrid of a cross between the horse (*Equus caballus*) and the donkey, or ass (*Equus asinus*). The mule combines most of the good qualities of its parental stocks. From the horse it inherits its speed, size, strength, and spiritedness; from the donkey, its surefootedness, lack of excitability, endurance, and ability to thrive on little food. Because of these qualities it is able to adapt itself to conditions in which both the horse and the donkey would fail. Hence, the mule fetches a higher market price than do animals of either of its parental stocks. The mule, however, is itself usually sterile. Knowledge of this fact has, perhaps, been responsible for the notion that hybridization generally results in sterility. This is, of course, quite erroneous except, for the most part, in those comparatively rare cases in which interspecific crosses are involved.

All ethnic groups of mankind belong to the same species, and all are mutually fertile, as are the resulting offspring of mating between the members of such groups. The evidence, though by no means conclusive, suggests that among human beings, as among other forms of life, anything resembling hybrid vigor is most markedly characteristic of the first generation of hybrids. In plants and in lower animals there would appear to be a gradual decline in vigor, possibly owing to the re-establishment of a relative homozygosity by inbreeding. Thus, one of the principal means of revitalizing any group of living forms is by hybridization, by introducing new genes or increasing the frequency of new combinations of genes having adaptive value. This is precisely what has occurred, from the earliest times, in man.

For early man, in process of evolution, we have one example of evolution by hybridization in the Neanderthaloid people, whose fossil

---

[24] For a discussion of such interspecific and intergeneric crosses in the non-human primates see Montagu, "A Hybrid Gibbon," *Journal of Mammalogy*, XXXI (1950), 150–53.

remains were discovered in 1931–32 at Mount Carmel in Palestine.[25] The variability presented by the skeletal remains of the Carmelites suggests hybridization even though that hybridization may have occurred between their ancestors long before.[26]

Inbreeding tends to stabilize the type and in the long run may produce a decrease in vigor. Outbreeding, on the contrary, tends to increase the variability of the type and, at least temporarily, to augment its vigor. This is particularly significant in the case of small breeding groups in which the rate of homozygosis is likely to be more rapid than in larger populations.

It has already been suggested that one of the principal agencies in the production of new human types has been in the past, as it is in the present, hybridization. In fact, at all times in man's evolutionary history he has unconsciously conducted his reproductive life in a manner which the professional stockbreeder would undoubtedly pronounce satisfactory.

Thus, in a treatise on stockbreeding, one of the world's foremost geneticists, Professor Sewall Wright, summarizes the facts relating to hybridization in these words: "By starting a large number of inbred lines, important hereditary differences in these respects are brought clearly to light and fixed. Crosses among these lines ought to give full recovery of whatever vigor has been lost by inbreeding, and particular crosses may be safely expected to show a combination of desired characters distinctly superior to the original stock, a level which could not have been reached by selection alone. Further improvement is to be sought in a repetition of the process—isolation of new inbred strains from the improved crossbred stock, followed ultimately by crossing and selection of the best crosses for the foundation of the new stock." [27]

This, by and large, is actually the way in which new human ethnic groups and varieties have come into being and evolved. First, by iso-

---

[25] For a description of these remains see McCown and Keith, *The Stone Age of Mount Carmel*, Vol. II. For a discussion of the hybridization hypothesis explanatory of the variability of these remains see Montagu's review of the above work under the section "Prehistory" in the *American Anthropologist*, XLII (1940), 518–22.

[26] Montagu, "Prehistoric Hybridization," *Man*, LXII (1962), 25.

[27] Wright, *Principles of Live Stock Breeding*, U.S. Department of Agriculture Bulletin 905 (1920).

lation and inbreeding and the action of various selective factors, then, by contact with other groups and crossbreeding with them, followed once more by isolation and inbreeding. This process has, of course, occurred with various degrees of frequency in different human groups, but that it has occurred in some degree in all is virtually certain.

The evidence indicates, as Julian Huxley has put it, that "The essence of man's success as an organism is that he has not evolved as a set of separated specialized types, but has kept all his genes in a common interbreeding pool." [28]

All that we know of the history of mankind points to constant migration and the intermingling of peoples. Today over the greater part of the earth human hybridization is proceeding at more rapid rates than at any previous period in the history of man, and a vastly greater number of peoples are being involved in the process at one and the same time. The tragedy, however, is that, while the genes combine to produce new types which are often recognizably superior in some traits to their parental stocks and generally novel, the prejudices of men for the most part conspire to render those novel traits worthless and their possessors miserable.

In many parts of the world where colored peoples live under the domination of the white man the hybrid is, by the white man, usually regarded as something of an outcast—"outcast" and "half-caste" being regarded as synonymous terms—an error which, being socially unallowed, if it is to be at all acknowledged, must be viewed with unconcealed disgust. There have been and will continue to be some exceptions to this kind of attitude, but on the whole it will be agreed by those who are at all acquainted with the facts that the hybrid, or mixed-breed, has received a raw deal at the hands of whites.

When, instead of being ostracized by whites, hybrid children and adults are given an opportunity to show what they can do, the results have often been so disconcerting to their alleged superiors that everything possible has been done either to suppress or to distort the facts.[29]

---

[28] Huxley, *Evolution in Action*, pp. 173–74.

[29] In a well-known textbook of psychology an account is given of a young girl who belongs in the genius class, without any mention being made of the fact that she is the daughter of a Negro father and a white mother. In Los Angeles, in nonsegregated public schools attended by Negro and white children, it was found that 500 Negro children ranked slightly higher in intelligence than the white group in the same schools with whom they were com-

It is certainly unequivocally clear to those who are capable of viewing the evidence dispassionately that biologically the offspring of mixed unions are, on the whole, *at least* as good human beings in most respects, and better in some, than their parents. Did we not have good reason to believe this from our daily experience of such offspring, we should expect it upon the grounds of such genetic evidence as we have already discussed.

Here we may briefly cite the evidence, such as it is, for existing populations whose mixed ancestry is known and which have been the subject of anthropological studies.

POLYNESIAN-WHITE CROSSES

In the year 1790 nine English sailors and about twelve Tahitian women and eight Tahitian men landed on the isle of Pitcairn in the mid-Pacific. The English sailors were the remnant of the mutineers of the English warship *Bounty* who had made their escape to this lonely island. The story is now well known. What is not so well known is that the descendants of the English mutineers and the Tahitian women are to this day living on Norfolk and Pitcairn islands. Dr. H. L. Shapiro, who has studied both groups in their island homes, found that the offspring of the initial white-Tahitian unions were numerous, being 11.4 children per female on Pitcairn and 9.1 on Norfolk Island.[30] A large proportion of these hybrids were long-lived, and they have had unusually long-lived descendants. The modern Norfolk and Pitcairn Islanders are taller than the average Tahitian or Englishman, are more vigorous, robust, and healthy, and mentally

---

pared. References to such findings are seldom seen or heard. See Clark, *Los Angeles Negro Children.* An outstanding example of distortion of the facts during World War II was provided by Representative Andrew J. May of Kentucky, chairman of the House Military Affairs Committee, who caused the suppression for use by the United States Army of a pamphlet, *The Races of Mankind,* written by two anthropologists, Professor Ruth Benedict and Dr. Gene Weltfish, of the Department of Anthropology, Columbia University. For an account of this "affaire" see Appendix D. In July, 1947, Mr. May was unlucky enough to be convicted and sentenced to prison for bribery and conspiracy while in office. New York *Times,* December 4, 1949, p. 64.

[30] *Descendants of the Mutineers of the Bounty* (*Memoirs of the Bernice P. Bishop Museum,* Honolulu, 1929, Vol. XI, No. 1), and *The Heritage of the Bounty.*

they are perfectly alert. The general conclusion is that after five generations of inbreeding these descendants of Polynesian-white unions show little if any diminution of the vigor of the kind which generally follows crossbreeding in the later hybrid generations. Hybridity may have little, and environmental factors a great deal, to do with the vigor of these people. One thing, however, is certain: the physical type of these populations is in every way perfectly harmonious, with white characters predominating. As Shapiro concludes:

"This study of race mixture on the whole rather definitely shows that the crossing of two fairly divergent groups leads to a physical vigor and exuberance which equals if not surpasses either parent stock. My study of the Norfolk Islanders shows that this superiority is not an ephemeral quality which disappears after the F_1 or F_2 generation, but continues even after five generations. Furthermore, the close inbreeding which the Norfolk hybrids have practiced has not led to physical deterioration.

"This conclusion regarding the physical vigor of the Norfolk hybrids applies also to their social structure, which on Pitcairn was not only superior to the society instituted by the Englishmen themselves, but also contained elements of successful originality and adaptability. Although the Norfolk Island society is much influenced by European contacts, it has maintained itself—a fact which acquires increased significance in view of the deterioration of the fiber of Polynesian life as a result of European influences." [31] This conclusion also holds good for the Pitcairn Islanders. "As far as the evidence goes, then," writes Shapiro, "the Pitcairn experiment lends no support for the thesis that race mixture merely leads to degeneration or at best produces a breed inferior to the superior parental race. In fact, we see in this colony some support for heightened vigour, for an extended variation and for a successful issue of the mingling of two diverse strains." [32]

Perhaps the best effects of human hybridization under favorable social conditions are seen in the character and the achievements of the offspring of Maori-white unions and their descendants in New Zealand. Both physically and culturally the hybrids combine the best features of both ethnic groups.[33] Native as well as hybrid Maoris have shown themselves in every way as capable as the whites. One Maori

---

[31] Shapiro, *Descendants of the Mutineers of the Bounty,* p. 69.

[32] Shapiro, *Race Mixture,* p. 44.

[33] Condliffe, *New Zealand in the Making;* Keesing, *The Changing Maori.*

has been acting prime minister of New Zealand, while several others have been ministers of high rank in government. A distinguished anthropologist, a physician and the foremost authority on Polynesian ethnology, the late Te Rangi Hiroa (Sir Peter Buck), was the son of a Maori mother and a white father. "I can truly say," he wrote, "that any success I may have achieved has been largely due to my good fortune in being born a mongrel. I am absolutely certain that I could not have accomplished what I have if I had been born a full Maori or a full pakeha [white]." [34]

The achievements of Maoris have been rendered possible by the fact that discrimination and the color bar, except in a few local areas, have never been intensely developed in New Zealand.[35]

AUSTRALIAN-WHITE CROSSES

Social conditions could not be more unfavorable for the offspring of aboriginal-white crosses than they are in Australia, yet all unprejudiced observers agree that the offspring of such crosses represent an excellent physical type and that both the aborigines and the hybrids are possessed of considerable mental ability.[36] There can be little

---

[34] Foreword, in Beaglehole and Beaglehole, Some Modern Maoris, p. xvi.

[35] Ibid., pp. 298–328; Nash, "Democracy's Goal in Race Relationships—with Special Reference to New Zealand," in Laidler (ed.), The Role of the Races in Our Future Civilization, pp. 12–16.

[36] The evidence for these statements is to be found in a large number of scattered books, periodicals, and newspapers. Among these I would particularly draw attention to the following: Wilkins, Undiscovered Australia, pp. 242–62 and the plate opposite p. 256 showing half-caste girls; McLaren, My Crowded Solitude; Cook, Report of the 27th of June, 1933, by the Chief Protector of Aboriginals in the Northern Territory of Australia, reprinted in the Report of the Commission on Mixed Marriages in South Africa (1939), p. 52; Terry, Hidden Wealth and Hiding People; Idriess, Over the Range; Bates, The Passing of the Aborigines; Love, Stone Age Bushmen of To-Day; Porteous, The Psychology of a Primitive People; Montagu, Coming into Being among the Australian Aborigines; Lefroy, "Australian Aborigines: a Noble-Hearted Race," Contemporary Review, CXXXV (1929), 22; Dover, Half-Caste; Dark, The Timeless Land; Herbert, Capricornia; Neville, Australia's Coloured Minority; Barnett, The Human Species, and plate 12 opposite p. 117; Gates, "Studies in Race Crossing," Zeitschrift für Morphologie und Anthropologie, XLVII (1956), 233–315; Gates, "The Genetics of the Australian Aborigines," Acta Geneticae Medicae et Gemellologiae, IX (1960), 7–50; Chewings, Back in the Stone

doubt that were the aborigines and half-castes treated as they deserve to be, they would do quite as well as the Maori or any other people. Cecil Cook, the chief protector of aboriginals in the Northern Territory of Australia, in an official report on the subject made to his government in 1933, stated: "Experience shows that the half-caste girl can, if properly brought up, easily be elevated to a standard where the fact of her marriage to a white will not contribute to his deterioration. On the contrary under conditions in the Territory where such marriages are socially accepted amongst a certain section of the population, the results are more beneficial than otherwise since the deterioration of the white is thereby arrested and the local population is stabilized by the building of homes. It is not to be supposed that such marriages are likely to produce an inferior generation. On the contrary a large proportion of the half-caste female population is derived from the best white stock in the country whilst the aboriginal inheritance brings to the hybrid definite qualities of value—intelligence, stamina, resource, high resistance to the influence of tropical environment and the character of the pigmentation which even in high dilution will serve to reduce the at present high incidence of Skin Cancer in the blonde European." [37] The half-caste males are, of course, to be bred back to "full-blood" aboriginal women. From Dr. Cook's report it is evident that the half-caste, in the Northern Territory at least, is considerably advantaged by his biological heritage. This is undoubtedly true of all half-castes in Australia.[38] In terms that Western peoples readily understand, such facts as the following should not be unimpressive.

Writing in 1899, the Rev. John Mathew states: "In schools, it has often been observed that aboriginal children learn quite as easily and rapidly as children of European parents. In fact, the aboriginal school at Ramahyuck, in Victoria, stood for three consecutive years the high-

Age; Miller and Rutter, *Child Artists of the Australian Bush;* Mountford, *Brown Men and Red Sand;* Berndt and Berndt, *From Black to White in South Australia;* Stuart, *Yandy;* Berndt and Berndt, *The First Australians;* Elkin, *The Australian Aborigines;* McCarthy, *Australia's Aborigines.*

[37] Cook, *Report on the 27th of June, 1933, by the Chief Protector of Aboriginals in the Northern Territory of Australia.*

[38] Tindale, "Survey of the Half-Caste Problem in South Australia," *Proceedings of the Royal Geographical Society, South Australian Branch,* session 1940–41, pp. 66–161.

est of all state schools of the colony in examination results, obtaining *one hundred per cent of marks.*"[39]

In May, 1926, an aboriginal, Jacob Harris, defeated the draughts (checkers) champion of New South Wales and Western Australia, being himelf subsequently defeated by the champion of Victoria. Harris had learned the game at the mission station by watching over the shoulders of the players and was entirely self-instructed.[40]

The extraordinary abilities of Australian aborigines to draw and paint in Western style has only recently been discovered, when for the first time both mixed and unmixed natives were afforded opportunities to exercise their artistic capacities in the style of the whites. The resulting performances have been quite astonishing, especially among the children. The book by Miller and Rutter, *Child Artists of the Australian Bush*[41] contains painting after painting by children, for the most part under the age of fourteen years, which have to be seen to be believed.

The story of the remarkable artistic abilities of the Australian aborigines is instructive because for many years their highly stylized aboriginal art impressed many observers as being rather crude, and was used by some as yet another evidence of the aborigine's behavioral incapacities. But capacities require opportunities for development if they are to be converted into abilities, as the story of the Australian aborigines' latent capacities for artistic creation so strikingly illustrates.

Tindale, who has made a survey of the half-caste problem in Australia, cites a number of cases which suggest that increased vigor is the rule in aboriginal-white crosses. Tindale also gives it as his

---

[39] Mathew, *Eaglehawk and Crow*, p. 78. Mathew's italics. Commenting on Mathew's report, Professor S. D. Porteous, in one of the most wrong-headed and condescending works ever published on the subject (and, of course, supported and made possible by one of our Foundations), says, "Whatever the explanation of the situation, the inference that the aboriginal children excelled the white children of the rest of Victoria in scholarship is, of course, ridiculous." *The Psychology of a Primitive People,* p. 380.

[40] Reported in the London *Daily Express,* May 27, 1926; see p. 11, note 4, in Montagu, *Coming into Being among the Australian Aborigines.*

[41] Miller and Rutter, *Child Artists of the Australian Bush.* See also McElroy, "Aesthetic Appreciation in Aborigines of Arnhemland. A Comparative Experimental Study," *Oceania,* XXIII (1952), 81–94. Read and Mountford, "Australia: Aboriginal Painting from Arnhemland," UNESCO World Art Series, New York, 1955.

opinion that the reproductive and survival rates of the latter are probably higher than among the whites. He concludes: "There seems little evidence to indicate that the difficulties of adjustment mixed breeds may have at present are particularly the result of marked ethnic inferiority. Physically many are of fine type, and have shown their physical superiority for example in sports such as running, football and boxing—their disabilities seem to be lack of education and home-training and the discouragement implicit in belonging to an outcast stock. There may be no mixed blood geniuses, but there are also on the other hand relatively few of markedly inferior mental calibre. The majority are of a mediocre type, often but little inferior to the inhabitants of small white communities which have, through force of circumstances remained in poverty, ignorance or isolation." [42]

ETHNIC MIXTURE IN HAWAII

Hawaii has afforded investigators an excellent opportunity for the study of the effects of the mixture of different ethnic groups. Here native Hawaiians, who are, of course, Polynesians, have intermixed with whites of many nationalities, with Japanese, Filipinos, Chinese, Koreans, Puerto Ricans, and others. All these have intermixed with each other, so that in Hawaii there are literally hundreds of varieties of mixed types. They are all in process of amalgamating, and it is likely that in the future the people of Hawaii will become a more or less distinctive ethnic group. In Hawaii is being repeated what has undoubtedly taken place on both greater and lesser scales innumerable times elsewhere in the world.

Here the evidence is clear that the descendants of the mixed Hawaiian unions are in many ways superior to their Hawaiian and non-Hawaiian progenitors. The part-Hawaiians have a much higher fertility rate than all the other ethnic groups, and they are more robust, while in height, weight, and in their physical characters, as well as mental characters, they appear to be intermediate between their Hawaiian and non-Hawaiian forebears.[43] The native Hawaiian

---

[42] Tindale, "Survey of the Half-Caste Problem in South Australia," *Proceedings of the Royal Geographical Society, South Australian Branch,* session 1940–41, p. 124.

[43] Krauss, "Race Crossing in Hawaii," *Journal of Heredity,* XXXII (1941), 371–78; Adams, *Interracial Marriage in Hawaii,* pp. 232–35.

is inclined to be over-heavy, a disadvantageous trait which tends to be reduced in the part-Hawaiian. The distribution of physical traits in the crosses follows the Mendelian laws of segregation and of independent assortment. That is to say, the children of crosses of the same ethnic groups, in a single family, segregate in their characters —some around the parents, while others resemble the stocks of the grandparents; furthermore, it has been observed that single hereditary characters are often inherited independently of each other.

As a result of six years of intensive study of the Hawaiian population, Dr. William Krauss has shown that not the slightest evidence of any disharmonies is to be found in the hybrids of their descendants and that, while there is no particular evidence of hybrid vigor, the mixed offspring are in every way satisfactory physical and mental types.[44]

Throughout Oceania, including the islands of Melanesia and Polynesia, aboriginal-white hybridization has been proceeding for centuries.[45] Handy, a careful student of Oceanic affairs, declares that throughout Polynesia the mixed breed "is one of the greatest assets which govern a community, both white and native phases," and that the mixed breed is "one of the most solid bonds between the white and the native." [46] This is also the conclusion stated by Krauss for the special case of Hawaii.

In concluding this section on Polynesian-Hawaiian ethnic crossing it is of interest to quote the comment of the former bishop of Honolulu, S. Harrington Littell: "In my opinion the peoples of Hawaii

---

[44] Krauss, *ibid.* Consult further Reece, "Race Mingling in Hawaii," *American Journal of Science,* XX (1914), 104–16; Finch, "The Effects of Racial Miscegenation," in *Papers on Inter-Racial Problems,* pp. 108–12; Hoffman, "Miscegenation in Hawaii," *Journal of Heredity,* VIII (1917), 12; Dunn and Tozzer, "An Anthropometric Study of Hawaiians of Pure and Mixed Blood," *Papers of the Peabody Museum of American Archaeology and Ethnology, Harvard University,* XI (1928), 90–211; Wissler, "Growth of Children in Hawaii: Based on Observations by Louis R. Sullivan," *Bernice P. Bishop Museum Memoirs,* pp. 105–207; Clark, "One World on an Island," '47, I (1947), 14–21; Burrows, *Hawaiian Americans;* and for a discordant view, MacCaughey, "Race Mixture in Hawaii," *Journal of Heredity,* X (1919), 41–47, 90–95; Morton, "Genetics of Interracial Crosses in Hawaii," *Eugenics Quarterly,* IX (1962), 23–24.

[45] For an account of some of these cases see Dover, *Half-Caste,* pp. 176–87; see also Oliver, *The Pacific Islands.*

[46] Handy, quoted by Keesing, *The Changing Maori.*

have gone farther than elsewhere in appreciating the contributions which men of all races and colors are bringing to cosmopolitan thinking and to interracial understanding and good will. They are not perfect, but they have made a good start toward the noble ideal of right and brotherly relationships within the family of God." [47]

ETHNIC MIXTURE BETWEEN INDIANS AND WHITES

In 1894 Professor Franz Boas published the results of a pioneer study on the "half-blood" Indian, in which he showed that the latter was taller and more fertile than the parental Indian and white stocks. In many of his physical characters, as was to be expected, the hybrid Indian presented an intermediate appearance.[48] Since increases in stature and fertility are among the most characteristic marks of hybrid vigor throughout the plant and animal kingdoms, it would be possible to claim hybrid vigor for the offspring of Indian-white crosses. A similar conclusion might be drawn from Sullivan's analysis of Boas's data on mixed and unmixed Siouan tribes.[49]

In a study of Indian-white crosses in northern Ontario, involving Ojibway Indians, Cree Indians, Frenchmen, and Englishmen, Gates found the descendants to be of an admirably hardy type. "They appear to have the hardiness of the native Indians combined with greater initiative and enterprise than the pure Indian would ever show. . . . They push the fringe of civilization farther north than it would otherwise extend, and help to people a territory which would otherwise be nearly empty." The evidence derived from this study, the author concludes, "serves to show that an intermediate race may be more progressively adapted to the particular conditions than either of the races from which it sprang." [50]

Williams's study of Maya-Spanish crosses in Yucatan, where much crossing and recrossing has gone on for almost four centuries, shows

[47] Littell, "All Races Necessary," New York *Times*, September 3, 1944.

[48] Boas, "The Half-Blood Indian: an Anthropometric Study," *Popular Science Monthly*, XIV (1894), 761–70; reprinted in Boas, *Race, Language and Culture*, pp. 138–48.

[49] Sullivan, "Anthropometry of Siouan Tribes," *Proceedings of the National Academy of Sciences*, VI (1920), 131–34. Wallis, "Variability in Race Hybrids," *American Anthropologist*, XL (1938), 680–97.

[50] Gates, "A Pedigree Study of Amerindian Crosses in Canada," *Journal of the Royal Anthropological Institute*, LVIII (1928), 530. See also the magnificent work of Girant, *Le Métis canadien*.

that after some twelve or thirteen generations the Maya-Spanish population, judged by any standard of biological fitness, is a vigorously healthy one.[51]

Goldstein's observations on the mestizo population of Mexico, which is largely a mixture of American Indian and Spanish, show that the mestizos are taller than the original parental stocks and more fertile. They are in every way a thoroughly vigorous group biologically, in spite of the debilitating effects of chronic poverty and primitive living conditions.[52]

The trihybrid Seminole Indians of Oklahoma are, as is well known, the recent descendants of a mixture between runaway Creek Indians, Negro slaves, and whites. The Oklahoma Seminoles have never been studied from the point of view of ethnic mixture, but they have been studied anthropometrically as a single population by Krogman.[53] From Krogman's observations and those of his fellow workers it is evident that the modern Seminole population exhibits, in varying degrees, the characters of all three ancestral types which have gone into its making. The physical types are, on the whole, good, and they are often very beautiful. There is not the slightest evidence of degeneration or disharmony in development.

The same is to be said of the recently described Moors and Nanticokes of Delaware, who are similarly the descendants of Indian, Negro, and white admixture. Furthermore, these two groups have been inbreeding for more than two centuries with no observable ill effects; on the contrary, they appear to be a hardy group indeed, who have managed to make a place for themselves under the most untoward conditions which have been forced upon them by their "white Christian" neighbors.[54]

NEGRO-WHITE CROSSES

The American Negro is, of course, the most obvious and best-known example of the Negro-white cross. Because of the clear-cut

---

[51] Williams, "Maya-Spanish Crosses in Yucatan," *Papers of the Peabody Museum of American Archaeology and Ethnology, Harvard University*, XIII (1931), 1–256.

[52] Goldstein, *Demographic and Bodily Changes in Descendants of Mexican Immigrants.*

[53] Krogman, *The Physical Anthropology of the Seminole Indians.*

[54] Weslager, *Delaware's Forgotten Folk.*

differences in pigmentation, hair color and form, and eye color, the offspring of Negro-white unions and of their descendants afford scientists an excellent opportunity of judging the effects of such hybridization and shuffling and reshuffling of genes. The studies of Herskovits on the American Negro,[55] of Davenport and Steggerda on the Jamaican Negro,[56] and of Little on the English Negro,[57] conclusively show that in his physical characters the mixed-breed Negro stands intermediate between the stocks which generated him. In the American Negro, to be brief, we are developing a distinctively new ethnic type. This type, there is every reason to believe, is a perfectly good one by the measure of biological goodness or fitness, that is to say, by the measure of the organism's ability to meet successfully every demand of its environment—an ability testified to by the fact that in the course of a century and a half the Negro population has increased by fifteen times its original number.

Davenport claimed that hybridization sometimes produces disharmonies, and he also asserted that he had discovered such disharmonies in some of the mixed Jamaicans who were examined and measured by Steggerda. In a work in which a simple table can be headed "Traits in Which Browns Are *Inferior* to Blacks and Whites," when the word "intermediate" would more accurately have described the facts recorded in the table, one is not surprised to discover that the findings upon which this assertion rests have been most strangely exaggerated. More revealing of Davenport's attitude of mind are the following remarks, which surely, as more than one critic has observed, deserve a prize of some sort. Davenport writes: "The Blacks seem to do better in simple mental arithmetic and with numerical series than the Whites. They also follow better complicated directions for doing things. It seems a plausible hypothesis, for which there is considerable support, that the more complicated a brain, the more numerous its 'association fibers,' the less satisfactorily it performs the simple numerical problems which a calculating machine does so quickly and

---

[55] Herskovits, *The American Negro* and *The Anthropometry of the American Negro.*
[56] Davenport and Steggerda, *Race Crossing in Jamaica.*
[57] Little, "Some Anthropological Characteristics of Anglo-Negro Children," *Journal of the Royal Anthropological Institute,* LXXIII (1943), 57–73, Little, *Negroes in Britain.*

accurately." [58] Even when the blacks do better than the whites an argument must be devised whereby their achievement is turned into yet another evidence of their inferiority!

Some of the hybrids measured by Steggerda showed a combination of "long arms and short legs." "We do not know," writes Davenport, "whether the disharmony of long arms and short legs is a disadvantageous one for the individuals under consideration. A long-legged, short-armed person has, indeed, to stoop more to pick up a thing on the ground than one with the opposite combination of disharmony in the appendages." [59]

Three out of four brown (hybrid) Jamaicans are cited in support of this generalization, a generalization which is made by Davenport as if it applied to his own findings on the Jamaican browns as compared to the Jamaican blacks and whites. Professor H. S. Jennings adopted this generalization and made it part of the basis of a discussion on the possible ill effects of hybridization which constitutes the only unsatisfactory section in an otherwise admirable book. [60]

Professor W. E. Castle has cogently disposed of both Jennings and Davenport's generalizations by stating the plain facts as represented by Davenport and Steggerda's own figures. Here are the figures:

TABLE I

LIMB PROPORTIONS AND STATURE IN JAMAICANS

	Black	Brown	White
Arm length in cm.	57.3±0.3	57.9±0.2	56.8±0.4
Leg length in cm.	92.5±0.4	92.3±0.3	92.0±0.4
Total stature in cm.	170.6±0.6	170.2±0.5	172.7±0.7

It will be seen from these figures that the arm length of the browns is, on the average, six-tenths of a centimeter greater than in blacks and 1.1 centimeters greater than in whites, and the leg length of the

[58] Davenport and Steggerda, *Race Crossing in Jamaica*, p. 469.
[59] *Ibid.*, p. 471.
[60] Jennings, *The Biological Basis of Human Nature*, p. 280. Jennings has somewhat modified this in his *Genetics* (p. 280). The same comment may be made on Jennings's "The Laws of Heredity and Our Present Knowledge of Human Genetics on the Material Side," in Corrigan (ed.), *Scientific Aspects of the Race Problem*, pp. 71–72.

browns is two-tenths of a centimeter less than in blacks. It is here that the alleged "disharmony" is presumably to be found. Now, it should be obvious that the order of the differences in total stature is so small —at most not more than 2½ centimeters (1 inch) between brown and white—that it could not make the slightest practical difference in the efficiency of stooping.

As Castle has said: "We like to think of the Negro as an inferior. We like to think of Negro-white crosses as a degradation of the white race. We look for evidence in support of the idea and try to persuade ourselves that we have found it even when the resemblance is very slight. The honestly made records of Davenport and Steggerda tell a very different story about hybrid Jamaicans from that which Davenport and Jennings tell about them in broad sweeping statements. The former will never reach the ears of eugenics propagandists and Congressional committees; the latter will be with us as the bogey men of pure-race enthusiasts for the next hundred years." [61]

In a study of the offspring of Negro-white unions made in the seaports of England and Wales, Fleming found that 10 per cent of the hybrids showed a disharmonic pre- or postnormal occlusion of teeth and jaws. The palate was generally well arched, while the lower jaw was V-shaped and the lower teeth slipped up outside the upper lip, seriously interfering with speech; this disharmony "resulting where a well arched jaw was inherited from the Negro side and a

---

[61] Castle, "Race Mixture and Physical Disharmonies," *Science,* LXXI (1930), 603–06. Davenport replied to this: "We certainly never drew the conclusion that the Negro-white cross is inferior to the Negro or the whites; but we did find some cases of browns that seemed to present greater extremes— and sometimes less well-adjusted extremes—than either of the parental races. Our conclusion is not as Castle suggests it is, that the browns 'are a degradation of the white race.' Our conclusion is given at p. 477: 'While on the average, the Browns are intermediate in proportions and mental capacities between Whites and Blacks and although some of the Browns are equal to the best of the Blacks in one or more traits still among the Browns, there appear to be an excessive per cent over random expectation who seem not to be able to utilize their native endowment.'" "Some Criticisms of 'Race Crossing in Jamaica,'" *Science,* LXXII (1930), 501–02. In another paper written in the same year Davenport expressed himself unequivocally in the matter of Negro-white crosses. These, he wrote, seem to be "of a type that should be avoided." "The Mingling of Races," in Cowdry (ed.), *Human Biology and Racial Welfare,* p. 565.

badly arched one from the white side." [62] No other "disharmonies" were observed.

Fleming states that a "badly arched" jaw was inherited from the white side. In other words, the disharmony was not due to the effects of crossing but to the fact that it was transmitted from the white parent to the child. Such "disharmonies" were limited to only 10 per cent of the cases. It is also possible that, while some of these cases merely represent the expression of inherited defects, not ncessarily exhibited in the jaws of the parents themselves, still others were due to malnutrition, and that the defect actually bears no relation whatever to the fact that one parent was a Negro and the other a white. If this were not so, it would be expected that more than 10 per cent of the hybrids would exhibit "disharmonies" of occlusion.

Little, who examined 220 children of Negro-English parentage in the seaports of Liverpool, Cardiff, and Hull, found no disharmonies of any kind. Only 12 children showed greater or lesser degrees of crowding of the teeth.[63] He did, however, find evidence of increased vigor in the greater stature and weight of these children as compared with unmixed English children of the same class and locality.[64]

I am fully convinced that the whole notion of disharmony as a result of ethnic crossing is a pure myth. Certainly there is some evidence of occasional asymmetric inheritance in hybrids, but this is rare, and it is more than doubtful whether such asymmetries occur any less frequently in the general population than they do among hybrids. The fact seems to be that the likenesses between human groups so far outweigh any differences that such differences as do exist are quite insufficient to produce any disharmonies whatsoever.

As a typical example of the loose kind of speculative argumentation which has marred the discussion of human hybridization, reference may be made to a typical pronouncement upon the subject by an anatomist, the late Professor Charles Stockard. It is perhaps not without significance that Professor Stockard lived for many years in the "black belt" of the South. In an elaborate work calculated to throw

---

[62] Fleming, "Physical Heredity in Human Hybrids," *Annals of Eugenics*, IX (1939), 68.
[63] Little, "Some Anthropological Characteristics of Anglo-Negro Children," *Journal of the Royal Anthropological Institute*, LXXIII (1943), 66.
[64] *Ibid.*, p. 72.

some light upon the effects of hybridization among artificially produced breeds of dogs, Stockard writes as follows:

"Since prehistoric time, hybrid breedings of many kinds have
occurred at random among the different races of human beings. Such
race crossings may have tended to stimulate mutations and genic
instability, thus bringing about freak reactions and functional disharmonies just as are found to occur among dogs. The chief difference has been that in dogs a master hand has selected the freak
individuals according to fancy and purified them into the various
dog breeds. No such force regulates the mongrel mixing of human
beings, and dwarf, giant, achondroplastic and acromegalic tendencies
have not been selected out or established in pure form. On the contrary, individuals carrying different degrees of these tendencies are
constantly being absorbed into the general human stock, possibly to
render the hybridized races less stable, and less harmonious in their
structural and functional complexes than were the original races
from which they were derived. Mongrelization among widely different human stocks has very probably caused the degradation and even
the elimination of certain human groups; the extinction of several
ancient stocks has apparently followed very closely the extensive
absorption of alien slaves. If one considers the histories of some of
the south European and Asia-Minor countries from a strictly biological and genetic point of view, a very definite correlation between the
amalgamation of the whites and the Negroid slaves and the loss of
intellectual and social power in the population will be found. The
so-called dark ages followed a brilliant antiquity just after the com-
pletion of such mongrel amalgamation. Contrary to much biological
evidence on the effects of hybridization, racially prejudiced persons,
among them several anthropologists, deny the probability of such
results from race hybridization in man." [65]

The astonishing conclusion, drawn from crosses between mon-
strously formed dogs which have not the slightest counterpart in

---

[65] Stockard, *The Genetic and Endocrine Basis for Differences in Form and
Behavior,* pp. 37–38. For an excellent independent criticism of Stockard's
views see Lipschütz, *El indoamericanismo y el problema racial en las Américas,* pp. 268–79. For a "racist" account of the decline of Portugal as a result
of intermixture see Landry, *The Cult of Equality,* pp. 92–96. Landry thinks
more highly of Spain, hence, her people "never committed race suicide by
marrying with inferior races" (p. 95).

man, that the disharmonies observed in such crosses offer no "encouragement to the indifferent attitude frequently expressed towards crossing and hybridizing the various human stocks," [66] has been adequately dealt with by Castle. He comments upon this statement: "What human stock, it may be asked, is characterized by monstrous body form, like that of the long inbred dachshund or the Boston terrier? What occasion for alarm about the physical consequences of human crosses have we, other than the actual results of such crosses as shown by anthropological and sociological studies?" Castle goes on to criticize Stockard's "suggestion, without any evidence which justifies it, that racial degeneration among humans is a necessary consequence of racial crosses. No human racial crosses have ever been made or can be made which involve gene controlled differences such as exist between short-legged and bulldog types of dogs, the reason being that such differences, though they may exist in certain families of various human races, do not characterize any race as a whole, to which Stockard extends by implication his caution against human racial crosses." [67]

As for the alleged ill effects of the "absorption of alien slaves," Castle points out that this is a pure assumption. "Besides, slave making in antiquity did not involve racial diversity but only social or political status. Hence his [Stockard's] argument involves a complete *non sequitur*." [68]

In short, the idea that hybrids from widely differing breeds of dogs are often deformed, sometimes infertile, or even unviable constitutes an unsound analogy when extrapolated to man. As Kalmus has pointed out: "In the first place breeds in dogs are not adaptations to natural conditions, but are usually products of fancy breeding, and are often already biologically unbalanced, especially so far as their endocrines are concerned. Secondly, the differences in such characters as size, hairiness and form of skeleton (skull and pelvis) that are found in the various breeds are infinitely greater than those found in the human races, where in numerous mixed populations no signs of incompatibility in mating have been observed." [69]

---

[66] Stockard, *ibid.*, p. 490.

[67] Castle, "Dog Crosses and Human Crosses," *Journal of Heredity*, XXIII (1942), 249–52.

[68] *Ibid.*, p. 252.

[69] Kalmus, *Genetics*, p. 158.

Stockard's reference to "some of the south European and Asia-Minor countries" presumably relates to some of the lands bordering upon the Mediterranean Sea, extending from Portugal and Spain on the west to Turkey on the east. The major lands in this region in which any appreciable "absorption of alien slaves" has occurred are Portugal and Spain. What are the facts? Interestingly enough, while the populations of the Iberian Peninsula are of exceedingly complex descent, North African Negroids have, from the earliest times, made only a relatively minor contribution to that descent. Phoenicians, Celts, Romans, Carthaginians, Teutons, Goths, Normans, Moors of Arab and Berber origin, and Jews, together with North African Negroids and some West African Negroes, have in various regions in differing numbers gone into the making of the populations of the Iberian Peninsula. Far more Negroids were probably absorbed into some of those populations in prehistoric times than have been since, and Negroid genes were probably more widely distributed throughout the populations of Spain and Portugal when both these nations were at the height of their power than were absorbed by them after they had embarked upon the slave trade in the middle of the fifteenth century.

On the basis of such reasoning as Stockard's, the people of Portugal and Spain should never have been capable of attaining anything like the degree of civilization which characterized them up to the middle of the seventeenth century, if Negroid genes could possibly exert a deleterious effect upon a population and its cultural activities. In reality the absorption or nonabsorption of Negroid genes had nothing whatever to do with the yielding to others of the political and social leadership which Portugal and Spain had maintained in Europe. An unprejudiced review of the evidence will show that this was entirely due to the far-reaching changes in the political and social fortunes of Europe as a whole, changes over which neither of these nations could exercise adequate control, and also to the peculiar social and economic organization of the peoples of the Iberian Peninsula itself.[70] The loss of the Spanish Armada, for example, seriously undermined both the power and the prestige of Spain. The fortunate intervention of a storm saved Britain from being reduced to a vassal power and almost instantly reversed the fortunes and status of the two nations. Did

[70] For an illuminating discussion of this see Brenan, *The Spanish Labyrinth*.

genes have anything to do with the storm? No doubt there are some who would maintain that they did.

Another case in point, to which Stockard does *not* refer, is ancient Greece. The civilization of ancient Greece was, all the evidence indicates, the creation of a highly hybridized people. The cranial and cultural[71] evidence leaves little doubt of that. The opponents of "mongrelization" would, no doubt, maintain that the ethnic elements which entered into the making of the Greeks were of a "desirable" type. But by what standard is desirability to be measured? Madison Grant would most certainly not have approved of some of the elements which entered into the ancestry of Socrates, Plato, Aristotle, and Pericles. It is highly probable that these were at least partly of Mediterranean origin, not to mention the possibility of Eurafrican and Alpine elements. It should be clear that any judgment of desirability must be made on the objective basis of the results of hybridization, and the facts show that there is no form of human hybridization which by objective biological standards is undesirable. Those who take the opposite view have thus far been unable to produce any evidence in support of their thesis which would withstand a moment's critical examination.

In individual cases certain unfavorable combinations of characters may occur, but such combinations are no more frequent under conditions of hybridization than they are under the opposite conditions. The point is that human populations are not, like the plants or dogs which the breeder crosses, even relatively purebred lines or species. The peoples of the earth are not sufficiently different from one another to produce the types of extreme or undesirable characters which are sometimes produced in plant and animal crosses of various sorts. The differences between men are simply not extreme enough, a truth which is itself proved by the fact of daily experience that the offspring of unions between members of different ethnic groups show no more disharmonious or undesirable characters than do offspring of unions

---

[71] See Angel, "Social Biology of Greek Culture Growth," *American Anthropologist*, N. S., XLVIII (1946), 493-533; Angel, "Report on the Skeletons Excavated at Olynthus," in Robinson, *Excavations at Olynthus;* and Angel, "A Racial Analysis of the Ancient Greeks," *American Journal of Physical Anthropology,* N. S., II (1944), 329-76. See also Myres, *Who Were the Greeks?;* McClure, "Greek Genius and Race Mixture," in *Studies in the History of Ideas,* III, 25-33.

between members of the same ethnic group. The determining factor in the organization of the new human being, the offspring of any union, is the genetic constitution of the parents, and nothing else. Since the evidence leads us to believe that no human group is biologically either better or worse than any other, it should be clear that hybridization between human beings cannot lead to anything but a harmonious biological development.

Blithely ignoring all the evidence which has made a shambles of the kind of "reasoning" indulged in by such writers as Stockard, Professor Henry E. Garrett, another native of the "black belt," unconcernedly repeats the identical canards.[72]

When we turn from Stockard's pronunciamentos on hybridization to his experimental work, we discover that this suffers from the serious defect that many of his experimental animals represented highly selected artificial strains, some of which were hereditary defectives. Such, for example, are the dachshund, the bulldog, and the Pekingese. The crossing of such defective stocks with normal breeds of dogs will certainly result in a number of defective offspring, and there will generally be as much disharmony as was present in the original defective progenitor. To jump from such an effect to the general supposition that "race crossings may have tended to stimulate mutations and genic instability, thus bringing about freak reactions and functional disharmonies just as are found to occur among dogs," is to abandon the last vestiges of scientific procedure for the hobbyhorse of irrational irresponsibility.[73]

In the first place, under normal conditions such defective animals would have become extinct within a short time, since they could not possibly compete with normal animals. And in the second place, even if the survival of such animals could be imagined, such defects as they transmitted would be due, not to "race" crossing, but simply to the fact that at least one of the animals involved was defective.

---

[72] Garrett, "The Equalitarian Dogma," *Perspectives in Biology and Medicine* IV (1961), 480–84. For the criticism of this article see the same journal, V (1961), 122–43, and later issues. See also Comas, " 'Scientific' Racism Again?" *Current Anthropology,* II (1961), 303–40; Garrett, "The Scientific Racism of Juan Comas," *The Mankind Quarterly,* II (1961), 100–06; Garrett and George, "Findings on Race Cited," *New York Times,* October 10, 1962, p. 46.

[73] Again, of course, this work was supported by one of our most respected Foundations, to the tune of several hundred thousand dollars.

It is not "race" crossing that is the cause of the defect in the off-spring, but the fact that one of the parents was a defective to begin with. As Castle has written in this connection: "Suppose that a white man who was affected with Huntington's chorea should marry a Negro woman and half their children should prove to be choreic (as in all probability they would), could we ascribe this unfortunate occurrence to race mixture? By no means, the same result would have followed had the wife been a white woman." [74]

To associate defectiveness with any "race" of which he himself is not a member is a common device of the racist, but in fact represents no more than a vicious invention which is thoroughly controverted and discredited by the facts.

An unprejudiced examination of the American Negro as a biological type[75] abundantly proves that he meets every test of biological fitness, while his vitality as measured by reproductive rates under adverse conditions exceeds that of the white population.[76]

One of the earliest studies of the descendants of Negro-white mixtures is that made by Eugen Fischer on the Rehoboth Bastaards of South Africa. They are represented by some three thousand individuals who are the descendants principally of Dutch and Low German peasant mixtures with Hottentot women.

If we were asked to name the two human types which would seem to stand at opposite extremes physically, we should probably place the Hottentot or Bushman at one end and the white at the other. The Hottentot is short, has peppercorn hair, is rather free of body hair, is yellowish and loosely skinned, steatopygous (large protruding buttocks), and in many cases characterized by overhanging upper eyelid folds. If disharmonies were likely to occur anywhere, we might expect to find them here; the fact is, however, that the Bastaards are an admirably and harmoniously developed people who exhibit something very like hybrid vigor. They are taller than their parental stocks and considerably more fertile.[77]

---

[74] Castle, "Race Mixture and Physical Disharmonies," *Science*, LXXI (1930), 604.

[75] Lewis, *The Biology of the Negro;* Cobb, "The Physical Constitution of the American Negro," *Journal of Negro Education,* III (1934), 340–88; Myrdal, *An American Dilemma,* pp. 137–53. See also Chapter 15 of the present volume.

[76] Holmes, *The Negro's Struggle for Survival;* Lewis, *The Biology of the Negro;* Myrdal, *An American Dilemma,* pp. 15–81.

[77] Fischer, *Die Rehobother Bastards und das Bastardierungsproblem beim*

These observations are more fully confirmed on a much larger variety of inhabitants of South Africa by Lotsy and Goddijn. These investigators studied the crosses of Bushmen, Basutos, Fingos, "Kaffirs," Mongoloids, Indians, whites, and many others, and their evidence unequivocally disproves any suggestion of the development of any ill effects from such crossings. It proves, on the contrary, that perfectly harmonious and often strikingly beautiful types develop as a result of such matings.[78]

Archdeacon Watts of Swaziland, South Africa, has written of the Swazi-white half-castes: "The half-caste becomes immoral, perhaps, in immoral surroundings, but, in good surroundings, he brings out the virtues of both races as well as their vices—the energy and ability of the European with the lack of greed, the natural obedience and the love of order of the Native. . . . These half-castes should be the natural leaders of the Native in the years to come." [79]

In Brazil, crossing between Negroes, Indians, and whites has been proceeding for more than four hundred years. The mixed population has increased enormously. The physical type of the descendants of such hybrid unions is in every respect biologically efficient and harmonious. Many Brazilians of mixed ancestry have attained the highest distinction in every walk of life.[80] Summarizing the studies of his colleagues and of his own on "race" mixture in Brazil, the late Professor Arthur Ramos, the Brazilian anthropologist, wrote, "Nothing justifies the idea that the Brazilian mestizos have any character of inferiority." [81]

Pourchet in the most recent analysis of Indian-white-Negro cross-

Menschen; Tobias, "On a Bushman-European Hybrid Family," _Man,_ LIV (1955), 179–82.

[78] Lotsy and Goddijn, "Voyages of Exploration to Judge of the Bearing of Hybridization upon Evolution. I. South Africa," _Genetica,_ X (1928), viii–315.

[79] Watts, _In the Mission Field,_ quoted by Cotton in _The Race Problem in South Africa._

[80] Roquette-Pinto, "Contribuição à antropologia do Brasil," _Revista de Imigração, e Colonização,_ III (1940); Pierson, _Negroes in Brazil;_ Bilden, "Racial Mixture in Latin America—with Special Reference to Brazil," in Laidler (ed.), _The Role of the Races in Our Future Civilization,_ pp. 49–54; Ribeiro, "Situação Etnica do Nordeste," _Sociologia,_ XV (1953), 210–59; Turner, "The Negro in Brazil," _Chicago Jewish Forum,_ XV (1957), 232–36; Ramos, _The Negro in Brazil;_ Price, "Race Barriers Broken," _The Spectator,_ 5 September 1952, 291–92.

[81] Ramos, _Introdução à antropologia Brasileira._

ing in Brazil[82] concludes, with Freyre,[83] that "Everything leads us to believe that miscegenation was a valuable contributing factor in the formation of the Brazilian, creating that ideal type of the modern man for the Tropics, the European with Negro or Indian blood to revive his energy."

Similarly, in Cuba, where conditions somewhat approximate those existing in Brazil, the descendants of Negro-white crosses are generally recognized to be of particularly fine physical type and socially among the most progressive.[84]

MONGOLOID-WHITE-NEGROID CROSSES

In a study of the hybrid population of the island of Kisar in the Timor Archipelago, which is the product of admixture between Mongoloid, Indo-Malayan, Oceanic Negroid, and European whites, Rodenwaldt found its members to be perfectly harmonic in type. There was not the slightest evidence of any developmental disharmonies. In their physical and cultural traits the Kisarese were intermediate between the native islanders and the whites, and with 7.3 children per marriage, were considerably more fertile than either.[85]

CHINESE-WHITE CROSSES

Studies of French-Annamite hybrids in Cochin-China and Tonkin by Bonifacy,[86] and also by Holbé,[87] Abel,[88] Huard and Bigot,[89] and

---

[82] Pourchet, "Brazilian Mestizo Types," in Steward (ed.), *Handbook of South American Indians*, V, p. 119.

[83] Freyre, *The Masters and the Slaves*, p. 74.

[84] Personal communication of Professor Armand Angulo.

[85] Rodenwaldt, *Die Mestizen auf Kisar*.

[86] Bonifacy, "Les Métis Franco-Tonkinois," *Revue Anthropologique*, XXI (1911), 259–66.

[87] Holbé, "Métis de Cochinchine," *Revue Anthropologique*, XXIV (1914), 281–93, XXVI (1961), 449–66.

[88] Abel, "Über Europäer-Marokkaner und Europäer-Annamiten-Kreuzungen," *Zeitschrift für Morphologie und Anthropologie*, XXXVI (1937), 311–29.

[89] Huard and Bigot, "Recherches sur Quelques Groupes Ethniques Observés en Indochine," *Travaux de l'Institut Anatomique de l'École Supérieure de Médicine de l'Indochine* (Hanoi), VI (1939).

Tao,[90] pay tribute to the biologically "beautiful results" of the admixture. Tao, for example, studied the offspring of 32 Chinese-French marriages and of 13 Chinese-German marriages in which, in almost every case, the father was Chinese. In every case the offspring were perfectly healthy, exhibiting no disharmonies of any kind.

Fleming examined 119 children who were the offspring of Chinese fathers and white English mothers. In only one instance was there any evidence of any asymmetric or disharmonious physical character in the hybrid. In a 14-year-old boy, "One orbit was Chinese in shape, the eye dark opaque brown and the Mongoloid fold marked. The other orbit was English in type, eye colour the grey with a brown net so common in English people, and there was no Mongolian fold."[91] Such abnormalities of inheritance are obviously extremely rare, as is suggested both by Fleming's findings and by experience.

Among the statements sometimes encountered regarding the alleged disharmonic effects of "race mixture" is that owing to differences in head shape of the "races" involved, as well as to differences in the form of the female pelvic outlet, "an important disharmony might result," that is, a baby inheriting the large head of the "race" of one parent might find itself in difficulties getting born to a mother of a "race" with a narrow pelvic outlet.[92] In the face of the extremely low maternal and infant mortality rates of the Hawaiian population, in which so many offspring of mixed marriages are born, and in the light of the American Negro—white experience (see pp. 304–05), such statements are without the slightest foundation. Investigation of the matter by the United States Army Medical Corps in Japan, in 500 cases where a Japanese woman was married to a white, led to the unequivocal conclusion that "The Japanese woman married to a Caucasian was found to present no greater difficulties in obstetric management than the Caucasian counterpart." [93]

Japanese-white, Malayan-white, East Indian and white, Arab-

---

[90] Tao, "Chinesen-Europäerinnen-Kreuzung," *Zeitschrift für Morphologie und Anthropologie,* XXXIII (1935), 349–408.

[91] Fleming, "Physical Heredity in Human Hybrids," *Annals of Eugenics,* IX (1939), 68.

[92] Davenport and Steggerda, *Race Crossing in Jamaica,* pp. 423–24.

[93] Sargent, Westfall, and Adams, "The Obstetric Risk of the Japanese Woman with a Caucasoid Husband," *American Journal of Obstetrics and Gynecology,* LXXVI (1958), 137–40. See also Morton, "Genetics of Interracial Crosses in Hawaii," *Eugenics Quarterly,* IX (1962), 23–24.

white, and Egyptian-white crosses have not been at all thoroughly studied, but such evidence as we have indicates strongly that the hybrids and the mixed-breeds resulting from these mixtures are in every way satisfactory types.[94]

The evidence here briefly summarized unequivocally indicates that human hybridization and ethnic mixture lead, on the whole, to effects which are advantageous to the offspring and to the group. Harmful effects, physical disharmonies of various alleged kinds, are of the greatest rarity, and degeneracies do not occur.

In this connection it has been said that one cannot get out of a mixture more than one puts into it. This is one of those facile generalizations which are too easily allowed to pass by the uncritical. When we combine oxygen and hydrogen, we obtain water, which is more than the two elements alone could yield. When we combine zinc and copper, we obtain an alloy, bronze, which has far greater strength, and numerous other superior qualities, than the unalloyed metals comprising it; that is certainly getting more out of a mixture than was put into it. When two purebred varieties of plants or animals unite to produce offspring, the latter often show many more desirable qualities and characters than the stocks from which they were derived. Surely the varieties which man presents in his varying ethnic forms would suggest that something more has been obtained out of the mixture of the elements than was originally brought into association. To maintain the contrary would be to subscribe to a genetic fallacy. All offspring of unions between human beings represent the expression of a unique contribution of genes. Some of these combinations may result in individuals superior or inferior or similar to the parents, but invariably one always obtains something different out of the mixture than that which originally entered into it.

---

[94] Dover, *Half-Caste;* Mahalanobis, "Anthropological Observations on the Anglo-Indians of Calcutta," *Records of the Indian Museum,* XXIII (1922–40), 1–187; Mahalanobis, "Analysis of Race Mixture in Bengal," *Journal of the Asiatic Society of Bengal,* XXIII (1927), 301–33; Smith, "The Influence of Racial Admixture in Egypt," *Eugenics Review,* VII (1915), 163–83; Frenchman, "Mixing of Races," *Eugenics Review,* XLI (1949), 98; Trevor, "Race Crossing in Man," *Eugenics Laboratory Memoirs,* XXXVI (1953), iv–45; Gates, "Studies in Race Crossing: The Japanese War Children," *Zeitschrift für Morphologie und Anthropologie,* XLIX (1958), 129–47; Battaglia, "La Genetica Umana e l'Incrocio Razziale," in Biasutti (ed.), *Le Razze e i Popoli della Terra,* I (1959), 323–54.

As Nabours has put it: "In a considerable number of hybrids, to be sure, especially among the higher animals and man, some of the respective characteristics may be blended or arranged in mosaics in such manner as to indicate certain of the qualities of the component races. Even so, such composites generally exhibit, in addition, qualities extraneous to any shown by the original organisms, and at the same time some of the properties of the latter are lost in the process. In this category probably belongs the mulatto, many of whose qualities, in spite of certain degrees of blending, are superveniently different from the mere sum or mosaic of the several characteristics of the white and black races. The respective properties of the ass and horse would not, by simple addition, or mosaically, make a mule, and the cattalo is far from displaying nothing but the sum or mosaics of the several attributes of buffalo and cattle. Nearly all the higher plants and animals when hybridized—and which are not?—exhibit extraneous qualities such that they largely, or completely effect the dissimilitude of the qualities of their several, contributive, primary races." [95]

All this, of course, does *not* mean that the emergent is independent of the genes that have entered into its making; it is, in fact, upon the genes contributed by each parent that, other conditions being equal, the combinations into which they enter to create the new individual will depend.

It should be remembered that gene distributions are not so much a matter of the distribution of genes of individuals as of the distribution of genes within populations. It is not, therefore, a matter of speaking of two individuals who, characterized by either a superior or a mediocre assortment of genes, transmit them to their offspring, but of the continuous interchange and shuffling and reshuffling of every kind of gene within a population to yield a large number of gene combinations. Some of these will be superior to others; in fact, there will be every possible form of variation within the limits set by the genetic equipment of the population. This is true of all populations. No population has a monopoly of good genes, and no population has a monopoly of bad genes; normal and defective genes are found in all populations of human beings. Furthermore, it is most unlikely

---

[95] Nabours, "Emergent Evolution and Hybridism," *Science,* LXXI (1930), 374.

that the kind of defective genes distributed in one population will be found to occur in anything like as great a frequency, if at all, in another population or ethnic group.

As Jennings writes: "In view of the immense number of genes carried by individuals of each race, and their separate history up to the time of the cross, the relatively few defects that have arisen are almost certain to affect genes of different pairs in the two. Hence, when the races cross, the individuals produced will receive a normal gene from one parent or the other in most of their gene pairs; and since the normal gene usually manifests its effect, the offspring of the cross will have fewer gene defects than either of the parents."[96] In a later work Jennings adds: "Thus the offspring of diverse races may be expected to be superior in vigor, and presumably in other characteristics. . . . Data on this point are not abundant, but it is probable that hybrid vigor is an important and advantageous feature of race crosses in man."[97]

Genes peculiar to each group are contributed by the parents to the offspring, and these genes express themselves in new traits and characters not possessed by either of the parents or their stocks. It is in this process that the creative power of "race" mixture shows itself.

The fact is that all ethnic groups and varieties are characterized by biologically fit qualities. Were this not so, they could not possibly have survived to the present time. Hence, when they are crossed, it is not surprising that the hybrids should show qualities which are capable of passing every test of biological fitness and efficiency. True hybrids are, of course, only the first filial generation of crosses; but since all human hybrids are polyhybrids—that is, hybrid for a very large number of genes—hybridization in mixed human populations will often extend over a period of many generations. Thus, because of such polyhybridization over several generations, the tendency will be to add more and more new genes to the common stock and for a considerable number of generations (depending upon the size of the

---

[96] Jennings, *The Biological Basis of Human Nature,* p. 280.

[97] Jennings, "The Laws of Heredity and Our Present Knowledge of Human Genetics on the Material Side," in Corrigan (ed.), *Scientific Aspects of the Race Problem,* p. 71. As "probable" disadvantages of "race" crossing Jennings refers to Davenport and Steggerda's inferences from their observations on Jamaican white and Negro crosses. Jennings, however, admits that "critical and unambiguous data on this matter are difficult to obtain for man," p. 72.

population) to maintain a high degree of variability or heterogeneity. Certainly some poor combinations of genes will occur in individual cases, resulting in some mediocre individuals, but these will take their chances with the rest, contributing perhaps a genius or two, or perhaps a few politicians, to the population before passing on their way or else being selectively eliminated.

Ernst Kretschmer, the distinguished student of human constitutional typology, found in his study of genius that most geniuses were of mixed ethnic ancestry.[98] He goes on to say: "One may assume, with some probability, that the rise of lofty civilizations, blossoming with genius, at other times and in other races and nations, was caused by a similar biological process of cross-breeding. For in individual human biology too, suitable cross-breeding gives rise to richly-developed 'hybrids' who easily outgrow the parental types from which they have sprung. The breeding of genius is thus assimilated to the same process which, in specialist biology, is known as the 'luxuriation' of hybrids [hybrid vigor]. Hence highly developed civilizations are usually produced within a definite time interval after the migrations of peoples and the invasions of conquering tribes which have gradually mixed themselves with the native populations." [99]

Kretschmer points out that it is an error to assume that the immigrating or invading group, as such, has brought genius with it, but rather that the blossoming of a new civilization is due to hybridization alone. This view would, however, tend to make the progress of culture dependent on biological factors, whereas it should be evident that it is cultural hybridization, not biological hybridization, which is principally, if not entirely, responsible for such blossomings of culture.

The more unlike two mating groups are genetically, the more likely it is that for many characters the hybrid offspring will be superior to either of the parental groups and will be a mosaic of their characters for the rest. It is far less likely that the offspring of such matings will exhibit anything like the frequency of defective characters which occurs in matings between members of the same

---

[98] Before this, two geneticists, East and Jones, had stated that "the great individuals of Europe, the leaders in thought, have come in great numbers from peoples having very large amounts of ethnic mixture." *Inbreeding and Outbreeding,* p. 99.

[99] Kretschmer, *The Psychology of Men of Genius,* p. 99.

ethnic group. This is due to the fact that most defective genes are carried in the recessive state and are more likely to be matched within the carrier's own ethnic group than in some other. Furthermore, genes for certain desirable characters unique to different ethnic groups are, of course, carried in the dominant state, and the offspring of such crosses will show the effects of the combination of these genes not only in the expression of certain characters of the parental stocks but also in others which are themselves unique.

While it may be true of plants that in some cases hybrids will combine some of the undesirable traits of both parental stocks, the traits of human beings over a large area of the globe are such that, when under hybridization they do combine, there appears to be a gain on the whole rather than a loss of biological fitness. This is a fact which has not been sufficiently emphasized, and it is one of the first importance. It would seem that all the ethnic groups of mankind possess qualities which under hybridization result, on the whole, in the emergence of novel and biologically fit types, not in reversionary unfit ones. The latter types are definitely the rare exceptions, which in the course of time are naturally eliminated; the former survive and reproduce not only their kind but also, again under conditions of hybridization, new kinds.

It will be seen, then, that the beliefs relating to the alleged harmfulness of hybridization are quite erroneous and that they constitute a part of the great mythology of "race." The truth is that ethnic group mixture constitutes one of the greatest creative powers in the progress of mankind. Professor F. H. Hankins has written that "in the ever-changing texture of racial qualities and in the infinite combinations still to be made there may in the future arise race blends quite as excellent as those which produced the Age of Pericles, the wonderful thirteenth century, the Renaissance, or the present era in European civilization." [100] It is possible to go even further than this and say that the future will see race blends not only "quite as excellent," but also undoubtedly greatly superior to those referred to. Superior in the very real sense that they will lack many of the defective qualities of which all ethnic groups are today more or less carriers. As Professor F. J. Trembley has said: "For a million years man has been fusing, with consequent great increase in form and structure and in cultural

---

[100] Hankins, *The Racial Basis of Civilization*, p. 351. This work contains an exellent discussion of "race" mixture.

heritage. He has produced an incomplete civilization along the way, but it is a civilization which possesses the potential seeds of a heaven on earth. Should we erect any artificial barriers to this fusion which seems to have done so much for man?" [101]

We may conclude with the words of a great American biologist: "So far as the biologist can see, human race problems are not biological problems any more than rabbit crosses are social problems. The rabbit breeder does not cross his selected races of rabbits unless he desires to improve upon what he has. The sociologist who is satisfied with human society as now constituted may reasonably decry race crossing. But let him do so on social grounds only. He will wait in vain, if he waits to see mixed races vanish from any biological unfitness." [102]

---

[101] Trembley, "Evolution and Human Affairs," *Proceedings of the Pennsylvania Academy of Science*, XXIII (1949), 192.

[102] Castle, "Biological and Social Consequences of Race Crossing," *American Journal of Physical Anthropology*, X (1926), 156. See also Barnes, "The Mixing of Races and Social Decay," *Eugenics Review*, XLI (1949), 11–16, and Dickinson, "Race Mixture: a Social or a Biological Problem?" *Eugenics Review*, XLI (1949), 81–85; Snell, "Hybrids and History. The Role of Race and Ethnic Crossing in Individual and National Achievement," *Quarterly Review of Biology*, XXVI (1951), 331–47.

II

Eugenics, Genetics, and "Race"

Human beings are complex organisms, and it is never an easy thing to analyze the motives involved in their behavior. The fact is that the individual himself is rarely able to give a satisfactory account of the motives for his conduct, since the elements entering into it are both numerous and complex. One should therefore be wary in attempting to interpret the behavior of others. This applies with especial force to eugenists. Eugenists are persons who believe that the human race, or their particular branch of it, is rapidly decaying and that, if the race is to be made safe for the future, steps must be taken to eliminate the undesirable decay-producing elements and to bring about a general improvement in man's physical and mental structure by selective breeding. Eugenics means good breeding. Galton, its founder, defined it as "the science of improving stock, which is by no means confined to questions of judicious mating but which, especially in the case of man, takes cognizance of all influences that tend in however remote a degree to give to the more suitable races or strains of blood a better chance of prevailing speedily over the less suitable than they otherwise would have had." [1] It is quite clear from this definition that the founder of eugenics was convinced of the existence of "higher" and "lower," "superior" and "inferior," "races," and that he considered it a desirable thing that the "superior" "races" should prevail over the "inferior" "races," and that as speedily as possible. Thus, we perceive that implicit in the eugenic movement from the outset was the doctrine of racism.

Eugenists are, in general, sincerely enthusiastic persons who are honestly anxious to be of service to their fellows, not to mention

---

[1] Galton, *Inquiries into the Human Faculty and Its Development*.

future generations, but they are also, in many instances, dangerous persons. A little knowledge is a dangerous thing, and a great deal of the world's unhappiness is due to well-meaning persons who, possessing a little knowledge, attempt on the basis of it to make decisions for others whose true nature they do not understand and whose future it would be impossible for anyone to predict. It is to be feared that a large number of the most vocal eugenists fall into this category. Furthermore, it is known that the sins of some eugenists are less venial than the sins of those who have merely acted on the basis of half-baked knowledge. In the United States, and elsewhere, eugenics was early converted into a movement in the service of class interests. This is well seen in the writings of such men, to name but two, as the late Madison Grant and Henry Fairfield Osborn. In this connection Professor E. G. Conklin wrote: "Nowadays one hears a lot of high sounding talk about 'human thoroughbreds,' which usually means that those who use this phrase desire to see certain narrow and exclusive social classes perpetuated by close inbreeding; it usually has no reference to good hereditary traits wherever found, indeed such traits would not be recognized if they appeared outside of the 'four hundred.' Such talk probably does neither harm nor good; the 'social thoroughbreds' are so few in number and so nearly sterile that the mass of the population is not affected by these exclusive classes." [2]

So long as no attempt is made to impose such views upon the population, no great harm can be done. All of us, however, have some knowledge of the tragic effects of the teaching of mythological "race" doctrines and of the practice of "race" hygiene in Germany. Similar attempts have frequently been made in the United States, bills having been introduced into state legislatures, and passed in thirty of them, making it either a criminal offense or unlawful for persons of different colors or "races" to intermarry, as well as in any way to assist such a union.[3] Such activities, among others, have caused eugenics to fall into disrepute among scientific students of eugenics and genetics, genetics being the science of heredity upon which eugenics is allegedly based. The clear stream of science must not be polluted by the murky visions of politicians and the prescriptions of

[2] Conklin, *Heredity and Environment*, p. 306. For a brilliant "anatomy" of some of the English eugenists see Hogben, *Dangerous Thoughts*, pp. 44–58.
[3] See Appendix G.

effete castes distinguished by a hypertrophied sense of their own importance.

While it is praiseworthy to look forward to, and to work for, a more humane humanity and a world with fewer imbeciles, degenerates, and criminals and greater numbers of highly intelligent and healthy persons, it is quite certain that such a state could never be achieved by such practices as the eugenists have in the past recommended.[4] Inherited disorders, such as certain extreme types of feeble-mindedness, may call for sterilization, but one is deceived if one believes that by such measures feeble-mindedness would be appreciably reduced. Were every feeble-minded individual to be sterilized for the next two thousand years, the reduction in the number of feeble-minded individuals in the population at the end of that time would not exceed 50 per cent. Superior methods are available, but they do not appeal to eugenists, who fail to understand that eugenics should be a social science, not a biological one.

The objections to negative eugenics are clear, unequivocal, and unanswerable. The recommendations of negative eugenics are: (1) theoretically unsound, and therefore (2) practically unjustifiable, not to mention the dangers of the political misapplication of such unsound ideas, as we saw in Nazi Germany; (3) fertility is generally reduced in those affected by recessively determined abnormalities; (4) even when such individuals breed, their offspring in most cases are normal; (5) even if it were possible, sterilization of the heterozygous carriers would waste an enormous potential of normal births; (6) conditions due to rare dominant genes usually result in infertile individuals; and in (7) other conditions due to unfavorable dominant genes the fertility is usually low, hence, (8) most conditions due to defective genes are self-limiting since their bearers do not propagate; (9) carriers of defective genes also carry a large number of normal genes which in homozygous state often give rise to above-average traits; (10) many hereditary disorders are amenable to environmental alleviation; (11) the increase in population mobility and the collapse of innumerable barriers to intermixture between large numbers of peoples who were hitherto separated reduces

---

[4] I say "past" because at the present time there are happy evidences of a return to sanity among some eugenists. See, for example, Frederick Osborn's *A Preface to Eugenics*. See also Huxley, "Eugenics and Society," in his *Man Stands Alone*.

the chances of deleterious genes coming together; (12) sterilizing homozygotes who show a defective trait due to recessive genes still leaves by far the greater number of individuals carrying the gene in heterozygous state to circulate freely throughout the population. If, for example, the frequency of a recessive gene in the general population were 1 in 1,000, that would mean that the homozygote in whom the defective trait was expressed would occur in 1 out of 1,000,000 individuals. Supposing the homozygous individual were sterilized, that would still leave 999 heterozygotes to distribute the gene. Clearly, a rather inefficient and ineffectual way of dealing with the problem; (13) since the number of genes of any given sort in the human species is usually very large, any artificially induced changes in their number in any local portion of the species is likely to have very little if any effect upon the total frequency; and finally (14) because negative eugenics overlooks such facts it would certainly do more damage to the human species than defective genes are capable of doing.

The very condition of feeble-mindedness, for example, one of the most popular of the biological bogeys of the eugenist, is often the expression of inadequate socialization or education in the process of becoming a social human being. In offering their dubious cures for our alleged ills the extremists among eugenists go even further and pretend to perceive biological differences between "races." They arbitrarily designate as "superior" the "race" or stock to which they happen to belong and as "inferior" all or most of the others. The corollary to this is that "race mixture" should be prevented if "racial" degeneration, according to their definition, is not to ensue. It is with this aspect of eugenics that we are concerned here.

The term "race," as we have seen, is an unscientific one. Science knows of nothing in the real world relating to human beings which in any way corresponds to what this term is usually assumed to mean, that is, a group of individuals marked off from all others by a distinctive heredity and the possession of particular physical and mental characters. In this sense there is actually only one race, or one thing which corresponds to it, and that is the human race, embracing every human being. It is, of course, clear that there exist certain groups within the human race which are characterized by differences in pigmentation, hair form, nose form, and other traits. These we have already called "ethnic groups." If, as seems clear, all human groups are derived from a common ancestry, then it is also clear that such differences represent the expression of the combined action of mutant genes, genetic drift, hybridization, natural and social selection. In any event, such ethnic groups would by the very fact of their existence prove, in the scale of natural values, biologically fit. There can, therefore, be no argument on the score of the physical or biological structure of any ethnic group—unless an appeal be made to purely arbitrary and irrelevant aesthetic standards. Actually, the argument is always based on the existence of alleged mental and cultural differences; these are invariably assumed to be biologically determined. For such an assumption there is not, as we have seen, a scrap of evidence. On the contrary, the substantial body of evidence now available proves that when the members of any variety of mankind are given for the first time adequate opportunities, they do, on the average, quite as well as any who have long enjoyed the advantages of such opportunities. And as Boas has said, "if we were to select the most intelligent, imaginative, energetic and emotionally stable third of mankind, all races would be represented." [5]

There exists no evidence whatever that mental ability and cultural achievement are functions which are in any way associated with genes linked with those for skin color, hair form, nose shape, or any other physical character. It is, therefore, from the genetic standpoint, impossible to say anything about a person's mental ability or cultural achievement on the basis of such physical characters alone. Cultural differences between peoples are due to a multiplicity of historical causes which have nothing whatever to do with genes and which are essentially and fundamentally of a social nature. To the same causes are due the differences in cultural conduct, the behavior, of the members of those different cultures. Hence, on biological grounds and as a consequence of the common ancestry of all peoples—however much they may differ from one another in their physical characters—there is every reason to believe that innate mental capacity is more or less equally distributed in all its phases in all human groups. If this is so, and this is a matter which can be tested, there can be not the slightest justification for the assertion that ethnic mixture would lead to the intellectual deterioration of any people. The evidence is

---

[5] Boas, *Anthropology and Modern Life,* p. 75.

all to the contrary, as the facts of hybridization among human beings prove.

In this connection Julian Huxley has written that he regards it as "wholly probable that true Negroes have a slightly lower average intelligence than the whites or yellows."[6] But neither this nor any other eugenically significant point of racial difference has yet been scientifically established.[7]

"Further, even were the probability to be established that some 'races' and some classes are genetically inferior to others, as a fact, it seems certain, on the basis of our present knowledge, that the differences would be small differences in average level, and that the ranges would overlap most of their extent—in other words, that a considerable proportion of the 'inferior' group would be actually superior to the lower half of the 'superior' group. Thus no really rapid eugenic progress would come of encouraging the reproduction of one class or race against another." [8]

Huxley commits a rather common methodological error when he opines that true Negroes probably have a slightly lower average intelligence than whites or yellows. The question must be asked: "Average intelligence measured by what standard?" Surely, it should at this late date be evident that intelligence, by whatever standard it is measured, is always a function of cultural experience[9] as well as of inherent quality. The fact that this is so is strikingly brought out with reference to the Negroes themselves and in relation to whites by the

---

[6] It is of interest to note that Huxley's grandfather, Thomas H. Huxley, wrote in 1865: "It may be quite true that some negroes are better than some white men; but no rational man, cognizant of the facts, believes that the average negro is the equal, still less the superior, of the average white man. . . . The highest places in the hierarchy of civilization will assuredly not be within the reach of our dusky cousins." "Emancipation—Black and White," in his *Science and Education*, pp. 64–65.

[7] Elsewhere Huxley states that "the genetic variability of the human species is so well distributed that the average genetic difference between classes or social groups and different nations or ethnic groups is negligible or small in its effects compared with the improvements which can be effected through better living conditions and education." *Heredity East and West*, p. 185.

[8] Huxley, *Man Stands Alone*, p. 53.

[9] Not to mention numerous other environmental factors, prenatal, nutritional, neuro-humoral influences depending upon the mother's psychological state, and the like. See Montagu, *Prenatal Influences;* Montagu, *Life Before Birth*.

results obtained in the Army intelligence tests carried out on Negro and white recruits during World War I. These tests showed that Northern Negro recruits on the average did better on the tests than Southern Negro recruits. The tests also showed that Negroes from certain Northern states on the whole did better in the tests than white recruits from almost all the Southern states. Here are the median scores of the groups concerned.

TABLE 2

ARMY COMPREHENSIVE ALPHA TESTS: WHITE RECRUITS FROM ELEVEN
SOUTHERN STATES COMPARED WITH NEGRO RECRUITS FROM
FOUR NORTHERN STATES[a]

WHITES		NEGROES	
State	Median Score	State	Median Score
Arkansas	35.60	Ohio	45.35
Mississippi	37.65	Illinois	42.25
North Carolina	38.20	Indiana	41.55
Georgia	39.35	New York	38.60
Louisiana	41.10		
Alabama	41.35		
Kentucky	41.50		
Oklahoma	43.00		
Texas	43.45		
Tennessee	44.00		
South Carolina	45.05		

[a] Computed from the data in Yerkes (ed.), "Psychological Examining in the United States Army," *Memoirs of the National Academy of Sciences*, XV (1921), 690 and 691, tables 205–06. Data for the Negro recruits was available for only twenty-four out of the forty-eight states and the District of Columbia. Had data been available for all areas of the United States, it is quite probable that several more states would have shown higher median scores for Negroes than for whites of some other states. See Montagu, "Intelligence of Northern Negroes and Southern Whites in the First World War," *American Journal of Psychology*, LXVIII (1945), 161–88.

From this table it will be seen that the Negroes from Ohio with a median score of 45.35 did better than the whites of eleven states, all of which happen to be Southern. The Negroes of Illinois with a score of 42.25 and the Negroes of Indiana with a score of 41.55 did better than the whites from seven Southern states, while the Negroes from New York with a score of 38.60 did better than the whites from three Southern states. All the evidence indicates that the Negroes from the Northern states who did better than the Negroes and whites from the Southern states listed did so not because of any inborn differences between them but because the social and economic opportunities of the Northern Negroes had been superior to those enjoyed by Southern Negroes and whites. The results of these tests have been fully corroborated by tests made on Northern and Southern Negro children.[10]

Marcuse and Bitterman have shown that the scores made on these tests are highly correlated with the yearly educational expenditures of the states from which the testers were drawn as well as with the per capita income prevailing in those states. These facts are well brought out in Table 3, and, as Marcuse and Bitterman remark, "It

TABLE 3

RANK-ORDER CORRELATIONS BETWEEN MEDIAN BETA SCORES FOR THE
VARIOUS STATES AND MEDIAN ALPHA SCORES,
ANNUAL EDUCATIONAL EXPENDITURES (1910)
AND PER CAPITA INCOMES (1919)[a]

	Educational Expenditures Per Capita Population 5–17 Years	Per Capita Income	Alpha[b] (White)	Alpha[b] (Negro)
Beta (white)[c]	.64 (.81)[d]	.50 (.64)[d]	.67	
Beta (Negro)[c]	.72 (.76)[d]	.67 (.72)[d]		.65

[a] From Marcuse and Bitterman, "Notes on the Results of Army Intelligence Testing in World War I," Science, CIV (1946), 231–32.
[b] Alpha tests were given to literates.
[c] Beta tests were designed for illiterates and foreigners.
[d] Figures in parentheses are comparable correlations with median Alpha scores.

is probably most warranted to conclude from the correlations presented here that Beta scores, like Alpha scores, are strongly influenced

---

[10] Klineberg, Negro Intelligence and Selective Migration.

by cultural factors concomitant with the socioeconomic levels of the states." [11]

It is not impossible that there exist differences in the distribution of the kinds of temperament, intelligence, and other behavioral traits in different ethnic groups, but if such differences exist, they must, as Huxley has pointed out, be very small. The important fact is, surely, that every living ethnic group has survived to the present time because it has been able to meet the demands of its particular environment or environments with a high order of intelligence, of mental plasticity and adaptability, and the necessary physical vigor. This is a truth which holds for the most isolated group of aborigines as for the most highly cultured peoples. Measured by such standards, it seems probable that there are no significant differences in the intelligence potentials of different ethnic groups.

When eugenists assert that there has been a great increase in degeneracy, criminality,[12] and feeble-mindedness and that the race is rapidly deteriorating, they do so generally without benefit of a full knowledge of the facts whereof they speak, for the truth is that except for the ex-cathedra manner in which such statements are usually delivered, little real evidence is ever forthcoming in support of their jeremiads. The good will to help is blind and often cruel if it is not guided by true insight based on knowledge. A physician can be of use only when he has first carefully investigated the cause of disease and when it is quite clear what his remedies can effect; otherwise he is a positive danger.

Dr. Irving Langmuir, in his presidential address to the American Association for the Advancement of Science, uttered a pertinent criticism in this connection. "We often hear realists," he said, "deplore the effects of charity which tend to keep the unfit alive. We are even told that the whole course of evolution may be revised in this way. Similar arguments could be used against the surgeon who removes an appendix or a doctor who uses a sulfa drug to cure pneumonia.

---

[11] Marcuse and Bitterman, "Notes on the Results of Army Intelligence Testing in World War I," *Science,* CIV (1946), 231–32.

[12] For an examination of the problem of crime in our society see Montagu, "The Biologist Looks at Crime," *Annals of the Academy of Political and Social Science,* CCXVII (1941), 46–57; Merton and Montagu, "Crime and the Anthropologist," *American Anthropologist,* XLII (1940), 384–408; Bonger, *Race and Crime;* Barnes and Teeters, *New Horizons in Criminology.*

"But what is the need of developing a race immune to appendicitis if we possess means of preventing their ill-effects? The characteristics that determine fitness merely change from those of immunity to those which determine whether a race is able to provide good medical treatment."[13]

Today our many varieties of recording facilities are immeasurably superior to those in existence a hundred years ago, and our hospitals, physicians, asylums, police, and incentives to crime are vastly more numerous. Yet, in spite of all these tokens of decline, the expectation of life of the average individual at birth has in modern times practically doubled, while some of the worst scourges of mankind, such as the vitamin-deficiency diseases, the venereal diseases, typhoid, typhus, yellow fever, diphtheria, tuberculosis, and many others, have been brought under control. During this period there has been such a burgeoning of invention and discovery, such a flowering of intellectual development, as the world has never before witnessed, and all this, presumably, as a sort of efflorescence of the process of deterioration. The swan song of a world the eugenist never made. Or have the great achievements of the past hundred years, perhaps, been due to the genius of a few individuals who have managed to carry the burden of the mediocrities along with them? This is a view which is frequently urged by "superior" persons. It is a sad commentary upon the understanding and the charity of those who hold it and it does scant justice to untold millions of individuals who were never given a chance, who made good as best they knew how—which was more often than not as best they were permitted—and who died unmourned and unremembered.

Let us give human beings equal social, cultural, and economic opportunities, and then we shall be able to judge how many, if any, genetically inadequate individuals we have among us. We shall then be in a position to judge the nature of the biological measures which ought to be instituted to ensure the welfare of our species. Surely it should be clear that these measures would not really be biological, but social, and that in their effects the social advantages would always be greater than the biological ones. This would, surely, be the most reasonable procedure, in view of the fact that in most cases it would take many hundreds of years to eliminate, even partially, a single de-

---

[13] Langmuir, "Science, Common Sense and Decency," *Science,* XCVII (1943), 6.

fective trait.[14] Only a few generations would be required for a purely social process to determine whether or not many of the alleged deteriorative factors which are said to be undermining the health of the "race" could be eliminated by improving the social environment. Our present social ills are, for the most part, produced not by genetically inadequate persons, but by socially inadequate ones, and the remedy for those ills therefore lies first in the improvement of the social environments of our species. Our troubles, it must be repeated, emanate not from biological defectives but from social defectives; and, in general, social defectives are produced by society, not by genes. It is social, not biological, therapy that is indicated.

The great fallacy committed by eugenists and by numerous others is that, having to some extent followed the work of geneticists in breeding certain characters in lower animals within the walls of a laboratory, they have extrapolated from the laboratory findings on such lower animals to conditions vastly more complex and obscure, and which have, moreover, never formed the subject of experimental investigation. Human beings are not representative of strains similar to the selected pure strains of mice and rabbits which form the geneticist's material. Naive and uninformed persons believe that if in the geneticist's breeding laboratory the genetics of a certain character is studied and the experimenter can at will breed his animals for that character, the same thing can be done for human beings. Theoretically and under certain ideal conditions and given scores of generations of selected human beings this could be done for some, but not for all, characters. Obviously this is impractical; if it were practical it would still be open to question whether it would be desirable.[15]

---

[14] Informed eugenists are well aware of this fact, but the informed eugenist in practice has often been indistinguishable from the extreme eugenist. Whatever the informed eugenist may say, we must judge him, as we must everyone else, by what he does or proposes to do.

[15] While breeding for certain desirable characters in plants or lower animals, it frequently happens that certain undesirable characters are developed. The genes for these, carried as recessives, under normal conditions remain unexpressed, but under controlled breeding find expression because of their unsuspected linkage with the genes physiologically associated with the character considered desirable. For example, Asdell has observed that "all the intersexual goats he had seen (about 200 now) were hornless. Hornlessness is inherited as a simple dominant. Since then much inquiry and observation have failed to unearth a single intersex. If they exist, they must be very rare. This sug-

Geneticists, to whose work the eugenist frequently appeals, have in some cases not been altogether guiltless in assisting the purposes of the eugenist, and some of them are scientifically almost as badly deluded as is the most uncritical of eugenists.[16] Much of the research of geneticists has been on breeds of domesticated plants and animals which have been rendered highly uniform by intense inbreeding and selection. Geneticists have also studied characters which are produced by mutant genes, and certain human congenital abnormalities. Others studied the effects of crossing between species. From these researches a great body of facts emerged which, by some geneticists, were at once extrapolated to man and uncritically applied to the differences between human groups. The error committed here lies in the assumption that human groups are genetically as simple as domestic races of plants or animals. They are not. And, as Haldane has pointed out, the attempt to build a human genetics on the basis of results obtained from domestic races, laboratory mutants, and species crosses is as erroneous as would be the attempt to build biochemistry on a study of the reaction of simple crystalloids. This does not mean that much needed and invaluable information for the better understanding of the genetics of man cannot be obtained from researches on natural and artificial populations of animals, but it does mean that one must be extremely cautious in making use of such data.

A special duty therefore devolves upon the geneticist to take special pains to minimize the possible misinterpretations which his findings may be given, for such misinterpretations can be socially extremely dangerous. He should himself be clear and make it clear to others that his findings are misleading when applied to human groups.

---

gests that there is a close linkage between the two genes, an important point economically, since selection for hornlessness has been practiced by pedigree goat breeders for some time. The goat breeders have evidently been increasing the gene frequency for intersex by selecting for hornlessness and are thus doing themselves harm." Asdell, "The Genetic Sex of Intersexual Goats and a Probable Linkage with the Gene for Hornlessness," *Science*, XCIX (1944), 124.

[16] See, for example, the article by the distinguished geneticist Cyril D. Darlington, "The Genetic Understanding of Race in Man," *International Social Science Bulletin* (UNESCO), II (1950), 479–88. See also the reply to this by Montagu, "Answer by an Anthropologist to a Geneticist about the Understanding of Race in Man," *International Social Science Bulletin* (UNESCO), III (1951), 1007–10.

Unlike many eugenists, scientists frankly confess that they do not know all the answers.

The truth is that we do not yet know enough about human heredity to meddle with human beings in order to improve the stock. Two mediocrities may produce a genius; two geniuses may produce a mediocrity. In view of the fact that the genes for defective characters are frequently carried in the recessive condition, it is generally impossible to spot them in apparently otherwise normal individuals, and it is in most cases therefore impossible to predict when they are likely to crop out. Selective breeding, as understood by the eugenist, is inbreeding, and that is a notoriously dangerous process, for by such means the chances are greatly increased of bringing together recessives of a character detrimental to the organism. By outbreeding such recessives become associated with dominants and therefore remain unexpressed. When selection is practiced on animals, we keep only those animals which exhibit a particular character; the others, showing undesirable characters, are killed. Mankind, it is very much to be feared, is not to be saved by being treated like a lot of race horses or a strain of dogs, at the fancier's discretion. Human beings must be treated as human beings, as something rather more than animals; for the ills from which our particular sample of mankind suffers result from the misuse of mankind's capacities for being human. Those ills are not due to the totally irrelevant fact that man is a member of the animal kingdom subject to the laws of genetics as is any other animal.

In effect, eugenists tell us that by random mating defective characters are accumulated in the recessive state until the whole population becomes affected. The defects so carried will then become expressed and will wreak havoc upon such a population. Upon this kind of fantastic reasoning Dobzhansky has made the following adequate comment:

"It is not an easy matter to evaluate the significance of the accumulation of germinal changes in the population genotypes. Judged superficially, a progressive saturation of the germ plasm of a species with mutant genes a majority of which are deleterious in their effects is a destructive process, a sort of deterioration of the genotype which threatens the very existence of the species and can finally lead only to its extinction. The eugenical Jeremiahs keep constantly before our eyes the nightmare of human populations accumulating recessive genes that produce pathological effects when homozygous. These prophets of doom seem to be unaware of the fact that wild species in the state of nature fare in this respect no better than man does with all the artificiality of his surroundings, and yet life has not come to an end on this planet. The eschatological cries proclaiming the failure of natural selection to operate in human populations have more to do with political beliefs than with scientific findings." [17]

Certainly we could do a great deal to reduce the number of the hopelessly defective among us. It is also important to realize that thousands upon thousands of seriously defective individuals are today alive who under natural conditions would not have survived long. It should, however, be clear that wherever in an ethnic group or nation such individuals exist they constitute a problem which can be dealt with by social means alone—social means based upon humane social principles and sound scientific knowledge. To proceed on the basis of the one without the other would be dangerous and undesirable.

It is among the white peoples of the earth that the greatest number of defectives are to be found. The nonliterate peoples of the earth generally sacrifice their defectives as soon as the defect, or anything approximating a defect in their eyes, becomes apparent. Such heroic measures are, fortunately, replaceable by more effective means of prevention. These are matters which each people must determine for itself, following procedures agreed upon preferably in international conference. At the present time the normal healthy person is in all ethnic groups far more numerous than the defective person, and the chances are excellent that crossbreeding between such groups will decrease rather than increase the incidence of defectives. Hence, we may conclude that there is nothing in the nature of any ethnic group, taken as a whole, which could upon either genetic or eugenic grounds be construed as leading to any bad effects under crossing.

In conclusion, then, until man has put his social house in order, it would be unwise for him to indulge in any strenuous biological exercises, for a rickety house standing on shaky foundations is not the proper place for such acrobatics.

---

[17] Dobzhansky, *Genetics and the Origin of Species,* 1st ed., p. 126.

12

"Race" and "Culture"

THE QUESTIONS are often asked: "Why is it that the cultures of different 'races' differ so much from one another? Is this due to the fact that 'race' and culture are inseparably connected?" "Do differences in 'race' have anything to do with the differences in cultural development as between the 'races'?"

The answer to these questions is really simple. Cultures differ from one another to the extent to which the history, the experience, of each of the interacting groups has differed. By "history," by "experience" we mean anything that a person or group of persons has undergone or lived, perceived, or sensed. No matter with what variety of mankind we may be concerned or with what groups of a particular variety, culture is in its broadest and fundamental sense not merely an aspect but a function of experience.

"Race" and culture do not appear to be in any way connected. As Klineberg has pointed out: "The argument from the cultural contributions of a particular ethnic group to the inborn racial characteristics of that group falls down for many reasons: cultures may vary while race remains unchanged, the same culture may be found in groups of different race, what looks like a superior cultural contribution from one point of view may seem much less significant when another criterion is applied, etc. Studies of race mixture are similarly inconclusive, since individuals of mixed racial heredity cannot be shown to be different in their inborn psychological characteristics from those of 'pure' race. Finally, there is no evidence that some racial groups are biologically more 'primitive' or undeveloped than others.

"This does not mean that heredity plays no part in the determination of behaviour. On the contrary, there is good evidence that

238

'individuals' and 'families' may be distinguished from others in terms of hereditary as well as acquired characteristics. As regards large racial groups, however, there appears to be about the same range of hereditary capacities in one group as in another. The fact that differences in behaviour between such groups obviously exist, is no proof that they exist because they are inborn." [1]

The reason the cultures of other ethnic groups are so often different from our own is that they have been exposed to experiences which differ as considerably from our own as do the cultures in question. If you or I, with our present genetic background, had been born and brought up among a group of Australian aborigines, we should be, culturally, behaviorally, Australian aborigines, though physically we should remain members of our own ethnic group. For experience is determined by the place and the culture in which groups and individuals live, and for this reason groups and persons belonging to different cultures will differ mentally from one another. Our physical structures would not have varied significantly, because they were for the most part genetically determined by our present parents, but our physical expression would almost certainly have been modified, and our cultural equipment would be that of an Australian aboriginal. Why? Because culture—and by "culture" is to be understood the way of life of a people; culture is a people's ideas, sentiments, religious and secular beliefs, its language, tools and other material products, its institutions, customs, and ideals—because culture is something that one acquires by experience, unlike one's physical appearance, which one acquires through the action, for the most part, of inherited genes, but which under the influence of culturalizing factors is subject to considerable modification. The culture of persons, as of groups, will differ according to the kinds of experience they have undergone.

Most illuminating in this connection is a study by Professor Erwin H. Ackerknecht, who has brought together the facts concerning white children who had been abducted from their parents by North American Indians during the eighteenth and nineteenth centuries.[2] Professor Ackerknecht gives us the accounts of eight fairly well-recorded life histories of such abducted children. All these children

---

[1] Klineberg, "Race Differences: The Present Position of the Problem," *International Social Science Bulletin* (UNESCO), II (1950), 465.
[2] Ackerknecht, "White Indians," *Bulletin of the History of Medicine,* XV (1944), 15–36.

were taken by the Indians when they were between the ages of four and nine years, with the exception of a girl who was taken in adolescence. All of them forgot their native culture, and even the girl who had been captured when she was fifteen years of age became completely Indianized. In every case these "white Indians" resisted all attempts to persuade them to return to their white relatives and to the culture of their birth. As Ackerknecht says, the "white Indians" seemed to have found "a kind of unity of thought and action and a kind of social cohesion which deeply appealed to them, and which they did not find with the whites, especially not with the pioneers. There is no doubt that this fact largely contributed to their staying with the Indians."[3] The remarkable fact about these "white Indians" is that they not only became completely Indianized culturally in the sense of manifesting purely Indian forms of social behavior, but they also developed all the physical powers of resistance said to be peculiar to Indians. Furthermore, most of them lived to be extremely old. Finally, all of them had acquired the facial expression and outward impassibility characteristic of the Indian. Samuel Stanhope Smith was among the first, if not the first, to comment upon this fact. In 1810 he wrote, "Another example of the power of society in forming the countenance is well known to all those who are acquainted with the savage tribes spread along the frontiers of these states. Among them you frequently meet with persons who have been taken captive in infancy from Anglo-American families, and grown up in the habits of savage life. These descendants of the fairest Europeans universally contract such a resemblance to the natives, in their countenance, and even in their complexion, as not to be easily distinguished from them; and afford a striking proof that the differences in physiognomy, between the Anglo-American, and the Indian depend principally on the state of society."[4]

Of many of these "white Indians" it is expressly recorded that having been accustomed to white ways they could no longer sleep in a house or in a bed.[5]

Such facts should go a long way toward disproving the view that culture is something which will express itself in genetically determined

[3] *Ibid.*, p. 34.

[4] Smith, *An Essay on the Causes of the Variety of Complexion and Figure in the Human Species,* 2d ed., pp. 171–72.

[5] Peckham, *Captured by Indians.*

form no matter what the environmental influences to which the person is exposed.

The culture of different peoples, as of different individuals, is to a large extent a reflection of their past history or experience. This is a point which is worth more than laboring. If the cultural status of any variety of man is determined merely by the kind of experience which it has undergone, then it is evident that by giving all people the opportunity to enjoy a common experience—supposing for the moment that this was desirable—all varieties would become culturally and mentally equal. That is, they would become equal in the sense that they would have benefited from exposure to the same kind of experience, always allowing, of course, for the fact that no two persons can ever be alike in their reception of and reaction to the same experience, and there will always, fortunately, continue to exist great differences between persons.[6]

There can be little doubt that genetic differences in temperament and intellectual capacity exist between the individuals comprising every variety of mankind, no two individuals in this respect ever being alike; but it takes the stimulus of a common experience to bring them out and to render them comparable. It is because of differences in history, in cultural experience, that individuals and groups differ from one another culturally, and it is for this reason that cultural achievement is an exceedingly poor measure of the cultural potentialities of a person or of a group.

For all practical purposes this was essentially stated by the great French statesman and economist Robert Jacques Turgot (1727–1781), when he wrote that "The human mind contains everywhere the germs of the same progress; but nature, partial in her gifts, has endowed certain minds with an abundance of talents which she has refused to others; circumstances develop these talents or relegate them to obscurity; and to the infinite variety of these circumstances is due the inequality in the progress of nations."[7]

For all practical purposes, and until further evidence to the contrary is forthcoming, we can safely take cultural experience to be the expression merely of a particular history of cultural experience.

---

[6] For a discussion of the moral and international consequences of these facts see Wootton, *Testament for Social Science*, pp. 146–52.

[7] Turgot, *Tableaux Philosophique des Progrès Successifs de l'Esprit Humain*, p. 214.

Obviously, all learned activities are culturally, not biologically, determined, whether those activities are based upon physiological urges or traditional practices. The generalized needs which all human beings inherit in common continue to be present in all human beings in all cultures; but how these needs are permitted to express themselves and how they are satisfied is something which is determined by tradition and varies not only in different cultures but within different groups within the same culture. For example, one of the fundamental needs which we all inherit is the need to eat. Different human groups, to whom the same foodstuffs may or may not be available, not only eat different foods but prepare them in different ways, and consume them, with or without implements, in various ways, usually established only by custom. The faculty of speech is biologically determined, but what we speak and how we speak is determined by what we hear in the culture in which we have been culturalized. Human beings everywhere experience, when they are tired, the desire to rest, to sit down, to lie down, or to sleep; but the manner in which they do all these things is culturally determined by the customs of the group in which they live. Many other instances will doubtless occur to the reader. The point to grasp here is that even our fundamental biological needs are more or less culturally controlled and regulated or culturalized and that their very forms and expressions, not to mention satisfactions, are molded according to the dictates of tradition. Culture, tradition, channels our biological processes.

In view of the tremendous number of different cultural influences which enter into the structure and functioning of different groups and the individuals composing them, it is surely the most gratuitous, as it is the most unscientific, procedure to assert anything concerning assumed genetic conditions without first attempting to discover what part these cultural influences play in the production of what is predicated. Obviously, no statement concerning the mentality of a person is of any value without a specification of the conditions of the environment in which that mentality developed. The introduction of genes or heredity as the *deus ex machina* to account for cultural differences between people may be a convenient device for those who must do everything in their power, except study the actual facts, to find some sort of support for their prejudices, but it is a device which will hardly satisfy the requirements of an efficient scientific method. Such devices must be accepted in a charitable spirit as the perverse efforts of some of our misguided fellows to maintain their own shaky feeling of superiority by depreciating the capacities of others. John Stuart Mill, more than a hundred years ago, in his *Principles of Political Economy* (1848), put the stamp upon this type of conduct. He wrote: "Of all the vulgar modes of escaping from the consideration of the effect of social and moral influence on the human mind, the most vulgar is that of attributing the diversities of conduct and character to inherent natural differences." In his *Physics and Politics* (1869) Walter Bagehot said much the same thing: "When a philosopher cannot account for anything in any other manner, he boldly ascribes it to an occult quality in some race." While the number of people who do this sort of thing has greatly increased since the days of Mill and Bagehot, the number who realize the absurdity of such practices has also grown considerably, so that on this count there is no necessary need of despair for the future. The situation often gets qualitatively better as it looks quantitatively worse. The facts which are now available concerning the peoples of the earth render it quite clear that they are all definitely brothers under the skin.

It is, perhaps, too much to expect those who have been educated in the contrary belief to accept such a view; the least, therefore, that we can do is to provide the children in our schools with an honest account of the facts instead of filling their guiltless heads with the kinds of prejudice that we find distributed through so many of the books and so much of the teaching with which they are provided. Surely, a sympathetic understanding of people who behave "differently," look "differently," cannot help but broaden one's horizons and lead to better human relationships all around. Socially this is, of course, greatly to be desired, and in the United States a beginning has already been made in this direction in several American cities.[8] Such enterprises, however, must be multiplied several thousand times. Here, obviously, there is much work to be done.

But let us return to our main discussion, for though school children and others have frequently heard of physical relativity, few, if any, children, and hardly anyone else (apart from anthropologists), ever encounter the concept of cultural relativity.[9] From the standpoint of

---

[8] See Appendix E.
[9] For an illuminating exposition of cultural relativity see Benedict, *Patterns of Culture*.

the well-being and happiness of mankind the latter is a vastly more important conception to grasp than the former.

Cultural relativity implies that all cultures must be evaluated in relation to their own history, and definitely not by the arbitrary standard of any single culture such, for example, as our own. Judged in relation to its own history, each culture is seen as the resultant of the responses to the conditions which that history may or may not record. If those conditions have been limited in nature, so will the culture reflecting their effects. If the conditions have been many and complex in character, then the culture will reflect that complexity. Culture is essentially a relation which is the product of the interaction between two correlates—the one a plastic, adaptable, sensitive, biological being, the other simply experience. If we agree that mankind is everywhere plastic, adaptable, and sensitive, then we can most satisfactorily account for the mental and cultural differences between the varieties of mankind on the basis of different experiences. And this, when everything is taken into consideration, seems to be the principal explanation of the mental and cultural differences which exist between the ethnic groups of man. Let me give one or two examples of cultural relativity, as it were, in action.

Five thousand years ago the ancestors of the present highly cultured peoples of Europe were "backward barbarians" settled in the wilds of Europe. The ancestors of the modern Englishman were living in a Stone Age phase of culture, being culturally not much more advanced than many peoples whom we today call primitive or nonliterate. When they were discovered and conquered by the Romans in the first century of our era[10] they were in a Bronze Age phase of

---

[10] It has been stated that Cicero had an extremely low opinion of the mental capacities of the Britons. Thus, he is alleged to have written in a letter to his friend Atticus, "Do not obtain your slaves from Britain, because they are so stupid and so utterly incapable of being taught that they are not fit to form part of the household of Athens." See Benedict, *Race: Science and Politics,* p. 10. The truth is that Cicero made no such derogatory remark. What he wrote was ". . . there is not a scrap of silver in the island, nor any hope of booty except from slaves; but I don't fancy you will find any with literary or musical talent among them." *Ep. ad Att.* 4.16.13. Loeb Library, vol. I, p. 324. Cicero was wrong. The talents were there, but it took some fourteen hundred years of development before they could find expression. This long period of cultural lag, in spite of the presence of the Romans in Britain for

cultural development. Five thousand years ago Europe was inhabited by hordes of "barbarians," at a time when the kingdoms of Upper and Lower Egypt were at their height. These have long since passed into history, but five thousand years ago and less the peoples of these great cultures could have looked upon the Europeans as barbarians who by nature were completely incapable of civilization—and hence better exterminated lest they pollute the "blood" of their superiors. Whatever sins the Europeans have since committed, they have at least shown that given a sufficient amount of time and experience they were capable of civilization to a degree not less than that to which the peoples of Egypt of the First and Second Dynasties (3200–2780 B.C.) attained.

It should be a sobering thought to learn that the great basic discoveries on which modern civilization rests—writing, and later the alphabet, the wheel, the astronomical calendar, metallurgy, and so on —were made in the Middle East, at a time when most of the peoples of Northwestern Europe were "backward barbarians."

Here we have an example of cultural relativity. If we use time as our frame of reference, we might ask: "Since the Egyptians have had a much longer time than we to develop culturally, why haven't they developed as far as we have?" Disregarding the dubious notion that any human group has enjoyed a longer time in which to develop than any other, the answer is that time is not a proper measure to apply to the development of culture or cultural events. Time is only a convenient framework from which to observe their development. Cultural changes which among some peoples it has taken centuries to produce are among other peoples often effected within a few years.[11] The rate of cultural change is dependent upon many different factors, but the indispensable condition for the production of cultural change is the irritability produced by the stimulus of such new experiences; cultural change is exceedingly slow. Hence, if new experience is the chief determinant of cultural change, then the dimension by which we may most efficiently judge cultures is that of the history of the

some four centuries is worth noting. It would be interesting to know who started the Cicero hare. It keeps recurring in the literature.

[11]Sorokin and Merton, "Social Time: a Methodological and Functional Analysis," *American Journal of Sociology*, XLII (1937), 615–29; Sorokin, *Sociocultural Causality, Space, Time*, pp. 158–225.

experience which has fallen to the lot of the cultures observed. In other words, to evaluate cultural events properly one must judge them by the measure of experience viewed through the framework of time.[12] We of the Western world have packed more experience into the past two thousand years than has probably fallen to the lot of the Australian aborigines, for example, as well as many other peoples, throughout their entire history.

Experience, or variety of cultural contacts, not time, is the all-important factor. It would obviously be wrong to expect an Australian aboriginal to behave like an Eton and Oxford man, but were he given all the cultural advantages of the Eton and Oxford man there can be little doubt but that he would do at least as well. Until the very recent period the Australian aborigines have been even more cut off from almost all cultural contact than the Britons were during the Upper Paleolithic and the Mesolithic. It was because Britain was situated well within the periphery of the eddying streams of European cultural development, because from Neolithic times onward Britons enjoyed the advantages of increasingly frequent and close contacts with the peoples of Europe, that the fructifying influence of such contacts gave them a considerable measure of civilization by the time Caesar landed on their shores in 54 B.C. The Australian aborigines, on the other hand, have been almost completely isolated upon their continent for countless generations without benefit of anything like such contacts with the cultures of other peoples.

Race and culture are not inseparably connected. The basic biological needs and the potentialities for behavior associated with them probably do not vary significantly from one ethnic group to another. What varies is the social stimulation to which these needs and potentialities are exposed and subsequently organized. The diversity of cultures which we encounter represents the adjustment which different human groups have made to the experiences and the problems they have been called upon to meet and solve.

Any judgments of value we may attempt to make between our own culture, whatever that may be, and that of other peoples will be invalid unless they are made in terms of history, of experience. Bearing this cardinal principle in mind, we shall be able to steer a clear

---

[12] Montagu, "Social Time: a Methodological and Functional Analysis," *American Journal of Sociology*, XLIV (1938), 282–84.

course. It cannot be too strongly emphasized, as Erich Kahler says, that the "historical evidence proves beyond doubt that the exact opposite of what the so-called race theory pretends is true; any decisive advance in human evolution has been accomplished not by breeds that are pure either mentally or physically, not by any cultural inbreeding, but by intermixture, by mutual impregnation of different stocks and cultures." [13]

It is, indeed, from the mixtures of cultural traditions that many of the major triumphs of civilization have come.

If the essential physical differences, then, between the varieties of mankind are limited to superficial characters, such as color of skin, form of hair, and form of nose, and the cultural and mental differences are due merely to differences in experience, then from the sociobiological standpoint all varieties of mankind must be adjudged fundamentally equal; that is to say, equally good in a biological sense and in cultural potentiality. All normal human beings are born as culturally undifferentiated animals; they become culturally differentiated according to the social group into which they happen to be born. Some of the culturally differentiating media are neither so complex nor so advanced as others; the individuals developed within them will be culturally the products of their cultural group. As individuals, they can no more be blamed or praised for belonging to their particular group than a fish can be either blamed or praised for belonging to its particular class in the vertebrate series. Culture, the culture of any group, is more or less determined by accidental factors, which the group, as a group, has usually done little to bring about. Members of the more advanced cultures have merely been luckier in that they have enjoyed the benefits of a broader experience and more stimulating contacts than members of the less advanced cultures.[14] Boas has said: "The history of mankind proves that advances of cul-

---

[13] Kahler, *Man the Measure*, p. 30.

[14] It is of interest to note here that the eighteenth-century students of man, such as Ferguson, Reid, Hume, Stewart, and Adam Smith, solved the problem of the cultural diversity of man in much the same way. "They were struck with the vast differences in culture, as well as with accounts of men of different physical features, but, on the basis of their major presupposition that human nature is fundamentally the same, they solved the problem of differences in achievement by judging the different peoples to be at different stages of maturity." Bryson, *Man and Society*, p. 53.

ture depend upon the opportunities presented to a social group to learn from the experience of their neighbors. The discoveries of the group spread to others, and, the more varied the contacts, the greater are the opportunities to learn. The tribes of simplest culture are on the whole those that have been isolated for very long periods and hence could not profit from the cultural achievements of their neighbors." [15]

In short, the history of mankind teaches us that there is no inherent tendency in any group of mankind which distinguishes it from any other to develop from a state of "barbarism" to one of "high culture." It is only under certain culturally stimulating conditions, which are for the most part accidentally determined, that any group will ever advance to a state of high culture, for man is the creature beyond all others who possesses the capacity for turning accidents into opportunities. In the absence of such conditions no human group will ever advance beyond the state of culture determined by the totality of conditions operative upon it. That should be obvious.

With respect to the alleged unchangingness of human nature, which racists almost always proclaim, consider, for example, the case of the Greeks. In spite of a remarkable biological continuity with their ancestors of classical times,[16] the people of modern Greece are comparatively backward culturally and nowhere nearly so creative as their ancestors of more than two thousand years ago. To what, then, is due this striking difference between the Greeks of the third century before Christ and those of the twentieth century? A study of the tragic history of political anarchy, war, massacre, social disorganization, conquest, and oppression which has been the lot of the Greek people during the past two thousand years suggests the direction, at least, in which we should look for an explanation.[17] As Professor

---

[15] Boas, "Racial Purity," *Asia*, XL (1940), 231–34.

[16] See the following studies by Angel: "Report on the Skeletons Excavated at Olynthus," in David M. Robinson, *Excavations at Olynthus, Pt. XI, Necrolynthia, a Study in Greek Burial Customs and Anthropology*, pp. 211–40; "A Racial Analysis of the Ancient Greeks," *American Journal of Physical Anthropology*, N. S., II (1944), 329–76; "Skeletal Material from Attica," *Hesperia*, XIV (1945), 279–363; "Social Biology of Greek Culture Growth," *American Anthropologist*, N. S., XLVIII (1946), 493–533.

[17] Brandes, *Hellas*.

Wilder Penfield, one of the world's great neurologists, has written, "The brains of the Greek patricians who rose to such superiority of intellectual achievement during the golden age of Classical Greece were no different structurally from the brains of Greeks in the so-called dark ages that followed. The subsequent low level of intellectual output was the result of changing environment, and the disappearance of fair competition, freedom and public rewards for excellence." [48]

The seafaring Scandinavians of the Bronze Age were undoubtedly the ancestors of the modern Scandinavians, yet how different is the cultural behavior of the modern relatively sedentary Scandinavians from that of their raiding forebears!

The boisterous joy of life of the English of Elizabeth's time and the lusty libertinism of the Restoration contrast sharply with the prudery of the Victorian Age. The Englishman's "nature" was different in the sixteenth as compared with that in the seventeenth century, and still more different in the nineteenth century.[19]

With respect to the Germans it would be difficult to do better than cite the comments of an eighteenth-century Scotsman, William Guthrie, who wrote: "The Germans are by nature honest, hospitable people, passionately fond of liberty, and very little versed in dissimulation and artifice. . . . The Germans are brave, and when led by able generals, particularly by Italians, have often performed great deeds." [20]

"Being led by able generals, particularly Italians" is a remark which in the light of later German-Italian military relations is quite too piquant, and should provide an interesting commentary in itself upon the mutability of human nature.

And what shall we say of the differences in cultural behavior of such biologically near kin as the New Mexican sedentary Pueblo and the nomadic Navaho Indians, or the behavior of those inhabitants of Mexican Indian villages which are completely Hispanicized?

---

[18] Penfield, "Letter to the Editor," *Perspectives in Biology and Medicine,* VI (1963), 540–41.
[19] For some interesting comments bearing on these points see Babington, *Fallacies of Race Theories,* pp. 235 ff.; also Gorer, "Some Notes on the British Character," *Horizon,* XX (1949–50), 369–79.
[20] Quoted in Kohl, *England, Wales, and Scotland,* p. 79. It is necessary to add that Kohl did not quite approve these statements.

What can have happened to the alleged "warlike nature" of the American Indians who today live at peace with their white and Indian "enemies"? [21]

Is the cultural behavior of the Japanese the same as it was a hundred or even fifty years ago?

Compare the great Polynesian maritime peoples with their descendants today in Hawaii and New Zealand. Biologically they are mostly the same people, but so far as the expression of their "nature" is concerned they are virtually completely Westernized.

The one thing characteristic of human nature is, surely, its changeability under changing conditions. The one characteristic of man as man is his ability to make all the necessary changes within himself to meet the demands of a changing environment. This trait, plasticity or educability or adaptability, is the one which, in the human species as a whole, has had the greatest demands made upon it by natural selection. Survival of the human species and its progress has depended upon this ability of human nature to change in adaptation to changed conditions.

What most people take to be human nature is really second nature, a nature which has been acquired in terms of the potentialities of being human in a specific culture. Human nature is a pattern of behavior, and this pattern of behavior is known to be capable of change not only from generation to generation but in the same person within a single generation.

It has often been argued that "racial" enmities between men will disappear only when all physical "racial" differences between them have been obliterated. This is a fallacious argument for the simple reason that the real source of "racial" hostilities is not physical, but cultural. It would be equally erroneous to argue from this that such hostilities will therefore disappear only with the obliteration of all cultural differences between men.

The world would be immensely the poorer for such a cultural leveling, and such a process would not, in any event, bring about the desired effect. Perfection of man's nature and achievements, it cannot

---

[21] During the making of a film on location in Florida which required the firing by Indians at Whites, the Seminole Indians who had been hired for the occasion balked on the ground that they had made a treaty with the United States that prohibited taking up arms against the white man. See *New Yorker,* XXVII (May 12, 1951), 23.

be too often emphasized, is not obtained by the ascendancy of one form of excellence, but by the blending of what is best in many different forms; by harmonizing differences, not by rendering them more discordant. The deep peril and disease of our age is that the cultural differences which exist between ethnic groups tend to become flattened out or swallowed up and annihilated too soon. In this obliterative process are often lost the unique virtues of a culture even before the dominant culture has grasped their meaning. And as often as this happens is mankind impoverished. As John Collier, former commissioner of Indian Affairs, has pointed out, the history of our species tells us that cultural diversity is the creative force in history. The ideal of a great way of life which we call Christianity, for example, represents the blending of the elements of many different traditions. Hebrew monotheism and morality, Greek philosophy, Oriental mysticism, Roman law, all entered into its shaping.

Christianity is only one of countless examples of the profound truth that cultural "diversity is the essential nurture of the spirit of man, the seed-bed of our human future. The cross-fertilization of contrasting cultures is the maker of our human power." [22]

Stressing superficial differences between people only helps to maintain the illusion that there may be more fundamental differences behind them. What in truth and in justice requires to be done is to stress the fundamental kinship of all mankind: to stress the likenesses which we all bear to one another, and to recognize the essential unity in all mankind in the very differences which individuals of all ethnic groups display. Unity neither implies nor necessitates uniformity. It is important that human beings shall be united, but not that they shall be uniform. We must learn to recognize the all-importance of our common humanity and the triviality of the things that divide us. The world must be re-established as a vast community in which every ethnic group is freely permitted to give as well as to receive. Such an ideal will never be achieved by the ignorant and vicious stressing of differences, but by the broader, saner, and more humane sympathetic recognition of the fundamental likenesses and, finally, by the utilization and interchange of the differences to strengthen each other in living a fuller, a more varied, a more interesting, and a more peaceful life.

---

[22] Collier, "The Creative Value of Cultural Diversity," *Trends & Tides,* II (1946), 5–6.

13

"Race" and War

ALMOST A HUNDRED YEARS have passed since that fatal morning when a dust-laden Prussian officer cantered into Paris at the head of a small advance party of Uhlans, thus signalizing the capitulation of the French and the unequivocal victory of the Germans in the Franco-Prussian War of 1870. Forty years later this selfsame Prussian officer, now a general, careered into Europe with a book which at once attained universal notoriety. This book was entitled *Germany and the Next War*. Few books have before or since been so fervidly and widely discussed. In this book the author, General Friedrich von Bernhardi, boldly threw down the gauntlet to the world and, virtually with saber in hand, called upon the German people to protest against the "aspirations for peace which seem to dominate our age and threaten to poison the soul of the German people."

It is understandably hard for an iron-headed soldier, after some forty years of comparative inactivity, to recall an event as stirring as the entry at the head of a victorious army into a defeated enemy's capital without feeling that if things were not actually going to the dogs, at least it was high time that something was done to prevent the possibility. And so, in order to convince the German people of the "unnaturalness" of that "inactivity which saps the blood from a nation's sinews," von Bernhardi did something he had never done before: he wrote and published a popular propagandistic book, making the pen, as it were, temporarily do service for the sword and ink for blood. "War," declared von Bernhardi, "is a biological necessity"; it "is as necessary as the struggle of the elements in Nature"; "it gives a biologically just decision, since its decisions rest on the very nature of things." "The whole idea of arbitration represents a presumptuous encroachment on the natural laws of develop-ment," for "what is right is decided by the arbitrament of War." [1] In proof whereof such Darwinian notions as "the struggle for existence," "natural selection," and "survival of the fittest" are invoked with a loud fanfare of trumpets. According to von Bernhardi, it is plainly evident to anyone who makes a study of plant and animal life that "war is a universal law of nature." [2]

Darwin himself regarded the biological influence of modern war as distinctly bad. In *The Descent of Man* he wrote: "In every country in which a large standing army is kept, the finest young men are taken by the conscription or are enlisted. They are thus exposed to early death during war, are often tempted into vice, and are prevented from marrying during the prime of life. On the other hand, the shorter and feeble men, with poor constitutions are left at home and consequently have a much better chance of marrying and propagating their kind."

As Professor S. J. Holmes, the distinguished social biologist, has put it: "One may be a strict orthodox Darwinian and maintain with entire consistency that, under present conditions, war is an evil of the very first magnitude." [3]

Von Bernhardi's declaration and fortification of Germany's will-to-war—for it had the highest official sanction and approval—was published in 1912. Two years later the greatest holocaust the world had yet known was launched upon its ghastly way by those

> . . . vultures sick for battle
> Those bloodless wolves whose dry throats rattle,
> Those crows perched on the murrained cattle,
> Those vipers tangled into one.
>
> —After Shelley, "To Sidmouth and Castlereagh"

---

[1] It would seem that this idea is at least as old as the sixth century before Christ. We find it clearly stated in a fragment left us by Heracleitus of Ephesus (*circa* 500 B.C.). "We must know," he writes, "that war is common to all and that strife is justice, and that everything comes into being by strife." *Heracleitus,* fragment LXII, trans. by W. H. S. Jones, p. 491.

[2] Bernhardi, *Germany and the Next War,* pp. 16–37. Compare with this the following passage written in 1942 by Lord Elton: "War, however we may hate it, is still the supreme agent of the evolutionary process. Blind, brutal and destructive, it remains the final arbiter, the one test mankind has yet contrived of a nation's fitness to survive." *Saint George or the Dragon.*

[3] Holmes, *Life and Morals,* p. 198. For a more extended discussion of Darwinism applied to man see Montagu, *Darwin, Competition, and Cooperation.*

—the confused, inhuman, militaristic von Bernhardis and the other legislators of a victimized Europe.

World War I came to a technical end in 1918, having cost the lives of eighteen million men. Eight million were slaughtered upon the field of battle and ten million civilians died either directly or indirectly as a result of the war. As for the maimed and wounded combatants, these amounted to a mere twenty million. The cost to the United States of running this fracas amounted to $125,000,000 a day during the first three years and $224,000,000 a day, or $10,000,-000 an hour, during 1918, the total cost of the killing amounting to some four hundred billion dollars.[4]

During World War II the United States was spending $250,000,-000 a day on the war, and by 1945 the total cost had run up to one thousand and thirty billion dollars.[5]

Although most human beings now living, with the exception of some militarists and politicians, can see neither sense, good, nor anything but misery in war, there are many who, like von Bernhardi, continue to aver that war has its biological justification. Among these was my old friend and teacher Sir Arthur Keith (1866–1955) who in many articles beginning in 1915 and in later books[6] maintained that the impulses which lead men to aggressive and defensive wars are "nature's mechanisms for preserving the individual and the tribe or nation" and "make individuals and nations willing to risk life itself to further the means and opportunities of life." In all theories of this kind "race" and "race" prejudice are conceived by their proponents to play a basic and "natural" part.

Sir Arthur Keith's opinions on this subject first received wide attention with the publication of his rectorial address to the students of Aberdeen University in 1931.[7] In the present chapter I propose to take Sir Arthur Keith's views on the nature of war and its relation to "race" prejudice and, treating them as representative of the "race-

---

[4] Bogart, *Direct and Indirect Costs of the Great World War*, pp. 265–68.

[5] Fairchild, *The Prodigal Century*, p. 244.

[6] Keith, *Essays on Human Evolution*, and *A New Theory of Human Evolution;* for the views of the American warmongers see Hofstadter's brilliant account in his *Social Darwinism in American Thought, 1860–1915*. See also Nasmyth, *Social Progress and the Darwinian Theory*.

[7] Keith, *The Place of Prejudice in Modern Civilization*.

prejudice-biological-nature-of-war" school, subject them to a brief critical examination.

Keith begins by declaring his firm conviction that "prejudices are inborn; are part of the birthright of every child." These prejudices "have been grafted in our natures for a special purpose—an evolutionary purpose." "They are essential parts of the evolutionary machinery which Nature employed throughout eons of time to secure the separation of man into permanent groups and thus to attain production of new and improved races of Mankind." "Nature endowed her tribal teams with this spirit of antagonism for her own purposes. It has come down to us and creeps out from our modern life in many shapes, as national rivalries and jealousies and as racial hatreds. The modern name for this spirit of antagonism is race-prejudice." "Race-prejudice, I believe," continues Keith, "works for the ultimate good of Mankind and must be given a recognized place in all our efforts to obtain natural justice in the world." [8] Here, sadly, we may recall von Bernhardi's "war renders a biologically just decision, since its decisions rest on the very nature of things." It is the same argument, endlessly repeated, in almost the same words.

And now for the passage from Keith which gained such widespread notoriety: "Without competition Mankind can never progress; the price of progress is competition. Nay, race-prejudice and, what is the same thing, national antagonism, have to be purchased, not with gold, but with life. Nature throughout the past has demanded that a people who seeks independence as well as peace can obtain these privileges only in one way—by being prepared to sacrifice their blood to secure them. Nature keeps her orchard healthy by pruning; war is her pruning-hook. We cannot dispense with her services. This harsh and repugnant forecast of man's future is wrung from me. The future of my dreams is a warless world." [9]

---

[8] In a book published in 1945 the author, echoing Keith, writes: "Whatever may be said against it, in so far as it keeps the race pure, race prejudice is admirable and even necessary." Landry, *The Cult of Equality,* p. 257. The nonsense of such statements is sufficiently refuted by the fact that whenever and whatever ethnic groups meet they have mixed, and by the very consequential fact that no human being alive today is of unmixed origin.

[9] Keith, *The Place of Prejudice in Modern Civilization,* p. 50. In *An Autobiography* Keith writes of this address: "I was soon to be aware of the disturbance to which my rectorial address had given rise. My good friend, Dr.

Essentially similar views were expressed by Sir Arthur Keith in his Robert Boyle Lecture *Nationality and Race,* published twelve years earlier, and were repeated by him in 1950.[10] Unlike von Bernhardi, Sir Arthur Keith was a distinguished physical anthropologist and, as all who knew him well know, a man of the noblest and most generous nature who was himself as free of anything resembling "race" prejudice as a man could well be. Nevertheless, in his treatment of the subject of "race" prejudice and war the fact was unfortunately betrayed that he had overstepped the frontiers of his own particular field, a field to which he has made lasting contributions. Charles Singer has well said that "even professional men of science, when they pass beyond the frontiers of their own special studies, usually exhibit no more balanced judgment or unprejudiced outlook than do non-scientific men of comparable social and educational standing." Sir Arthur Keith's views on war and "race" prejudice may be taken as a case in point.

What, we may ask to begin with, is this "Nature," always, it is to be observed, spelled with a capital N? Keith's Nature is apparently a very intelligent being, working things out purposefully with much premeditation. I use the term "intelligent" here in a generic sense to cover the operations of what is conventionally understood as the intellect; I make no comment on the quality of that putative intelligence, beyond saying that an intellect which can conceive of no better device to improve its breed than by warfare must be a very poor intellect indeed. For surely the biological vitality of a species can be preserved and improved by many immeasurably more effective means than this—means which do not necessitate or require the annihilation of a single individual. But what, in fact, *is* this Nature of von Bernhardi and Keith which, according to them, justifies "race" prejudice and renders war a biological necessity?

Apparently it is an anthropomorphism akin to the *élan-vital* of Bergson or the "life-force" of Bernard Shaw. In other words, it would appear to be some form of directing Godhead with the capital G in

Katherine Trail, widow of my venerated mentor of early days, wrote me a most indignant letter accusing me of fanning the embers of war. Other critics laid hold of an unfortunate metaphor I had used—the 'pruning-hook of war.' . . . My little booklet met with no demand. And all the time Hitler was demonstrating to the world the truth of my thesis" (pp. 565-66).
[10] Keith, *An Autobiography.*

very much the old style, divested here and there of a few sacraments
and perfectly clean shaven, but otherwise much the same. Voltaire's
gibe that if God had made men after his own image they had returned
the compliment is as appropriate a truth today as it ever was. Nature
or God today is an anthropologist as well as a mathematical physicist
—sometimes an entelechist and often enough merely a set of differential equations, unlimitedly limited and with an infinite number
of functions at one and the same time, but if the truth were really
known, merely a set of conditioned reflexes in the cosmic movement
continuum. In fact, Nature may mean anything, according to the
whim of the user.[11] Nature, says Aristotle, makes some men slaves
and others free. In Nature, says Hobbes, "the life of man is solitary,
poor, nasty, brutish, and short"; it is a condition of "war of every man
against every man," in which "the notions of right and wrong, justice
and injustice have no place" and "force and fraud are the two cardinal
virtues." "The state all men are naturally in," replies Locke, is "a
state of perfect freedom to order their actions . . . as they think fit,
within the bounds of the law of nature . . . a state also of equality."
"Nature," writes Wordsworth, "to me was all in all, she never did
betray the heart that loved her." "Nature," rejoins Tennyson, "red
in tooth and claw, shrieks against the creed of man." And as Professor
A. F. Pollard has remarked of these antinomies, "Some see red,
others see God; it all depends upon the kingdom that is within them."
In fact, Nature is the name we give to the projection of the totality
of our ignorance concerning the forces which are conceived to be
involved in, or responsible for, the generation of life and its maintenance. Nature is not a "thing-in-itself" which operates upon other
things. The term denotes, rather, if it denotes anything at all, an
artificial construct whose function is to serve as a general stereotype
for our ignorance, in addition to serving as a *deus ex machina* to

---

11 "Nature is a word, always very loosely used, to which time has brought
increasingly sentimental connotations. The decline of one superstition has
encouraged the growth of another. God the Father has been dethroned from
many simple hearts only to be replaced by Nature the Mother, an entity of
strikingly similar characteristics, mingling benevolence and vindictiveness in
quite the old familiar proportions. Nature has consciousness and makes rules
and plans, and takes revenge. She is jealous and cannot bear interference.
Her workmanship is perfect. Her desire for mastery is always overwhelming,
and no one ever gets the upper hand of her for long." Moore, *The Vulgar
Heart*, p. 126.

which, in a quandary, we may appeal in order to be comfortably relieved of our perplexities. For most people to say that a thing is "natural" explains it. But does it? What do we mean by "natural"? Prejudices are natural according to Keith and others, prose as Monsieur Jourdain was surprised to learn, warfare according to von Bernhardi, and "the golden lie" according to Plato and some of his modern successors. Nature, it is further added, operates according to definite laws. All, in fact, is determined by law. The movements of the planets are determined by laws as immutable as those which determine the behavior of a dog or a man. But all this is mythical.

The universe, as far as we know, is composed of a system of ever-changing *relations*, in the form, for example, of electromagnetic fields, gases, stresses, forces, strains, velocities, dimensions, substances, and so forth, truly *ad infinitum*.

Nothing in it is fixed; all is flux.[12] Between certain limits of infinity or finity, that is, in a given space-time continuum, the relations of certain planetary velocities, for example, may remain (relatively) constant. The recurring averages in which these relations manifest themselves may be calculated to a high degree of probability, and when so calculated they may be stated as laws. These laws are always probability laws, and are valid only as long as the relations of the planetary velocities, as well as numerous other factors, remain (relatively) constant. Should any of these relations change, the old laws will have to be modified, or entirely new ones will have to be elaborated.

With this in mind we may proceed further, and for the purpose in view let us be deliberately brief and therefore oversimple. A unicellular organism living at the bottom of a stagnant pool and environed by a stable universe of internal and external stimuli will tend to undergo little change as long as the constancy of these stimuli persists; but modify its relations, the form and nature of the stimuli acting upon it, alter its internal and external environments, and if you go on long enough—let us say for a few thousand million years—sufficiently and adequately varying the nature of the environmental stimuli, and allowing for the important part played by the inherent tendency of the organism to vary, you will, let us suppose, produce a man. And your man, as an organism, will obviously represent the sum of the effects of the responses to the totality of the environments

---

[12] Hoyle, *The Nature of the Universe;* Weizsäcker, *The History of Nature.*

organically made by his ancestors. Organically, your man will be the product of an innumerable variety of conditions—the changing relations collectively called "heredity" and "environment." So will be, and so indeed is, any plant or any other form of animal life. Thus, all plant and animal life is not *produced* according to definite laws, but in response to a series of arbitrary or *chance* alterations in the relations of the conditions affecting it. Nature is thus not an intelligent, teleologically directed process which acts according to predetermined law, but is a composite of *chance* relations which may be arbitrarily observed as unit groups of recurring averages of relations, the behavior of the independent variables, or the quanta[13] of which both are indeterminable and unpredictable, whence the *principle of indeterminacy* or, more accurately, *limited meaningful measurability*. Man, indeed, may owe his present supremacy to just such a series of undetermined chance relations, which may be more briefly described as an accident, the accident referred to having been initiated in the early Miocene epoch approximately twenty-eight million years ago, when according to those who hold this theory, owing to the denudation of the forests, due to causes which can at present only be conjectured, a group of unspecialized anthropoidlike creatures, resembling the extinct ape known to paleontologists as *Sivapithecus sivalensis,* were forced down from the trees and were constrained to assume a life upon the ground. This revolutionary change in their environment must be considered an important factor in contributing to the ultimate development of all those physical characteristics which we have learned to recognize as distinctive of man. Those apes who lived in the unaffected regions stayed up in the trees, descending to earth only when, presumably, their weight became too great; they remain apes.

Was there any directive, purposeful, intelligent, natural force at work here? None at all. A gradual series of environmental changes accidentally precipitated may have been responsible for the descent from the trees, or the cause may simply have been the cumulative changes produced by mutation—and all mutation is random. The colossal number of varied forms of life, extinct and living, which are to be found upon this earth today have arisen because of the operation of very similar causes. Every form of life with which we are acquainted

---

13 On quanta and genes see Schrödinger, *What Is Life?*

owes its peculiar form to the enormous number of changes which have been and are in process of taking place both in the materials of its inherent structure and in the environment peculiar to each—the internal as well as the external environment. These changes are not regulated by law, but by chance. The processes of the universe of life are discontinuous and practically infinitely variable. The universe consists of an infinitely changeable and changing series of relations. Action and reaction, stimulus and response, take place always *relatively,* never *absolutely.* Nature, in short, in the determined immutable sense of the traditionalists, does not exist save as a procrustean fiction.

The law and order that man sees in nature he introduces there, a fact of which he seems to have grown quite unconscious. Natural systems of classification work so well that, following an unconscious pragmatic principle, they are assumed to be true, or at least representative of the truth, the latter being conveniently defined as correspondence with the reality of whatsoever it may be; in this way the tacit assumption is made that one has but to seek and one will find the law and order that undoubtedly exists in nature. This process is termed "discovery."

Now, while systems of classification are of incalculable value in aiding the process of discovery and understanding, such systems are nonetheless quite artificial and do not in any way reflect a law and order which characterizes the operation of the processes we commonly ascribe to nature itself. Nature is a fiction which uses neither measuring rod nor timetable. It is man alone who uses such instruments in order that he may the more fittingly orient himself in relation to this self-created fiction. The classificatory systems of man are *interpretative devices* and merely represent the attempt—and it is a grand attempt—to unravel the tangled skein of some of the relations of the various forms of life to one another, but no more, "a compromise between the complexity of biological fact and the logic of practical convenience." Of this man loses sight, and confuses himself with the belief that the law and order which he has worked out into an arbitrary scheme *is* the law and order according to which nature "works." "Homo additus Naturae," remarked Bacon long ago. Nature, if it consists of anything, represents a discontinuous series of processes, a network of entangled gossamer strands, which man attempts to gather together and spin into a web which he naively imagines is the *real thing,* the "real thing" being merely as he sees it, and he sees it in an infinite number of ways, according to the kingdom that is within him. Nature comes in this way to mean anything, and what may mean anything in fact means nothing. It is a personification of purely imagined purposes. Logically, the conception of nature is without the slightest value; psychologically, perhaps, the term may not be without some significance in the sense of Nietzsche's words in *The Joyful Wisdom*: "Laws and laws of nature are the remains of mythological dreaming." Such "laws of nature" can be a menace. If one thing is natural to man it is to be artificial. And the artificial, it has been said, is the highest form of the natural.

Julian Huxley has, I think, adequately disposed of the type of purposive personification in which Sir Arthur Keith has indulged. "The ordinary man," he writes, "or at least the ordinary poet, philosopher, and theologian, is always asking himself what is the purpose of human life, and is anxious to discover some extraneous purpose to which he and humanity may conform. Some find such a purpose exhibited directly in revealed religion; others think they can uncover it from the facts of nature. One of the commonest methods of this form of natural religion is to point to evolution as manifesting such a purpose. The history of life, it is asserted, manifests guidance on the part of some external power; and the usual deduction is that we can safely trust that same power for further guidance in the future.

"I believe this reasoning to be wholly false. The purpose manifested in evolution, whether in adaptation, specialization, or biological progress, is only an apparent purpose. It is just as much a product of blind forces as is the falling of a stone to earth or the ebb and flow of the tides. It is we who have read purpose into evolution, as earlier men projected will and emotion into inorganic phenomena like storm or earthquake. If we wish to work towards a purpose for the future of man, we must formulate that purpose ourselves. Purposes in life are made, not found." [14]

Professor A. P. Pollard has said: "The statement that 'war is natural' has no meaning, and any comment on it must be mainly speculation as to what those who make it imagine they mean when they repeat the words. 'Natural' to whom, when, and under what conditions? 'Let dogs delight to bark and bite, it is their nature to.'

[14] Huxley, *Evolution: The Modern Synthesis,* p. 576.

Is it the nature, too, of men of science?" [15] About as natural as the alleged "universal law of Nature" which makes the whole of nature "fight" and some scientists "bark and bite." We are told that even trees and flowers "fight." Do they? There is not the slightest evidence that they do. And if they do, what connection has this "fighting" with the warfare practiced by men? Some flowers digest insects; some plants "strangle" others. Does this constitute war between the flowers and the insects concerned? Do the plants that strangle others have to plead guilty to murder? Are these "warlike" actions of plants and flowers advance or rearguard actions?

Apropos of plants, Professor Frits Went writes, "In our minds the struggle for existence is usually associated with a ruthless extermination of the less well adapted by those better adapted. There is no cold war or even aggression in the desert or jungle. Most plants are not equipped with mechanisms to combat others. All plants grow up together and share whatever light or water or nutrients are available. It is only when the supply of one of these factors becomes critical that competition starts. But it appears likely that in the jungle, as in the desert, survival is taken care of by the control of germination. ... As a general moral we conclude that war as man wages it finds no counterpart in nature, and it has no justification on the basis of evolution or natural selection." [16]

It would be extremely helpful to know whether it is defensive or offensive war that is natural. Sir Arthur Keith believed that both are. The illegitimate use of such terms as "struggle," "fighting," "force," and so forth, when applied to plant and animal life, and the deliberate confusion of these terms with "war" occur too often, and too frequently are allowed to pass unchallenged.[17] Professor Pollard has entertainingly remarked of this confusion: "The sun and the moon, we suppose, declare war with great regularity because they get into opposition every month. Parties in the House of Commons are per-

---

[15] Pollard, "The War of Nature and a Peace of Mind," *Vincula* (University of London Students Journal), 14 December 1925, p. 60.

[16] Went, "The Ecology of Desert Plants, *Scientific American,* CXCII (1955), 75.

[17] This confusion could not be better illustrated than by Hitler's remark that "war is the most natural, the most every-day matter. War is eternal, war is universal. There is no beginning and there is no peace. Any struggle is war." Rauschning, *The Voice of Destruction,* pp. 7–8.

petually at war because they are opposed. The police wage war because they are a force; for 'naturally' if we use force against a criminal, we must needs make war upon other communities. War, indeed, will last for ever, because men will never 'cease to struggle.' So the League of Nations has obviously failed whenever a stern parent is caught in the act of chastising a peccant child; and 'fighting' will go on without end because drowning men will fight for life, doctors will fight disease, and women will fight for places at drapery sales. And this is war!" [18] The semantic fallacy could not be pointed more neatly.

Man kills a variety of animals for the purposes of food and various other uses, but he does so as a husbandman, a domesticator of animals, not as a maker of war upon animals. He breeds animals in order to eat them. Does this constitute war? In any event, is the domestication and slaughtering of these animals natural? It is certainly not natural to man, who commenced the domestication of animals not more than ten thousand years ago. Moreover, it is more unnatural for the vast majority of the animals who are members of the same order of mammals as man, namely, the primates, to attack other animal groups or, except on rare occasions, consume any part of them. The anthropoid apes are vegetarian. The fact is that man possesses the gastrointestinal tract of an herbivore, like the anthropoids. Man's meat eating is undoubtedly an acquired taste forced upon him under conditions of scarcity. But it is neither innate in the psychophysical disposition of man nor necessary that he may live, to kill any animal whatever, or plant, for that matter, at least not for men living in the highly civilized centers of the Western world. Man's taste in food is culturally determined, like his taste in tobacco and alcohol. Under primitive conditions of life he is forced to kill animals for food and apparel, just as it was considered "natural" for some nations, not so long ago, to kill prisoners of war in order that the food supply might not unnecessarily be depleted. Animals in the wild state kill digestible numbers and varieties of other animals, where they are available, for the satisfaction of their hunger, for the very good reason that they have no other means of remaining alive—but man has.

In medieval England it was considered natural and perfectly legal for all claims to real property to be settled and tried by battle. Since

---

[18] Pollard, "The War of Nature and a Peace of Mind." *Vincula,* 14 December 1925, p. 60.

those days man has elaborated more peaceful means of settling such disputes, not by blood but by reason, because of an understanding and sympathy made possible by a more enlightened form of culture. For culture, if it means anything, represents the fact of man's ability to elaborate and improve upon the normal processes of the universe, commonly called Nature. It is through the agency of culture that man is able to elaborate and improve upon his original endowment, to turn first into second nature. It is not so much that culture is an extension of him as that he is an extension of culture. Indeed, today, by means purely cultural, man is in a position to control and regulate, in almost every possible respect, his own future evolution. He holds the power within himself of total self-extermination or more complete development, and it will be by the weakness or strength of his humanity alone that either the one or the other effect will eventually be brought about. Fundamentally, man is quite an intelligent animal, but he is a victim, alas, of the two-handed engine of his culture which distorts his mind and renders him unintelligent. Outworn traditional teachings have made of Western man a shockingly unintelligent creature who lives under the continuous and unrelieved domination of a chaos of ideas more degrading, more stupid, more idiotic, and more saddening than it may ever be possible to describe. This confused morality has without question been substantially responsible for his present deplorable state, for the reflexes and patterns of thought of every child born into the Western world today have been conditioned according to the prescriptions of these teachings, so that culturally Western man has come to be a function almost entirely of the reigning spirit of confusion and prejudice. And since in his conduct he functions without effort as a victim of confusion and prejudice, he arrives at the belief that it is *natural* to act and think thus. In this way is produced the mentally and spiritually bludgeoned person who gropes his way confusedly through life—and whose number is legion. The frustrations which he has suffered seek an outlet in aggressiveness, and it is in his world alone that force and war still remain a legitimate and defensible means of settling a difference.

With regard to Keith's "race prejudice," that, of course, is an acquired sentiment, a constellation of socially acquired emotions, as Sir Arthur Keith would undoubtedly have known had he made as deep a study of cultural as he had of physical anthropology. Nature, according to him, secures the separation of man into permanent groups by means of the operation of "race" prejudices, which express themselves as national rivalries and jealousies, in order to produce "new and improved races of mankind." This, presumably, is a form of natural selection operating from inherited psychological bases, a form of selection peculiar to man alone, for no other animal, as far as we know, exhibits the slightest symptom of anything akin to what Sir Arthur Keith calls "race prejudice." So-called "race" prejudices among lower animals, like their so-called "natural" fears and terrors, are *acquired*, not inborn. This is probably true of the psychological barriers which exist between different groups of birds and in various other animals. Experiments on young animals first carried out by Benjamin Kidd many years ago, and by numerous investigators since, conclusively prove that the so-called "instinctive" fear and terror, exhibited in the presence of their allegedly natural enemies by the adult members of the species, are emotions which are generally completely absent in the young and that they are acquired only by *learning* from other members of the species or by individual experience.[19] A lamb, or any other animal, for example, which has had no long association with members of its own species from whom it could have acquired the fear—or past experience with lions—will exhibit not the slightest fear of a lion when confronted with one. On the other hand, when chickens raised in complete isolation are first brought into association with other chickens they sometimes exhibit both fear and aggressive reactions.[20] A certain amount of social, of cooperative, experience would seem to be necessary if the fears nurtured by isolation or any other factors are to be overcome.

No animal or human being is born with any prejudice or specific fear whatever, either of snakes, mice, or the dark, to mention a few of the most familiar common fears usually considered of "instinctive" origin; all these fears or prejudices are *acquired* by learning and may, and usually do, act very like conditioned reflexes, simulating physical reflexes which are innate, but which in these cases are conditioned to react culturally, not biologically or instinctively.

Upon the theory that "race" prejudice is innate, how are we to

---

[19] This is not to say that certain *general* fears and aggressive reactions may not have an innate basis, they may and probably do have; but it is to deny that such reactions are innately determined for any *specific* creature or group.

[20] Brückner, "Untersuchungen zur Tiersoziologie, insbesondere zur Auflösung der Familie." *Zeitschrift für Psychologie,* CXXVIII (1933), 1–110.

account for the well-authenticated fact, familiar to most people of experience, that children of one nation, brought up in the milieu of a "foreign" nation, feel no prejudices whatever, in wartime or in peacetime, against the nation of their adoption but, on the contrary, are generally to be found in the ranks of their adopted land fighting against the motherland of their ancestors, whether it be with ideas or with powder? No more impressive demonstration of this is to be found than in the case of the thousands of Japanese-Americans who in World War II bravely fought on all fronts as American citizens and soldiers against the Axis forces. Japanese-Americans especially distinguished themselves in action against Japanese forces.[21] In fact, the Japanese-American 442d Regimental Combat Team was the most decorated unit in United States history.[22]

A notorious example of transmutation is the case of Houston Stewart Chamberlain, the egregious author of that stupendous miracle of nonsense *The Foundations of the Nineteenth Century*, in which the spectacle is witnessed of an apostate Englishman glorifying the Teutonic spirit, the German brand in particular, at the expense, among others, of his ancestral land and heritage. One may well wonder what happened to Chamberlain's "birthright" of prejudice when as an adult he became a champion of German prejudices. Possibly William James's law of transitoriness of instinct may be invoked here. And what shall we say of Sir Thomas Browne (1605–1682), the author of *Religio Medici*, who wrote: "I am of a constitution so general, that it consorts and sympathiseth with all things; I have no antipathy, or rather idiosyncrasy, in any thing. Those national repugnances do not touch me, nor do I behold with prejudice the French, Italian, Spanish, or Dutch"?

Or of Oliver Goldsmith (1728–1774) who wrote, "Among all the famous sayings of antiquity, there is none that does greater honor to the author, or affords greater pleasure to the reader, (at least if he be a person of a generous and benevolent heart,) than that of the philosopher, who, being asked what countryman he was, replied that he was a citizen of the world. How few are there to be found in modern times who can say the same, or whose conduct is consistent with such

---

[21] Full accounts of the activities of Japanese-American members of the forces of the United States may be read in the files of the Japanese-American newspaper *Pacific Citizen,* published at Salt Lake City, Utah.

[22] *Ibid.,* XXI (October 6, 1945), 1; Murphy, *Ambassadors in Arms.*

a profession! We are now become so much Englishmen, Frenchmen, Dutchmen, Spaniards, or Germans, that we are no longer citizens of the world; so much the natives of one particular spot, or members of one petty society, that we no longer consider ourselves as the general inhabitants of the globe, or members of that grand society which comprehends the whole human kind.... Let a man's birth be ever so high, his station ever so exalted, or his fortune ever so large, yet, if he is not free from the national and all other prejudices, I should make bold to tell him, that he had a low and vulgar mind, and had no just claim to the character of a gentleman. And, in fact, you will always find, that those are most apt to boast of national merit, who have little or no merit of their own to depend on, than which, to be sure, nothing is more natural: the slender vine twists around the sturdy oak for no other reason in the world, but because it has not strength sufficient to support itself."[23]

Or of that great and universal genius Thomas Young (1773–1829), who, as a young man, wrote: "A man who has formed intimacies and friendships with inhabitants of different parts of the globe will find enough to love and to disapprove among every people; and perhaps one who has acquired the faculty of communicating his thoughts with equal ease and pleasure to the individuals of several nations, will find himself as much at home in the one as in the other. Certainly one who is totally destitute of this attainment can never be admitted to judge with impartiality of the character of any country."[24]

As we have seen in an earlier chapter, there is every reason to believe that "race" sentiment and antipathies are comparatively recent developments in the societies of Western man.

In America, where white and black populations frequently live side by side, it is an indisputable fact that white children do not learn to consider themselves superior to Negro children until they are told that they are so,[25] a fact which is revealingly illustrated by the words of a white American farmer from the South who, in answer to the query as to what he thought of the Negro, replied, "I ain't got any-

---

[23] Goldsmith, *On National Prejudices.*

[24] Peacock, *Life of Thomas Young*, p. 107.

[25] Horowitz, "The Development of Attitudes toward the Negro," *Archives of Psychology*, No. 194 (1936); Radke and Trager, "Children's Perceptions of the Social Roles of Negroes and Whites," *Journal of Psychology*, XXIX (1950), 3–33; Trager and Yarrow, *The Learn What They Live.*

thing against niggers; I was fourteen years old before I know'd I was better than a nigger." Numerous other examples could be cited of the cultural acquisitions of prejudices, but we have already dealt with the mechanism of "race" prejudice upon an earlier page, where we have seen that all ideas of "race" prejudice are inherited in just the same manner as are our clothes, not innately but culturally. Man as a social being is custom made, and his own ideas are tailored according to the prevailing fashion. The statement so frequently heard that "war is a universal and everlasting law of Nature" is at best a shallow judgment, for it seems never to occur to those who make it that the conflicts which they are pleased to term "war" and which are alleged to take place between animals in the wild state are pertinent only in referring to conflicts between animals of widely separated species, genera, orders, and, almost universally, classes. Under certain conditions lions will attack almost anything that moves; so will, to a lesser extent, wolves and hyenas; domestic cats will kill small rodents and birds; monkeys will kill birds and insects; baboons will sometimes kill and eat a small monkey; but in all these examples, selected at random, not a single animal will fight with a member of its *own* species in the sense that it will fight with members of other species, orders, or classes of animals.

Under natural conditions it is not usual for animals of one species to prey upon, or to fight with, each other, but rather to attack only animals of different breeds. To this rule there are few exceptions. Of course, hungry animals will devour, upon occasion, members of their own species, but this is a form of conduct which is normally resorted to only because of extreme necessity. In serious conflicts between wild or domesticated animals of the same species the fight is rarely between more than two animals, and usually the causes and the motives which have provoked the fight are similar to those which influence men, namely, the will to possess a sexually desirable mate or an object of physical value such as food. Gibbons feed contentedly in the same tree with monkeys such as macaques and langurs, but will not tolerate the presence of another gibbon group of the same species or any other. Practically all vertebrates defend themselves against attack by members of other groups of their own species. But this sort of defensive fighting is quite different from war. War is an organized attack of one community upon another community, and as such is never fought by animals other than those of the "human" variety. It is impossible to produce a single instance from the animal kingdom, outside of man, to show that within a single species a form of behavior resembling warfare is waged by one group of its members upon any other group of the same species—as a means of improving the species or what not.

Pliny the Elder (23–79 A.D.) is perhaps the earliest writer to have pointed out that man is the only creature that makes war upon his own kind. "In fine, all other living creatures pass their time worthily among their own species: we see them herd together and stand firm against other kinds of animals—fierce lions do not fight among themselves, the serpent's bite attacks not serpents, even the monsters of the sea are only cruel against different species; whereas to man, I vow, most of his evils come from his fellow man."[26]

It was Leonardo da Vinci who defined man as the creature that persecutes its *own* as well as other living species.

If one thing is certain, it is that it is *not* natural for members either of the same species or of any other to wage "war" upon one another. "One species of animal may destroy another and individuals may kill other individuals, but *group* struggles to the death between members of the same species, such as occur in human warfare, can hardly be found among nonhuman animals."[27] As Dr. L. P. Jacks wrote, while World War I was raging, "there is nothing in the life of the lowest beasts which can be compared for utter senselessness with the mutual rending to pieces of the Nations."

War, let it be said at once, is the most unnatural, the most artificial, of all human activities, for it originates in artificial causes, is waged by artificial entities called "states," and is fought from artificial motives, with artificial weapons, for artificial ends. Like our civilization, war is an artificial product of that civilization itself, the civilization that has been achieved by the repeal and the repudiation of those very processes of so-called "Nature" which our von Bernhardis are pleased to regard as an everlasting universal law.[28]

---

[26] Pliny, *Natural History*, Bk. VII, 1.5.

[27] Allee, *Cooperation Among Animals*, p. 200. It is even likely that the ants who are in any event too far removed from man to have any relevance for his behavior, form no exception to this rule. See Maier and Schneirla, *Principles of Animal Psychology*, pp. 164 ff., and Schneirla, " 'Cruel' Ants—and Occam's Razor," *Journal of Comparative Psychology*, XXXIV (1942), 79–83.

[28] For an interesting discussion of "animal warfare," in which the author

First among ten pertinent and basic principles subscribed to by over two thousand American psychologists is the following: *"War can be avoided: War is not born in men; it is built into men.* No race, nation, or social group is inevitably warlike. The frustrations and conflicting interests which lie at the root of aggressive wars can be reduced and re-directed by social engineering. Men can realize their ambitions within the framework of human cooperation and can direct their aggressions against those natural obstacles that thwart them in the attainment of their goals." [29]

We have seen that there is good reason to believe that aggressive "race" sentiment and prejudice are comparatively recent developments of civilized man. So, too, there is good reason to believe that warfare is but a recent development resulting from the artificial and perverted activities of men living in highly civilized groups. Among the extinct varieties of men of whom we have any knowledge no evidence of anything resembling warfare has ever been found. Plenty of weapons of a rather simple nature have been discovered in association with the remains of ancient man, but they appear to have been made for use against animals, not against his fellow men. Throughout the Old Stone Age (Paleolithic), a period which occupies 96 per cent of man's entire history, all known human groups lived by food gathering and hunting, as did the Middle Stone Age (Mesolithic) groups who succeeded them. Adam Smith long ago pointed out that a hunting population is always thinly spread over a large area and possesses but little accumulated property. Primitive man was, and in many cases still is, a food gatherer and a hunter, and no doubt, as in the case among most existing nonliterate peoples, his hunting grounds were marked off by definite boundaries, boundaries separating different communities; "these boundaries were sacred, and as no one would think of violating them they could not form a cause of war."

"Savages," writes Ellis, "are on the whole not warlike, although they often try to make out that they are terribly bloodthirsty fellows; it is only with difficulty that they work themselves up to a fighting pitch and even then all sorts of religious beliefs and magical practices restrain warfare and limit its effects. Even among the fiercest peoples

---

extends the meaning of "warfare" to embrace attacks upon animals of widely separated species, see Wright, *A Study of War*, pp. 42–52, 479–518.

[29] Allport, "Human Nature and the Peace," *Psychological Bulletin*, XLII (1945), 376.

of East Africa the bloodshed is usually small. Speke mentions a war that lasted three years; the total losses were three men on each side. In all parts of the world there are people who rarely or never fight; and if, indeed . . . the old notion that primitive people are in chronic warfare of the most ferocious character were really correct, humanity could not have survived. Primitive man had far more formidable enemies than his own species to fight against, and it was in protection against these, and not against his fellows, that the beginnings of cooperation and the foundation of the State were laid." [30]

The late Professor W. J. Perry wrote: "Civilized people are far more ferocious than the majority of 'savages,' and whenever 'savages' are uncommonly ferocious, it is usually possible to detect the influence of civilized men. It is the civilized man who is the savage." [31]

A recent student of the subject, Dr. Ragner Numelin, has stated his conclusions as follows: "Warfare as such, *i.e.*, organized warfare, is . . . not customary among primitive peoples. When war occurs it is obviously more of the nature of robbery and plundering raids. The simplest communities do not organize war, and war for expansion is relatively rare in the primitive world. . . . Further, we have found that peaceable relations dominate among the primitive, wandering peoples, the food-gatherers, the fishing and hunting tribes. The rather peaceful character of such peoples is usually confirmed by their traditions and legends which often form a rich ethnological treasure-house. Instead of spending their days in fighting they lead peaceful lives when left undisturbed. They seldom use violence in their personal relations and they do not fight as communities. Savages do not usually live at odds with their neighbors." [32]

War came into being only after men had begun to cultivate the land upon which they were then able to settle permanently. Such an agricultural stage of development, we know, first appeared among men about ten thousand years ago, in Upper Neolithic times. [33] The

---

[30] Ellis, *The Philosophy of Conflict*, pp. 51–52. Ellis was here summarizing the work of Holsti, *The Relation of War to the Origin of the State*. For confirmatory views see Wright's chapter "Primitive Warfare," in *A Study of War*, pp. 53–100, and Hambly, "Primitive Warfare," *Chicago Natural History Museum Bulletin*, XVII (1946), 4–5.

[31] Perry, "Man the Primeval Pacifist," *Vincula*, 14 December 1925, p. 64.

[32] Numelin, *The Beginnings of Diplomacy*, p. 104.

[33] Childe, *The Dawn of European Civilization; Man Makes Himself;* "War in Prehistoric Societies," *Sociological Review*, XXXIII (1941), 126–38.

agricultural life results in the accumulation of property, the accumulation of property eventually results in more or less organized industry, industry in wealth, wealth in power, power in expansive ambitions, and the desire to acquire additional property—the source of additional power—necessary to gratify those ambitions, and thus, by no very complicated process, in war. Such conditions, which are peculiar to the industrial civilizations of today, are, of course, highly artificial, as are the prejudices and the "race" sentiment which they serve to generate.

In the modern world undoubtedly the most potent cause of war is economic rivalry, a cultural phenomenon having no biological basis whatever. The desire for foreign concessions and markets, an expanding population, the lust for *Lebensraum*—such things will upon little provocation set nations in opposition and at each other's throats.[34] It is from such economic causes that patriotism, chauvinism, and the widespread fear of aggression, which more than anything else serves to consolidate the group and is responsible for the generation of "race" prejudice and sentiment, are born. As Malinowski has put it, "human beings fight not because they are biologically impelled but because they are culturally induced, by trophies, as in head-hunting, by wealth as in looting, by revenge as in punitive wars, by propaganda as it occurs under modern conditions." [35]

If all this is true, then it is apparent that war arises not as the result of natural or biological conditions but from purely contrived artificial social conditions created by highly "civilized" modes of interaction between human groups.

With respect to the "natural antagonisms" with which man is alleged to be endowed, it may be said at once that these are pure creations of Sir Arthur Keith's imagination, for certainly there exists no evidence that man is born with any antagonisms whatever.[36] The evidence is, on the other hand, quite contrary to such a suggestion.

---

[34] See Bernhardi, *Germany and the Next War,* for a most illuminating exemplification of this view. See also Nef, *War and Human Progress;* Bernard, *War and Its Causes.*

[35] Malinowski, "War—Past, Present, and Future," in Clarkson and Cochran (eds.), *War as a Social Institution,* pp. 23–24.

[36] Bender, "Genesis of Hostility in Children," *American Journal of Psychiatry,* CV (1948), 241–45; Montagu, *On Being Human;* Montagu, *The Direction of Human Development;* Ausubel, *Theory and Problems of Child Development.*

Sir Charles Sherrington has set out some of this evidence in his masterly book *Man on His Nature*, while Professor W. C. Allee has recently given reasons together with some of the evidence, observational, inductive, and experimental, which indicates that the spirit of altruism, of cooperation, is very much more natural to man than is that of egoism or antagonism. "After much consideration," writes Professor Allee, "it is my mature conclusion, contrary to Herbert Spencer, that the cooperative forces are biologically the more important and vital. The balance between the cooperative, altruistic tendencies and those which are disoperative and egoistic is relatively close. Under many conditions the cooperative forces lose. In the long run, however, the group-centered, more altruistic drives are slightly stronger.

"If cooperation had not been the stronger force, the more complicated animals, whether arthropods or vertebrates, could not have evolved from the simpler ones, and there would have been no men to worry each other with their distressing and biologically foolish wars. While I know of no laboratory experiments that make a direct test of this problem, I have come to this conclusion by studying the implications of many experiments which bear on both sides of the problem, and from considering the trends of organic evolution in nature. Despite many known appearances to the contrary, human altruistic drives are as firmly based on an animal ancestry as is man himself. Our tendencies towards goodness, such as they are, are as innate as our tendencies toward intelligence; we could do well with more of both." [37]

Prince Petr Kropotkin arrived at similar conclusions at a time when such ideas were scarcely mentioned; these he set out in a remarkable book, *Mutual Aid*. "If," wrote Kropotkin, "we resort to an indirect test, and ask Nature: 'Who are the fittest: those who are continually at war with each other, or those who support one another?' we at once see that those animals which acquire habits of mutual aid are undoubtedly the fittest. They have more chances to survive, and they attain, in their respective classes, the highest development of

---

[37] Allee, "Where Angels Fear to Tread; a Contribution from General Sociology to Human Ethics," *Science*, XCVII (1943), 521. See also the same author's *Cooperation among Animals* and his *Animal Aggregations*. Along similar lines see Montagu, *On Being Human*, and Darwin, *Competition and Cooperation*.

intelligence and bodily organization." More recently J. B. S. Haldane has concluded that "in so far as it makes for the survival of one's descendants and near relations, altruistic behaviour is a kind of Darwinian fitness, and may be expected to spread as the result of natural selection." [38] And this, indeed, is what Darwin believed. "As man advances in civilization," he wrote, "and small tribes are united into larger communities, the simplest reason would tell each individual that he ought to extend his social instincts and sympathies to all members of the same nation, though personally unknown to him. This point being once reached, there is only an artificial barrier to prevent his sympathies extending to the men of all nations and races." [39]

Professor William Patten has devoted a highly original book to the consideration of cooperation as a factor in evolution. [40] Indeed, many distinguished students of evolutionary process have dealt with the evidence pointing to the cardinal importance of the role which cooperation has played in evolution, but their work is only now being rescued from the neglect into which it has fallen. [41]

Professor A. E. Emerson's views on the biological basis of social cooperation are identical with those of Allee. Emerson points out that: "Just as the cell in the body functions for the benefit of the whole organism, so does the individual organism become subordinate to the population. It is in harmony with natural law to have an individual function for the benefit of other contemporary individuals and also for future generations. This principle gives us a scientific basis for ethics." [42]

Professor Emerson goes on to say: "Coöperation is probably not an end in itself, but is rather a means to an end. The all-over directional

---

[38] Haldane, *The Causes of Evolution*, p. 130.

[39] Darwin, *The Descent of Man*, Chap. IV, pp. 187–88.

[40] Patten, *The Grand Strategy of Evolution*.

[41] Geddes and Thomson, *Evolution*; Geddes and Thomson, *Sex*; Bernard, *Some Neglected Factors in Evolution*; Reinheimer, *Evolution by Coöperation: a Study in Bio-economics*; Reinheimer, *Symbiosis; a Socio-physiological Study of Evolution*; Berg, *Nomogenesis*; Gibson, *The Morality of Nature*; Delage and Goldsmith, *The Theories of Evolution*; Allee *et al.*, *Principles of Animal Ecology*; and numerous other works. For a discussion of these works see Montagu, *Darwin, Competition and Cooperation*; Montagu, *The Direction of Human Development*.

[42] Emerson, "The Biological Basis of Social Cooperation," *Illinois Academy of Science Transactions*, XXXIX (1946), 9–18.

trend in organic evolution seems to have been toward optimum conditions for existence. What was the uncontrolled external environment of the cell became the balanced internal environment of the multicellular organism. Selection of variations leads toward more efficient division of labor and more integration and coöperation between the parts. Differentiation would be useless without integration, and integration would be useless without differentiation. Natural selection has constantly guided organic evolution in the direction of increasing complexity and increasing coöperation. This trend is easily seen in the study of the evolution of intraspecific populations and reaches its culmination in the social insects and in man." [43]

Certainly aggressiveness exists in nature, [44] but there is also a healthy nonruthless competition and strong basic drives toward social and cooperative behavior. These forces do not operate independently, but together, as a whole, and the evidence strongly indicates that of all these drives the principle of cooperation is dominant and biologically the most important. The coexistence of so many different species of animals throughout the world is sufficient testimony to the importance of that principle. It is probable that man owes more to the development of his cooperative drives than to any other in his biological and social evolution. [45] His future lies with their further development, not with their suppression.

In 1939 a group of leading scientists formulated the principle naturally operative in governing human conduct as follows: "The probability of survival of a relationship between individual humans or groups of humans increases with the extent to which that relationship is mutually satisfying." This principle being but a special case of the more general principle that "the probability of survival of individual, or groups of, living things increases with the degree with which they harmoniously adjust themselves to each other and their environment." [46] This, essentially, is the principle of cooperation, of mutual

---

[43] *Ibid.,* p. 15.

[44] Collias, "Aggressive Behavior among Vertebrate Animals," *Physiological Zoölogy,* XVII (1944), 83–123; Scott, *Aggression.*

[45] Allee speaks of "the great drive toward natural altruism that extends throughout the whole animal kingdom." "Biology and International Relations," *New Republic,* CXII (1945), 817; see also Montagu (ed.), *Culture and the Evolution of Man;* Washburn (ed.), *Social Life of Early Man.*

[46] Leake, "Ethicogenesis," *Proceedings of the Philosophical Society of Texas,*

aid, the conscious recognition of which has been the basis of most religious and ethical systems. The biological corroboration of the soundness of that ethical principle must be counted one of the greatest discoveries in the history of mankind. That principle has played a great part in the development of mankind. It must be made to play an even greater role in the future.

Our efforts to obtain natural justice in the world will be rewarded only when we have banished such pathological phenomena as "race" prejudice and the causes which give rise to it from our sick societies. The original conception of natural justice which was held by men down to the nineteenth century was one that was valid for the whole community of mankind. It was in principle an explicit recognition of the intrinsic worth of human personality, implying universal equality and brotherhood. The shift in meaning, in the nineteenth century, from nature as harmony and design to nature as struggle brought about the eclipse of the concept of justice as an ideal of human relations, and the emergence of the idea that what is just is determined by the arbitrament of force, the survival of the fittest.[47]

Without strong drives to cooperation, sociability, and mutual aid, the progress of organic life, the improvement of the organism, and the strengthening of the species becomes utterly incomprehensible. Indeed, Haldane and Huxley suggest that competition between adults of the same species is on the whole a biological evil. The biological effects of such competition, it seems likely, writes Haldane, "render the species as a whole less successful in coping with its environment. No doubt weaklings are weeded out, but so would they be in competition with the environment. And the special adaptations favoured by interspecific competition divert a certain amount of energy from other functions, just as armaments, subsidies, and tariffs, the organs of international competition, absorb a proportion of the natural wealth which many believe might be better employed."[48]

Not "nature red in tooth and claw" but cooperation is the primary law of natural conduct.

X (1944), 32–33; also included in Montagu (ed.), *Studies and Essays in the History of Science and Learning.*
[47] For an excellent discussion of this subject see Stapleton, *Justice and World Society.* See also Bryson, *Man and Society;* Baker, *The Dignity of Man;* Miller, *The Community of Man; Idem, Progress and Decline.*
[48] Haldane, *The Causes of Evolution,* pp. 125–26.

There remains to be examined the statement given expression by Sir Arthur Keith and implied in the writings of many before him that war is nature's "pruning-hook," "Nature's method of keeping her orchard healthy." This, of course, is supposed to mean that war acts as a process of natural selection—an idea which on the face of it is absurd; for, as everyone knows, the manner in which modern war acts is to kill off the best members of the group while jealously preserving the worst, such as the mentally and bodily diseased and the generally unfit. And in any case, as World War I fully proved, the nation superior to all others in the processes of waging war, the most ingenious and fertile in the invention and use of the instruments of destruction, may in spite of this lose the war by the selectively irrelevant fact of being overwhelmingly outnumbered. Referring to World War I, Professor Pollard has aptly remarked that "if the result had depended on scientific invention the Germans would have won. As it was, they neutralized enormous odds in numbers to such an extent that for four years the principal front hardly shifted on an average more than half a dozen miles in either direction. The Allied victory was due not to scientific superiority but to the economic exhaustion of the foe, and to the fact that in Foch's decisive campaign America was pouring more fresh troops into the line of battle in a month than the Germans could raise in a year."[49] From the standpoint of natural selection it is apparent to all those who lived through it that the Germans, who proved themselves the most intelligent and certainly not the least valorous of all the combatants, should, on the basis of "brains" alone, have won the war of 1914–1918. Instead, they lost it. Something clearly had gone wrong with "natural selection," or, rather, with war as an agency of it. It was, indeed, the confidence in "reeking tube and iron shard" which led the Germans from an even and peaceful development into the disaster of war and humiliation.

As a matter of fact, the whole concept of war as an agency of natural selection in the case of man breaks down when we consider that throughout the historic period there were numerous instances of victories in war gained by peoples who were culturally inferior to the peoples whom they conquered. It must, however, be freely acknowledged that on the whole up to the modern era the peoples victorious in war were generally superior to the people whom they

---

[49] Pollard, "The War of Nature and a Peace of Mind," *Vincula,* 14 December 1925, p. 61.

conquered—superior in the strict sense of the *military* superiority of the combatant *individuals*. In former times men actually fought with one another, the superior warrior (who may have been superior simply because he had been better fed) generally killing the inferior in hand-to-hand combat. But in modern warfare the combatants scarcely ever see each other, and when they do it is not military skill or native superiority which decides who shall die, but a shell fired from a battery some miles away or a machine gun hundreds of yards distant, or a bomb dropped from an airplane thousands of feet above them. In actual battle the superior men are the first to go over the top; in dangerous and generally useless raids they are the first to be chosen—and killed. Where, in all this slaughter, is there to be detected any evidence of natural selection? Selection, certainly, in that the superior are selected for death and the inferior are protected against it—in this way does modern warfare act as an agency of unnatural selection, for the worst.[50]

Man has reached his present supremacy through the inhibitive and integrative powers of his mind, through a unique educability and ability to reject and suppress what he considers to be undesirable, the ability to *control*. Human society depends upon the maintenance of that ability of the mind to control, not so much the brute in man—for there is really nothing that is brutal in him that is not forced upon him—but those elements which under miseducation are capable of making a brute of him. All that is fine, noble, beautiful, and desirable in our civilization has been achieved through the resolute determination of individual minds not so much to conquer and to vanish what is customarily called "Nature," red in tooth and claw, but to enlist the aid of "Nature" in the service of man and to control it effectively. It may be an oversimplification, but it is not far from the truth to say that so much that is ugly, inhuman, and destructive in our civilization is largely due to the activities of those who are anxious to exploit their fellow men to their own advantage and use measures of control only toward that end. To them war is a profitable activity, for it increases their power as well as their fortunes. It is individuals of this order, in all countries and from the earliest historical times, who help to make wars, not nature. Others who assist have the *status quo* to maintain.[51] "The fault, dear Brutus, lies not in our stars, but in ourselves."

---

[50] Kellogg, *Military Selection and Race Deterioration*, p. 178.
[51] Rowse, *Appeasement*.

Man has too long been deceived by a chaos of ideas for which there is not the slightest basis in fact, ideas which represent, as Spinoza said, the errors of the ages grown hoary with the centuries. The flowers that bloom in the verbal spring of such writers as von Bernhardi and Sir Arthur Keith, not to mention the Hitlers of this world, have nothing whatever to do with either the logical case or the factual reality. Nay, in spite of Kant and others, there is no instinct toward peace in man just as there is none toward war. The early Egyptians, the Cretans, and the people of Mohenjo-Daro, in India, did not wage war, for the good reason that it was totally unnecessary for them to do so, since socially and economically they were entirely sufficient unto themselves. Aboriginal Australians, however, have on occasion fought with one another, because for economic reasons—such as a dog or a wife—it seemed necessary for them to do so. Men, it seems, fight only when and if they want to; and under primitive conditions that appears to be very seldom indeed. There is nothing within the nature of men, no *primum mobile*, no innate prejudice, save for such prejudices as have been cultivated in them by education, which forces them to do so.[52]

I conclude this chapter with a paragraph from an article published in an obscure student journal not long after the First World War. "There looms a day of judgment, a day of judgment pronounced by man upon himself as having committed suicide because he was not fit to live. For we come to a common issue between a common mind to live and common 'nature' to kill. If there is Armageddon all will be taken, none will be left, and Fate will be common to victors and vanquished, rich and poor, all the nations, and both the hemispheres. To learn lest we perish is the logic of the League of Nations; learn to destroy is the teaching of 'natural' war. Whether mankind survives depends less on its science than on its humanity, upon whether we trust an increasing control over physical forces to men with a decreasing sense of responsibility for their use, and whether we regard as more 'natural' the war we think rooted in Nature or the peace we owe to our mind."[53]

---

[52] For an admirable discussion of "race" relations and war see Andrews, "Racial Influences," in Porritt (ed.), *The Causes of War,* pp. 63–113.

[53] Pollard, "The War of Nature and a Peace of Mind," *Vincula* (University of London Students Journal), 14 December 1925, p. 61.

14

"Race" and "Blood"

I~N HIS INSPIRING~ and provocative book *Man: Real and Ideal*, Professor E. G. Conklin writes: "Ashley Montagu would discard wholly the word 'race' in the case of man because of social prejudices associated with that word and substitute for it 'ethnic group' or 'caste.' I wholly sympathise with his desire to get rid of race prejudice, but not by denying the existence of races or by giving them another name, for 'What's in a name?' " [1] Apparently I have been unclear in my proposals, for these statements do not correctly represent my viewpoint,[2] but it is not with these statements that I am here concerned, but with Professor Conklin's question, "What's in a name?"

What, indeed? I suggest, with most students of language, that names are words and that words rule the lives of men; that in this sense words are among the most important things we have to deal with in the course of our lives. I suggest that the meaning of most, if not all, words is to some extent emotionally determined and that man is, in large part, a creature of emotion. It is Freud who said: "Words and magic were in the beginning one and the same thing, and even to-day words retain much of their magical power. By words one of us can give to another the greatest happiness or bring about utter despair; by words the teacher imparts his knowledge to the student; by words the orator sweeps his audience with him and determines its judgments and decisions. Words call forth emotions and are universally the means by which we influence our fellow

---

[1] Conklin, *Man: Real and Ideal*, p. 20.
[2] See Appendix B, 372–80.

creatures." [3] Henry James remarked, "All life comes back to the question of our speech—the medium through which we communicate." And as Bacon said before him, "Men believe that their reason is lord over their words, but it happens, too, that words exercise a reciprocal and reactionary power over our intellect. Words, as a Tartar's bow, shoot back upon the understanding of the wisest, and mightily entangle and pervert the judgment."

Finally, names, words, not only serve to describe, but also often serve to create ideas and stereotypes. As Goethe once remarked, "Where an idea is wanting a word can always be found to take its place." The modern movement of semantics and semantogenetics is devoted to the analysis of this form of human behavior and the tracing of its serious consequences.[4] Words fashion the thoughts of men, and most men become the puppets of their vocabularies.

Where words are concerned there are two classes of men—those who control their words by critical analysis, they are in the minority; and those whose words, whose verbal habits, control their thoughts, they are in the great majority. The latter are the "word supporters," the "word sentimentalists," the "racists," unconscious or declared. With them, to whom a name, a word, a very little word, often means the difference between life and death, we are here concerned. A first step toward clear thinking is the removal of words that create muddled thinking.

There are many words in the vocabulary of Western man which are characterized by an exaggerated emotional content; words distinguished by a high emotional and a low rational, or reasonable, quality. "Race" is such a word; "blood" is another. The word "race" has assumed a high emotional content in relatively recent times; "blood," on the other hand, is a word which, from the beginning of recorded history, and certainly long before that, has possessed a high emotional content.

That blood is the most immediately important constituent of the human body must have been remarked by men at an early period in their cultural development. The weakening effect or actual death produced by an appreciable loss of blood can hardly have escaped

---

[3] Freud, *Introductory Lectures on Psycho-Analysis,* p. 13.
[4] See Korzybski, *Science and Sanity;* Hayakawa, *Language in Action;* Chase, *The Tyranny of Words;* Ogden and Richards, *The Meaning of Meaning;* Walpole, *Semantics: The Nature of Words and Their Meanings.*

their notice. Hence, the identification of blood as a vital principle with life and its endowment with special strength-giving qualities must have been almost inevitable steps in the process of endowing this red fluid with meaning. Among all primitive peoples blood is regarded as a most powerful element possessed of the most varied and potent qualities. To enumerate these and the functions they are believed able to perform would alone fill a volume.

In the cultural dynamics of Western civilization the concept of "blood" has played a significant and important role. From the earliest times it has been regarded as that most quintessential element of the body which carries, and through which is transmitted, the hereditary qualities of the stock. Thus, all persons of the same family stock were regarded as of the same "blood." In a community which mostly consisted of family lines whose members had, over many generations, intermarried with one another, it is easy to understand how, with such a concept of "blood," the community or nation would come to regard itself as of one "blood," distinct, *by blood,* from all other communities or nations. This, indeed, is the popular conception of "blood" which prevails at the present time. Thus, for example, if one turns to the Oxford English Dictionary and looks under "blood," the following statement is found: "Blood is popularly treated as the typical part of the body which children inherit from their parents and ancestors; hence that of parents and children, and of the members of a family or race, is spoken of as identical, and as being distinct from that of other families or races."

As Dobzhansky has put it: "Before the re-discovery of Mendel's work the transmission of heredity was thought of in terms of inheritance of 'blood.' Parental 'bloods' mix and give rise to the 'blood' of the child which is a compromise between those of the parents. In a sexually reproducing population the available variety of 'bloods' mingle owing to intermarriage. If such a population is left undisturbed, the continuous mixing process will result in an uniform solution which will represent the 'blood' of a race or a variety. When a complete or near complete uniformity is reached you will have a 'pure race'—a group of individuals with identical germ plasms. If two races mingle, a mixed race arises; if race miscegenation ceases, a new 'pure race' will eventually result.

"It is most unfortunate," Dobzhansky adds, "that the theory of 'blood' though invalidated decades ago, still colors not merely the thinking of laymen but finds its way, explicitly or implicitly, into text books."[5]

It is this conception of 'blood' as the carrier of the heritable qualities of the family, "race," or nation which has led to its application in such extended meanings as are implied in terms such as "blue blood," "blood royal," "pureblood," "full blood," "half blood," "good blood," "blood tie," or "blood relationship," and "consanguinity." Supposed "racial" and national differences are, of course, recognized in such terms as "German blood," "English blood," "Jewish blood," and "Negro blood"; so that today the words "race" and "blood" have come to be used as synonyms.

When the meaning of these terms is analyzed, the manner in which the general conception of "blood" operates may be more clearly perceived. Thus, the term "blue blood," which refers to a presumed special kind of blood supposed to flow in the veins of ancient and aristocratic families, actually represents a translation from the Spanish *sangre azul,* the "blue blood" attributed to some of the oldest and proudest families of Castile, who claimed never to have been contaminated by "foreign blood."[6] Many of these families were of fair complexion, hence in members of these families the veins would, in comparison with those of the members of the predominantly dark-complexioned population, appear strikingly blue. Hence, the difference between an aristocrat and a commoner could easily be recognized as a difference in "blood"; one was a "blue blood," and the other was not.

The expression "blood royal" refers to the generally accepted notion that only persons of royal ancestry have the "blood of kings" flowing in their veins. No person, however noble his ancestry, can be of the "blood royal" unless he has the blood of kingly ancestors in his veins. Thus, kings have usually been held to belong to a special class of mankind principally by virtue of the supposed unique characters of their blood. In order to keep the "blood" of the royal house pure, marriages were arranged exclusively between those who were of "the royal blood."

---

[5] Dobzhansky, "Genetics and Human Affairs," *Teaching Biologist,* XII (1943), 101–02.

[6] The blood in the veins is dark red in color, while the veins themselves are creamy-white. The blue appearance of the veins through the skin is due to the refractive properties of the tissues through which they are observed.

In common parlance and in the loose usage of many who should know better, terms like "full blood," or "pure blood," and "half blood" clearly illustrate the supposed hereditary character of the blood and the manner in which, by simple arithmetical division, it may be diluted. Thus, "full blood" and "pure blood" are expressions which are alleged to define the supposed fact that a person is of unadulterated blood; that is, he is a person whose ancestors have undergone no admixture of "blood" with members of another "race." Within the last century these terms have come to be applied almost exclusively to persons who are not of the "white race," to persons, in short, whose place is considered to be on the allegedly inferior rungs of the "racial" ladder. It is possible that this restricted usage has been determined by the fact that these expressions have generally done most service in the description of native peoples or of slaves, as in "full-blooded Negro," "pureblood Indian," or merely "full blood," or "pureblood." Such an imputed lowly association would be sufficient to secure the nonapplication of the term to any member of the self-styled superior "races."

A "half blood," in contradistinction to a "full blood," or "pure-blood," is supposed to be half of one "race" and half of another— for example, the offspring of an Indian and a white. What is actually implied is that while a full blood or pureblood may claim relationship through both parents, a half blood may claim relationship through one parent only. For example, a mulatto, that is, the offspring of a white and a Negro, is for all practical purposes classed with the group to which the Negro parent belongs, and his white ancestry is, for the same purposes, ignored. In practice, it often works out that the half blood is not fully accepted by either of the parental groups, because of his "adulterated blood," and he becomes in the true sense of the expression "half caste," belonging to neither caste; for in Western society, as we have seen in an earlier chapter, the so-called "different" "races" are, in reality, treated as if they were different castes.

A person is said to be of "good" or "gentle" blood if he is of "noble" birth or of "good" family. Here the assumed biological de-terminance of social status by blood is clearly exhibited; that is to say, a person's rank in society is assumed to be determined by his "blood," when, in fact, it is in reality the other way around, "blood" is actually determined by rank. The ancestors of all noblemen were once common people, plebeians. It was not a sudden metamorphosis in the composition of their blood which caused them to become noble; it was rather an elevation in social status, which endowed them with supposedly superior qualities which are not biological in any sense whatever and belong purely to the ascriptive variety of things. That is to say, they have no real, but a purely imagined, existence.

The statement that a person is of "bad blood," in the sense that he is of common or inferior character or status, is rarely encountered, for the reason, presumably, that those who use such terms have not considered the "blood" of such persons worth mentioning at all. Thus, for example, while there is an entry in the Oxford English Dictionary for "blood worth mention," there is *none* for blood *not* worth mention. In the sense in which "blood" is considered as the seat of the emotions, "bad blood" is taken to be the physiological or serological equivalent of ill feeling. In this sense, of course, "bad blood" may be created between persons of "good blood."

The term "blood relationship" and its Anglicized Latin equivalent "consanguinity," meaning the condition of being of the same "blood" or relationship, by descent from a common ancestor, enshrine the belief that all biological relationships are reflected in, and are to a large extent determined by, the character of the blood. This venerable error, along with others, requires correction.

The brief analysis of the variety of ways in which "blood" is used and understood in the English language and in Western civilization in general renders it sufficiently clear that most people believe that blood is equivalent to heredity and that blood, therefore, is that part of the organism which determines the quality of the person. By extension, it is also generally believed that the social as well as the biological status of the person is determined by the kind of blood he has inherited. These beliefs concerning blood are probably among the oldest surviving from the earliest days of mankind. Certainly they are found to be almost universally distributed among the peoples of the earth in much the same forms, and their antiquity is sufficiently attested by the fact that in the graves of prehistoric men red pigments are frequently found in association with the remains. These pigments were, probably, used to represent the blood as the symbol of life and humanity, a belief enshrined in the expression "He is flesh and blood," to signify humanity as opposed to deity or disembodied spirit. There in the grave was the flesh, and the pigment was introduced to represent the blood.

As an example of a myth grown hoary with the ages and for which there is not the slightest justification in scientific fact, the popular conception of "blood" is outstanding. Were it not for the fact that it is a bad myth, harmful in its effects and dangerous in its possible consequences, it might well be allowed to persist; but since great harm has already been done and will continue to be done unless this myth is exposed for what it is—one of the most serious misinterpretations of fact ever perpetrated by mankind—it is today more than ever necessary to set out the facts about blood as science has come to know them.

In the first place, blood is in no way connected with the transmission of hereditary characters. The transmitters of hereditary characters are the genes which lie in the chromosomes of the germ cells represented by the spermatozoa of the father and the ova of the mother *and nothing else.* These genes, carried in the chromosomes and cell substance of a single spermatozoon and a single ovum, are the *only* parts of the organism which are concerned with the transmission of heredity.[7] Blood has nothing whatever to do with heredity, either biologically, sociologically, or in any other manner.

As Dobzhansky says: "Germ plasms are not miscible 'bloods.' They are sums of discrete genes which, if unlike but present in the same individual, do not mix but segregate according to the rules established by Mendel. In sexually reproducing organisms, an individual inherits only one-half, not all of the genes each parent possesses; and it transmits to its children one-half of its genes. Every sex cell produced by an individual is likely to contain a somewhat different complement of genes from every other sex cell of the same individual. Brothers and sisters have different hereditary endowments. The variety of genes present in populations of many sexually reproducing species, including man, is so great, and the number of combinations which they are capable of producing is so colossal, that it is unlikely that any two individuals (identical twins excepted) ever have exactly the same germ plasms."[8]

---

[7] Montagu, *Human Heredity.*

[8] Dobzhansky, "Genetics and Human Affairs," *Teaching Biologist,* XII (1943), 102.

The belief that the blood of the pregnant mother is transmitted to the child in the womb, and hence becomes a part of the child, is ancient but erroneous. Scientific knowledge of the processes of pregnancy have long ago made it clear that there is normally no actual passage of blood from mother to child. The developing child manufactures its own blood, and the character of its various blood cells, both morphologically and physiologically, is demonstrably different from that of either of its parents. The mother does not contribute blood to the fetus nor the fetus to the mother.[9] This fact should forever dispose of the ancient notion, which is so characteristically found among nonliterate peoples, that the blood of the mother is continuous with that of the child. The same belief is to be found in the works of Aristotle on generation.[10] Aristotle held that the monthly periods, which fail to appear during pregnancy, contribute to the formation of the child's body. Modern scientific investigation demonstrates that this and similar notions are quite false, and thus completely disposes of the idea of a blood tie between any two persons, whether they be mother and child or even identical twins. Hence, any claims to kinship based on the tie of blood can have no scientific foundation of any kind. Nor can claims of group consciousness based on blood be anything but fictitious, since the character of the blood of all human beings is determined not by their membership in any group or nation but by the fact that they are human beings.

The blood of all human beings is in every respect the same, with only two exceptions, that is, in the agglutinating properties of the blood which yields the four blood groups and in the Rh factor. But these agglutinating properties of the four blood groups and the twenty-one serologically distinguishable Rh groups are present in all varieties of men, and in various groups of men they differ only in statistical distribution. This distribution is a matter not of quality but of quantity. There are no known or demonstrable differences in the character of the blood of different peoples, except that some traits of the blood are possessed in greater frequency by some than by others. In that sense St. Paul's *obiter dictum* "[that] God hath made of one blood all nations of men for to dwell on all the face of the earth" [11] is literally true.

---

[9] Montagu, *Prenatal Influences.*
[10] Aristotle, *De generatione animalum,* i. 20.
[11] *Acts* 17:26.

Scientists have for many years attempted to discover whether or not any differences exist in the blood of different peoples, but the results of such investigations have always been the same—*no difference has been discovered,* except in the statistical distribution of the traits which all human beings possess in common and the presence of a blood type which is absent in other populations or the absence of one which is present in other populations.[12] In short, it cannot be too emphatically or too often repeated that in every respect the blood of all human groups is the same, varying only in the frequency with which certain of its chemical components are encountered in different populations. This similarity cuts across all lines of caste, class, group, nation, and ethnic group. Obviously, then, since all people are of one blood, such differences as may exist between them can have absolutely no connection with blood.

Such facts, however, did not in the least deter Nazi propagandists from using the "blood" myths to set human beings against one another. The official Nazi view of the matter was presented to the Congress of the Nazi Party at Nuremberg, exactly six years before the invasion of Poland, by the official Nazi distorter of the truth, Alfred Rosenberg—who was subsequently hanged as a war criminal at Nuremberg. "A nation," said Rosenberg, "is constituted by the predominance of a definite character formed by its blood, language, geographical environment, and the sense of a united political destiny. These last constituents are not, however, definitive; the decisive element in a nation is its blood. In the first awakening of a people, great poets and heroes disclose themselves to us as the incorporation of the eternal values of a particular blood soul. I believe that this recognition of the profound significance of blood is now mysteriously encircling our planet, irresistibly gripping one nation after another." [13]

The concept of "race" which equates the inheritance of the individual or of the group with the transmission of hereditary characters

---

[12] Mourant, *The Distribution of the Human Blood Groups;* Race and Sanger, *Blood Groups in Man;* Montagu, *An Introduction to Physical Anthropology,* 3rd ed.; Boyd, *Genetics and the Races of Man.*

[13] *Vossische Zeitung,* September 3, 1933. Rosenberg himself was a Baltic Russian, and did not become a "German" till 1923 when the Russians refused to allow him to return to Reval, where he was born. See *Memoirs of Alfred Rosenberg.* Rosenberg's chief collection of essays is entitled *Blood and Honor (Blut und Ehre).* See also Chandler, *Rosenberg's Nazi Myth.*

or qualities through the blood dates from a period when the nature of heredity was not understood and the existence of such things as genes was unknown. During that period, the eighteenth and nineteenth centuries, the "race" concept was developed. It has been seen that this concept is false and misleading, producing absurdities of thought and conduct which are atrocious.

The extravagant and preposterous claims which the Nazis made on the basis of the blood myth are only equaled by the superstitions which prevail among others in the same connection. During World War II these were given much publicity when the Red Cross segregated the blood of Negroes for the purposes of transfusion. In July, 1958, in the State of Louisiana a law came into effect requiring the segregation of the blood obtained from Negroes. The blood segregation bill was the result of the efforts of Louisiana's Joint Legislative Committee on Segregation. In other words, the myth of "blood" seems almost as strongly entrenched in this country as it was among the Nazis. This is an undesirable and dangerous situation and the sooner the facts concerning blood are made known the better.

The astonishing thing about the objection to Negro blood is not so much that it is based upon a misconception, but that the same person who refuses to accept Negro blood may be willing to have his children suckled by a Negro wet nurse just as he had been as an infant. The same person will be ready to submit to an injection of serum derived from a monkey, a horse, a cow, or some other animal, and while he himself may have been suckled by a Negro wet nurse and may even entertain the greatest affection for Negroes, he will violently object to any "pollution" of his blood by the injection of Negro blood into his own blood stream.

This is a false belief, a superstition for which there is no ground in fact. In reality the blood of the Negro is similar to that of all other human beings, so that for purposes of transfusion, or any other purposes, it is as good as any other blood.[14]

The objection to Negro blood is, of course, based on the antique misconception that the blood is the carrier of the hereditary characters,[15] and since the Negro is regarded as possessing "racially"

---

[14] For an able analysis and discussion of the character of the blood in the varieties of man see Lewis, *The Biology of the Negro*, pp. 82 ff.

[15] It was the ancient belief that the seed comes from all parts of the body and is carried in or is merely a specialized portion of the blood. For a clear ex-

inferior characters, it is feared that these may be transmitted to the receiver of the transfusion. Both prejudices are groundless.

But observe how real unreal names and words may become if only they are believed to be real. If I say that certain persons belong to certain "globglubs" and their "zebzebs" differ from my zebzebs because I belong to a different globglub, I may be talking utter nonsense; but if I believe that what I am saying is actually meaningful and true, it may be nonsense to others, but it is very fact to me. When, however, most people believe in the existence of globglubs and call them "races" and in zebzebs, which they call "blood," these words become the meaningful counters of their lives, the means by which they handle "reality." But what we take for reality is often only appearance, hence, we must be on our guard against words which pass for capsules of reality, but are, in fact, nothing but imaginative inventions—bags into which we have breathed our own hot air. "Words," said Thomas Hobbes, "are wise men's counters, they do but reckon by them. But they are the money of fools."

What modern science has revealed about blood, then, renders all such words as "blood royal," "half blood," "full blood," "blood relationship," and the others to which reference has been made meaningless in point of fact and dangerously meaningful in the superstitious social sense.

Is it too much to expect that this false belief, the myth of "blood," will soon make way for the scientifically established universal truth that all human beings, no matter of what creed or complexion they may be, and allowing for all the interesting variations in the frequencies of certain blood types, are fundamentally of one and the same blood?

---

pression of this view, which has persisted down to modern times, see Hippocrates, *Airs, Waters, and Places*, xiii. 14. Such views, it may here be mentioned in passing, formed the basis of the erroneous belief in the inheritance of acquired characters, for if the blood gathered the seed from every part of the body, any modification of the body would be reflected in the seed, and hence would be transmitted to the offspring.

15

Myths Relating to the Physical Characters of the American Negro

AMONG THE MANY MYTHS concerning "race," those which relate to the physical characters of the American Negro are of especial interest. These myths illustrate rather clearly the manner in which any trait may be seized upon and transformed into an "inferior character" by the simple device of asserting it to be so.

The chief visible characters which are popularly held to distinguish the Negro from the whites are the color of his skin and the form of his hair. These characters represent the immediately "visible" differences. Other characteristics in which Negroes are popularly held to differ from whites are in form of nose, length of arms and hands, "body odor," size of genitalia, size of brain, vocal cords, and so forth.

Before we proceed to examine his physical characters it should be stated that the American Negro must be regarded as one of the newest varieties of mankind. He represents the end effect of a considerable amount of mixture between different African varieties, some American Indians, and whites of every description—principally whites of British origin. Out of this mixture has emerged the unique type or ethnic-group-in-the-making represented by the American Negro. The type is even yet not fully consolidated, but is still in process of formation. All the evidence indicates that while at the present time the American Negro occupies, so far as his physical characters are concerned, a position intermediate between the African Negro, on the one hand, and whites and a relatively small proportion of American Indians, on the other, he will, if the social barriers against intermarriage and "miscegenation" are maintained, tend to stabilize around a type which is rather more Negroid than otherwise. Even so, his physical structure will continue to be characterized by many elements bearing the indubitable marks of his white and, to a much lesser extent, American Indian ancestry.[1]

The results of investigations thus far carried out make the following summary of the physical characters of the typical American Negro possible.[2] It is to be understood that the findings on the characters here cited have been repeatedly substantiated and confirmed by different investigators working independently of one another. The characters described here are to be read as conditions in the American Negro as compared with Old American whites,[3] or mixed Europeans.

ANTHROPOMETRIC CHARACTERS OF NEGROES

Head slightly longer and narrower

Head height less

Cranial capacity less

Hairline lower on forehead

Interpupillary distance greater

Nose height less

Bridge of nose lower

Nose broader

Prognathism (projection of upper jaw) greater

Lips thicker

External ear shorter

Torso shorter

Arms longer

Chest shallower

Pelvis narrower and smaller

Legs longer

Weight greater

Stature shorter

EXTERNAL FEATURES

Skin contains greater amount of black pigment

Hair, wavy, curly, frizzly, or woolly

Distribution of hair less profuse

Sweat glands in greater number[4]

---

[1] See Herskovits, *The American Negro;* Cobb, "The Physical Constitution of the American Negro," *Journal of Negro Education*, III (1934), 340–88; Cobb, Physical Anthropology of the American Negro," *American Journal of Physical Anthropology*, XXIX (1942), 113–223.

[2] This summary is based on the work of Davenport and Love, *Army Anthropology;* Todd and Lindala, "Dimensions of the Body, Whites and American Negroes of Both Sexes," *American Journal of Physical Anthropology*, XII (1928), 35–119; Davenport and Steggerda, *Race Crossing in Jamaica;* Herskovits, *The Anthropometry of the American Negro;* Cameron and Smith, "The Physical Form of Mississippi Negroes," *American Journal of Physical Anthropology*, XVI (1931), 193–201; Day, *A Study of Some Negro-White Families in the United States.*

[3] The comparisons are made with the Old American series of Hrdlička because these represent the type of the ancestral white stock of the American Negro. See Hrdlička, *The Old Americans.*

[4] Homma, "Apocrine Sweat Glands in White and Negro Men and Women,"

A large number of characters have been omitted from this summary for several reasons; some because Negroes and whites do not differ in many characters, others because information is lacking, and still others because for them the available evidence is unsatisfactory and requires separate discussion. We may now briefly consider the significance of the summarized differences.

SIGNIFICANCE OF ANTHROPOMETRIC DIFFERENCES

In general the head of the American Negro is about 2 mm. longer and about 1 mm. narrower than the head of the white. In accordance with this form the Negro head is lower by about 5 mm. than that of the white. This difference in the height of the head is probably significantly associated with the slightly smaller brain of the Negro. The mean cubic capacity of the interior of the Negro skull—which affords one a fairly accurate idea of the volume of the brain—as compared with that of the white, as determined by Wingate Todd at Cleveland on a dissecting-room population, was 1,350.25 cc. for 87 Negro males, and 1,391.08 cc. for 167 white males.[5] The difference, in the males, is here a matter of 41 cc. in favor of the whites. Cranial capacity and brain weight are variable characters, and there are few observations into which the personal factor enters so much as in the determination of these characters. But when all is said and done, Todd's difference of 41 cc. is probably as reliable and as accurate an estimate on small samples of American Negroes and whites of similar social status as it is possible to obtain. In a later report of work done under Todd's direction Simmons gives the average cranial capacities of groups of American Negro and white American skulls obtained by water measurement of large samples. Capacities were 1,467 cc. for Negro males and 1,517 cc. for white males, a difference of 50 cc. in favor of the white males.[6] In discussing head size and brain size it

---

Johns Hopkins Hospital Bulletin, XXXVIII (1926), 367–71; Glaser, "Sweat Glands in the Negro and the European," *American Journal of Physical Anthropology,* XVIII (1934), 371–76.

[5] Todd, "Cranial Capacity and Linear Dimensions," *American Journal of Physical Anthropology,* VI (1923), 97–194. The water method for determining cranial capacity was used.

[6] Simmons, "Cranial Capacities by Both Plastic and Water Techniques with Cranial Linear Measurements of the Reserve Collection, White and Negro," *Human Biology,* XIV (1942), 473–98.

is necessary to bear in mind that the American Negro is some 2 mm. shorter in total stature than the white; while this difference may not account for the whole of the difference in brain size of the Negro, it probably does account for part of that difference.

As far as the diameters of the heads are concerned the Negro head tends to be long as compared to the tendency toward reduction in length and a compensatory increase in breadth and height in the white. Reliable evidence is lacking on the relative thickness of the bones of the Negro as compared with the white skull, but if there is any real difference, it must be slight and would make, except in aged individuals, little difference in the cranial capacity. In short, the size of the Negro head is slightly smaller than that of the white, and different in shape, being long rather than broad. A difference of some 41 to 50 cc. in cranial capacity suggests a slightly smaller brain volume in the Negro as compared with the white. In point of fact, a difference of 40 to 50 cc. is so small, falling well within the normal range of variation of white cranial capacities, that it can hardly be regarded as significant from any but a statistical point of view. But since a difference in brain size, which is not quite the same thing as cranial capacity, has formed one of the chief subjects of general discussions concerning differences between Negroes and whites, it is necessary to discuss this matter somewhat more in detail here.

As illustrating the kind of pseudo-scientific and popular beliefs which are generally held in these connections a few examples may be quoted. The following quotation is taken from a work typical of the anti-Negro literature, and is by R. W. Shufeldt, M.D., "Major, Medical Department, United States Army (Retired)":

"In the skull of the negro the cranial capacity of the brain itself is much undersized. On the average, the former will hold thirty-five fluid ounces, as against forty-five for the Caucasian skull. In the negro the cranial bones are dense and unusually thick, converting his head into a veritable battering-ram. Moreover, the cranial sutures unite very early in life. This checks the development of the brain long before that takes place in other races, and this fact accounts to some extent for the more or less sudden stunting of the Ethiopian intellect shortly after arriving at puberty." [7]

---

[7] Shufeldt, The Negro a Menace to American Civilization, p. 35. This book, which is dedicated to the great paleontologist Edward Drinker Cope, con-

Another example, this time from the work of a clergyman interested in race relations, may be given on the same theme:

"The older schools of anthropologists agreed among themselves in assigning to the Negro branch of humanity a smaller and a less highly developed brain than is exhibited by other races. By charts, and otherwise, some of them sought to show the areas of the Negro brain not yet developed to the standard of the Caucasian. The logical results of the findings of these men, with their prodigious industry and patience, are distinctly discouraging to the Negro. Accepting their findings, there is provided an unanswerable argument against the degradation of the white group through the absorption of the Negro group." [8]

For each of the statements made by these two writers a certain amount of support could be found in the writings of the "older anthropologists." There are also several contemporary "anthropologists" who would lend many of these statements their support. To what lengths certain writers can go in these matters may be illustrated by the case of Dr. Lidio Cipriani, lately of the National Museum and the University of Florence, Italy. During the progress of the Italian campaign in Ethiopia Dr. Cipriani published a book for the purpose of justifying that campaign, and here we have Dr. Cipriani's own summary of Chapter V of that remarkable work:

"Researches conducted on the brain of the African and on its physiological and psychological functions reveal the existence of a mental inferiority which it is impossible to modify and which excludes the possibility of its development in our own manner. The Africans are particularly unadapted to assimilate European civilization. Since this depends upon the characters of the race, which are transmissible, then, with crossing, it is necessary to develop certain eugenical norms, above all for Europeans living in contact with the Africans. In this connection the important observations which have been made on the Negroes imported into America since the seventeenth century have the greatest value." [9]

The subjective determination and evaluation of the evidence are

---

stitutes one of the most virulent attacks—under a pseudo-scientific guise—upon the American Negro ever perpetrated.

[8] Shannon, *The Negro in Washington*, p. 320.

[9] Cipriani, *Un assurdo etnico: L'Impero Etiopico*, p. 177.

apparent here. One of the revealing classical examples of bias in this field is represented by the late Professor R. Bennett Bean's study of the Negro brain. In this study[10] Bean (who was a Southerner) described certain alleged racial differences in the Negro brain, such as its relatively small size, the reduction in the volume of the frontal and temporal lobes, and the anterior part of the corpus callosum—the great association tract connecting the two hemispheres of the brain.

Professor Franklin P. Mall, in whose laboratory at Johns Hopkins University this research was conducted, was so dissatisfied with Bean's interpretation of the evidence that he was led to investigate the problem for himself. It should be stated here that Mall was the outstanding American anatomist of his time and that he was responsible for training a large majority of America's most notable anatomists. Utilizing the racial criteria of Bean and others, Mall and his colleagues were quite unable to distinguish Negro from white brains, and after pointing out the technical, instrumental, personal, and other errors, as well as the contradictory results involved in Bean's work, Mall concluded: "In this study of several anatomical characters said to vary according to race and sex, the evidence advanced has been tested and found wanting. It is found, however, that portions of the brain vary greatly in different brains and that a very large number of records must be observed before the norm will be found. For the present the crudeness of our method will not permit us to determine anatomical characters due to race, sex or genius and which if they exist, are completely masked by the large number of marked individual variations. The study has been still further complicated by the personal equation of the investigator. Arguments for difference due to race, sex and genius will henceforward need to be based upon new data, really scientifically treated and not on the older statements." [11]

Similar criticisms of Bean's work were made by Wilder.[12]

Alleged differences said to exist in the character of the sulci of the Negro brain compared with the white are unfounded. Except for a difference in "a general way" of the fissural pattern of the frontal

[10] Bean, "Some Racial Peculiarities of the Negro Brain," *American Journal of Anatomy*, V (1906), 353–415.
[11] Mall, "On Several Anatomical Characters of the Human Brain, Said to Vary according to Race and Sex," *American Journal of Anatomy*, IX (1909), 1–32.
[12] Wilder, *The Brain of the American Negro*.

lobes, no differences whatever were perceptible, and "one could not distinguish a particular brain as belonging to a particular race on the basis of a difference in fissuration of the frontal lobes." [13]

Poynter and Keegan noted that the Negro brain generally displays "a prominent parietal lobe in contrast to the 'ill filled' frontal region." [14] But quite clearly this so-called "characteristic" merely represents an accommodation of the shape of the Negro head, which, it will be recalled, is longer, narrower, and lower than the head of the white. Poynter and Keegan wisely recognize that, since their findings demonstrate that the Negro brain displays characters which fall within the limits of variation of the white brain, "it is not possible to establish a single morphological feature which can be claimed as absolutely characteristic." Similarly, Fischer concluded that "the convolutions and the furrows or sulci between them vary so much from individual to individual that no racial distinctions can be ascertained." [15]

Levin, of the Bechterew Institute for Brain Research at Leningrad, has shown that the available evidence affords no ground whatever for any belief in racial or "inferiority" signs in human brains, whether they be of great men or of "savages." [16]

Actually, if the Negro brain is somewhat smaller than that of the white, the difference will be found to be so small that it can hardly be considered significant for the mental functioning of the Negro compared with that of the white. Within the limits of normal variation, differences in brain size have about as much relation to intelligence and cultural achievement as differences in body size, and as far as the available evidence goes, that is none. Weidenreich has put the matter succinctly: "The length of the alimentary canal of man," he writes, "varies between 14 and 45 feet, but no physiologist has ever ventured that an individual with a long intestine has a more effective digestion than one with a short intestine. In principle, it is against all

---

[13] Connolly, *External Morphology of the Primate Brain*, p. 203; see also Levin, "Racial and 'Inferiority' Characters in the Human Brain," *American Journal of Physical Anthropology*, XXII (1937), 345–80; Paterson, *Physique and Intellect*.

[14] Poynter and Keegan, "A Study of the American Negro Brain," *Journal of Comparative Neurology*, XXV (1915), 183–202.

[15] Fischer, "Variable Characters in Human Beings," in Baur, Fischer, and Lenz, *Human Heredity*, pp. 114–66.

[16] Levin, "Racial and 'Inferiority' Characters in the Human Brain," *American Journal of Physical Anthropology*, XXII (1937), 345–80.

that we know of the relation between function and structure of the organs to suppose that greater size guarantees superior function." [17] The Negro "Kaffirs" and Amahosa of Africa, the Japanese, the American Indians, the Eskimos, and the Mongols all have brains which are larger than those of the average white.[18] On the same grounds as some whites proclaim themselves superior to the American Negro they should proclaim these peoples superior to themselves— thus far, however, there is no indication that they are likely to do so. The fact is that the external morphology of the human brain, or the characters of size and weight, have little or nothing to do with its functional capacities; these, on the other hand, must be considered as due to a complex of characters, such as the genetically determined internal chemical structure of the cells and neurones and the organization to which these are subjected by experience, the abundance of the blood vessels, the character of their walls, and the efficiency of the drainage.[19]

Upon these matters we have no evidence adequate for a definitive judgment beyond the statement that at the present time there exists no evidence in support of the popular belief that significant differences exist between the brain of the Negro and that of the white. So far as the brain itself is concerned we may conclude with the words of a distinguished neuroanatomist and physical anthropologist, Professor W. E. Le Gros Clark, that "in spite of statements which have been made to the contrary, there is no microscopic or macroscopic difference by which it is possible for the anatomist to distinguish the brain in single individuals of different races." [20]

Recent work on the electrical activity of the brain has turned up some differences in what have been claimed to be racial patterns of activity. But the world's leading authority on electroencephalography ("brain waves") has this to say on that subject: "Slight differences there seem to be, as Mundy-Castle has found in Africa, but scarcely more than can be accounted for by the varying traditions and stand-

[17] Weidenreich, *Apes, Giants, and Man*, p. 100.

[18] For a table of brain or cranial capacities see Montagu, *An Introduction to Physical Anthropology*, 3rd ed., pp. 458–59.

[19] Donaldson, "The Significance of Brain Weight," *Archives of Neurology and Psychiatry*, XIII (1925), 385–86; Bonin, "On the Size of Man's Brain as Indicated by Skull Capacity," *Journal of Comparative Neurology*, LIX (1934), 1–28; Klineberg, *Race Differences*, pp. 77–92.

[20] Le Gros Clark, *Fitting Man to His Environment*, p. 19.

ards of life and nourishment. And did not the brains of these people establish and elaborate these traditions, accept or modify these standards? Unluckily for our peace of mind, there do exist precipitous gradients of economic and political differences; but brain physiology detects no incompatibilities; indeed in regions where the shades and textures of the human race are freely blended, there is found the richest variety, the most lively growth." [21]

With respect to the commonly repeated statement that the cranial sutures in the Negro unite earlier than in other races "and thus cause a stunting of the Ethiopian intellect shortly after arriving at puberty," it can now be quite definitely stated, as a result of the fundamental studies of Todd and Lyon on suture closure in Negroes and whites, that no significant differences in the character of suture closure exist between the two groups. The authors conclude their studies with the statement: "We repeat that there is one modal type of human suture closure upon outer and inner faces of the cranium, common to white and Negro stocks." [22]

As far as the growth and development of the skull are concerned, there are no significant differences in the pattern and rate of growth in certain bones of the skull, and these differences are already apparent during fetal development; as Schultz has said, "These differences are essentially the same as those which distinguish adult Whites from adult Negroes." [23]

Thus, Limson[24] found that in Negro fetuses the occiput was more prominent and convex and the external occipital protuberance more strongly formed than in white fetuses. Limson also found that the dental arch projects farther forward and that the anterior nasal spine is smaller in Negro than in white fetuses. These are precisely the regions of differential growth which Todd and his coworkers[25] have

[21] Walter, *The Living Brain*, pp. 189–90.

[22] Todd and Lyon, "Cranial Suture Closure; Its Progress and Age Relationship. Part IV. Ectocranial Closure in Adult Males of Negro Stock," *American Journal of Physical Anthropology*, VIII (1925), 149–68. Parts I–III of these studies were published in preceding numbers of the same journal.

[23] Schultz, "Fetal Growth in Man," *American Journal of Physical Anthropology*, VI (1923), 389–400.

[24] Limson, "Observations on the Bones of the Skull in White and Negro Fetuses and Infants," *Contributions to Embryology*, No. 136 (1932), 204–22.

[25] Todd, "The Skeleton," in *Growth and Development of the Child*, Part II (White House Conference on Child Health and Protection), 107–09.

shown to distinguish the adult Negro cranium, namely, greater expansion of the occipital bone at the back of the head and greater forward growth of the upper jaw and dental arch. This difference in the detailed growth pattern of the jaw has been shown to hold good in Negro fetuses in respect to the premaxillary bone, which tends to lose its independence later than in the white. This fact is significantly correlated, of course, with the somewhat greater projection of the upper jaw in the Negro than in the white.[26] This projection of the upper jaw is not a true *prognathism* similar to that which occurs in the anthropoid apes, for in the latter the early arrest in the growth of the brain case and the continued growth of the jaws and dental arches is a syndrome which does not occur in any form of man. The projection of the upper jaw in the Negro is accentuated as compared to the conditions in the white because in the latter there is an earlier arrest of growth in the upper jaw than in the Negro. This greater growth of the maxilla in the Negro is also responsible for another apparent, though unreal, difference in the appearance of the head. This is the apparently greater projection of the white cranium beyond the face—this appearance does not reflect any real difference in the character of the cranium, but rather constitutes the reflection of the lesser projection of the jaws in the white—in whom the jaws have tended, as it were, to shrink under the top of the head rather more than in the Negro. From every point of view the reduction in the size of the upper jaw in whites must be considered unfortunate, for the resulting restriction in space is responsible for a large number of disorders, such as failure of development of teeth, the noneruption, crowding, or rotation of teeth, deflection of the nasal septum, cleft palate and harelip, and so forth.[27] The retention of the ability for continued growth by the Negro maxilla as compared with the loss of this ability in whites would here, indubitably, confer a distinct advantage upon the Negro.

With respect to the shape of the nose in the Negro, this is very variable, but it stabilizes around a rather shorter, flatter, and broader

---

[26] Montagu, "The Premaxilla in the Primates," *Quarterly Review of Biology*, X (1935), 182–84; Montagu, "The Premaxilla in Man," *Journal of the American Dental Association*, XXIII (1936), 2043–57.

[27] For a discussion of these matters see Montagu, "The Premaxilla in Man," *Journal of the American Dental Association*, XXIII (1936), 2043–57, and "The Significance of the Variability of the Upper Lateral Incisor Teeth in Man," *Human Biology*, XII (1940), 323–58.

nose than that of the average white. It has been suggested that the broad nose and larger nasal passages of the African Negro are adapted to meet the requirements of air breathed at relatively high temperatures, whereas the relatively long narrow nose of the white is adapted to the breathing of air at relatively low temperatures. A statistical investigation of this problem supports this suggestion with some degree of probability.[28]

Statements to the effect that the Negro nose is more primitive than that of the white are unsound. For example, Dr. Victor Heiser has stated that the fact that the Philippine Negritos "were true Negroes is shown by the one piece cartilage in their spreading noses; all other races have a split cartilage. Even the octoroons show this negroid test of Negro blood." [29] This statement was repeated and elaborated in November, 1936, in the now defunct *Collier's* magazine. In a more recent work we are told that "There is a great difference between whites and blacks in the structure of the nasal cartilages." [30]

Professor Montague Cobb has thoroughly disposed of these myths by citing the facts which prove that no split cartilage occurs in any monkey, ape, or man and that there are no significant characters of the nasal cartilages, except those of size, which distinguish the American Negro nose from the white nose.[31]

Actually, the Negro nose merely exhibits a difference in form, and there is every reason to believe that the original form of the African Negro nose persisted in Africa as an adaptively valuable character and that in the American Negro the form of the nose, while still variable, presents a form intermediate between African Negro, white, and American Indian. The greater the admixture of white ancestry the more Caucasian does the form of the nose appear. Even so, there is a marked tendency toward persistence of the broad nose. This, among other characters, has been termed an "entrenched Negro character," [32] that is to say, a character which shows relatively great stability

---

[28] Thomson and Buxton, "Man's Nasal Index in Relation to Certain Climatic Conditions," *Journal of the Royal Anthropological Institute of Great Britain and Ireland,* LIII (1923), 92–122.

[29] Heiser, *An American Doctor's Odyssey,* p. 146.

[30] Landry, *The Cult of Equality,* p. 175.

[31] Cobb, "Your Nose Won't Tell," *Crisis,* LXV (1938), 332–36.

[32] Todd, "Entrenched Negro Physical Features," *Human Biology,* I (1929), 57–69.

under hybridization. Other such features are lip thickness, mouth width, interpupillary distance, and ear height. As for the apparently larger eye of the Negro, this is an illusion resulting from the comparatively less angular orbit of the Negro. On the other hand, Mrs. Day's careful observations[33] clearly show that two of Todd's most dominantly entrenched Negro characters, namely, lip thickness and breadth of nose, readily undergo change toward the type of the white lip and nose under hybridization. It would seem, however, that an appreciable amount of admixture must usually occur before these two characters actually assume the "ideal" white form.

The slope of the forehead in Negroes is not significantly different from that in whites, and we have already seen that this apparent "difference" is an illusion due to the greater "prognathism" of the Negro.

A still more significant contribution to the alleged low-foreheadedness of the Negro is the fact that the level at which the hair grows on his head is lower upon the forehead than it is in the white. Under hybridization this low level of the hairline appears to be one of the first characters to yield—as a glance through Mrs. Day's photographs of Negro-white individuals will at once show.

In African Negroes the chin is not so prominent as it is in whites, but in American Negroes the chin prominence is intermediate between the condition in Africans and that in whites, as may be seen from Mrs. Day's figures,[34] which both Hooton and I believe to show an exaggeratedly high proportion of lack of chin protrusion, 38.9 per cent in females and 50.5 per cent in males. It is clear, however, that chin protrusion increases with increase in the proportion of white ancestry.

In view of the fact that statements are frequently made which refer to the alleged apelike hands of the Negro and his long arms or long legs, as those who make such statements see fit, we shall briefly consider these matters here.

The Negro torso is slightly less than an inch and a quarter shorter than that of the white, the Negro leg a little less than an inch and a quarter longer.[35] The Negro arm is about an inch longer, the upper

---

[33] Day, *A Study of Some Negro-White Families in the United States,* pp. 96–99.

[34] *Ibid.,* p. 100.

[35] Davenport and Love, *Army Anthropology;* Todd and Lindala, "Dimen-

arm being relatively shorter and the forearm relatively longer than in the white. As for breadth and length of hands, Todd and Lindala found no significant differences in these dimensions, a fact which led these investigators to remark: "It is rather astonishing to find that the 'long narrow hand' of the Negro vanishes on the average." [36] It was considered by these authors that this finding could not be imputed to the admixture of white ancestry, since their series gave many evidences of relative purity of strain. Herskovits also failed to find any significant difference in the width of the Negro hand.[37] While the Negro hand as a whole is not longer than the hand of the whites, the fingers are, on the whole, longer, for Herskovits found that the middle finger is longer in Negroes than in whites. This would then make that portion of the hand in the Negro which extends from the wrist to the base of the fingers shorter than in the white, but this supposition requires confirmation. With respect to the length of the thumb there exist some observations on the skeletal thumb in nine African Negroes and fifteen whites which indicate that the African Negro thumb is about 1.7 mm. shorter in relation to the length of the middle finger than the relative thumb length of the average Englishman.[38] These findings corroborate in a striking manner the earlier findings of Schultz, who found the length of the thumb in relation to the middle finger in 18 adult Negroes to be 1.8 mm. less than in 14 adult whites.[39] In relation to the length of the hand, Schultz found that in both Negro fetuses and Negro adults the thumb was relatively shorter than in whites.[40]

Hence, as far as the upper extremity is concerned it would appear that every part of it is perfectly proportionate to the other, and that the greater length of the Negro arm is actually due to a compensatory adjustment in relation to the shorter torso. As for "apelike" characters

---

sions of the Body, Whites and American Negroes of Both Sexes," *American Journal of Physical Anthropology*, XII (1928), 35–119.

[36] Todd and Lindala, *ibid.*, p. 73.

[37] Herskovits, *The Anthropometry of the American Negro*, pp. 67–68.

[38] Montagu, "On the Primate Thumb," *American Journal of Physical Anthropology*, XV (1931), 291–314.

[39] Schultz, "The Skeleton of the Trunk and Limbs of Higher Primates," *Human Biology*, II (1930), 381–83.

[40] Schultz, "Fetal Growth of Man and Other Primates," *Quarterly Review of Biology*, I (1926), 493–95.

of Negro hands or arms, they are entirely wanting, both in the proportions and in the deeper structures.

The lower limb of the Negro is 26 mm., that is, just over an inch, longer than in the white and, unlike the case of the arm, there is no difference in the proportions of the length of the thigh or lower leg. "The long shin of the Negro is an illusion of its circumference, as his long foot is an illusion of its flatness." [41] The length and breadth of the Negro foot show no significant differences from those features of the foot of whites and are entirely proportional to leg length.[42]

Attempts to show that Negro athletes enjoy an unfair advantage owing to their alleged possession of a longer heel bone and longer calf muscles have been critically examined by Professor Montague Cobb, who has made a careful study of this matter and has shown that many of the outstanding Negro athletes have legs and feet which are predominantly white in character and that Negroid physical characters are not in any way significantly associated with Negro athletic ability.[43] In this connection it may be noted that Malafa, in an investigation of the bodily characters of sprinters and nonathletes, carried out on 100 white students from the grammar schools of Brno, Czechoslovakia, found that long legs were one of the principal characters which distinguished the athletes from the nonathletes.[44] This character constitutes, of course, a selective factor—and is not correlated with race or racial characters. One more fact concerning the Negro foot. The alleged longer heel bone is nonexistent, but in both fetuses and adults the appearance of greater length is "caused entirely by a thick layer of subcutaneous fat." [45]

It is frequently stated that the Negro pelvis differs from that of the white in being longer and narrower. This statement is not quite true. The Negro pelvis is smaller in all its dimensions. Todd and Lindala

---

[41] Todd, "Entrenched Negro Physical Features," *Human Biology*, I (1929), 57–69.

[42] Todd and Lindala, "Dimensions of the Body, Whites and American Negroes of Both Sexes," *American Journal of Physical Anthropology*, XII (1928), 74–75.

[43] Cobb, "Race and Runners," *Journal of Health and Physical Education*, VII (1936), 1–8.

[44] Malafa, *On the Bodily Differences between Sprinters and Non-Sportsmen*, pp. 1–11.

[45] Schultz, "Fetal Growth of Man and Other Primates," *Quarterly Review of Biology*, I (1926), 499.

write: "The male Negro pelvis is small in all its dimensions compared with the male White and its true pelvic component is long compared with the height of the iliac crest over perineum or over tuber ischii. Superposed on a common bodily size the female White pelvis is relatively some 10 mm. longer and broader than the male though its absolute dimensions are less. The female Negro pelvis is relatively only 6 mm. longer than the male but 21 mm. broader." [46]

It is to be doubted whether there is any truth in the statement sometimes made that because the Negro female has a narrower pelvis than the white female she is more likely to experience a less satisfactory termination to a pregnancy produced by a white male than to one produced by a Negro male. The implied suggestion here is that the rounder-headed white is likely to produce a fetus which will have a head larger and rounder than can be safely delivered through a small, narrow pelvis "intended" for the delivery of Negro-fathered children. We have already seen that in the only investigation made of this subject, in the case of Japanese-white unions, that there is not the slightest support for such beliefs. [47]

Caldwell and Moloy have, from the obstetrical point of view, investigated the anthropometric characters of the pelvis of Negro and white females. [48] These investigators find that female pelves may be classified into three types: (a) the gynecoid, or average female type, which occurs in 42 per cent of Negro females and in the same percentage of white females; (b) the android type, more closely approximating the male form than the female pelvis, which occurs in 15.7 per cent of Negro females and in 32.5 per cent of white females; and (c) the anthropoid type, with a long antero-posterior diameter and a relatively narrow transverse diameter, occurring in 40.5 per cent of Negroes and in slightly less than half that percentage of whites.

Obstetrically, the most dangerous form of the pelvis is the android type, which occurs among white females with double the frequency that it occurs among Negro females. The other two types of pelvis

[46] Todd and Lindala, "Dimensions of the Body, Whites and American Negroes of Both Sexes," *American Journal of Physical Anthropology,* XII (1928), 97–98.

[47] See p. 217 ante.

[48] Caldwell and Moloy, "Anatomical Variations in the Female Pelvis and Their Effects in Labor, with a Suggested Classification," *American Journal of Obstetrics and Gynecology,* XXVI (1933), 479–514.

present no especial obstetrical difficulties. It therefore seems improbable that the form of the Negro pelvis plays any more significant role in difficult labor and delivery than in the case of white females.

Davenport and Steggerda "entertained the hypothesis that, in the case of the Black woman who carried a mulatto child *in utero,* her narrow pelvic outlet and the child's large head might offer an important disharmony." [49] In order to test this hypothesis they proceeded to examine the heads of newborn colored and white children. They found that the heads of the newborn colored infants were slightly smaller at birth than those of white newborn infants, and it is evident from their findings that no disharmonies between pelvic outlet and shape of the head occurred in the Jamaica series examined by these authors. Data on the pelves were not available to Davenport and Steggerda, but the data which have since appeared render the suggestion of a significant disharmony of the kind hypothecated highly improbable.

Skin color is a complex character and depends upon a multiplicity of factors for its expression. As is well known, every gradation from black to white occurs among American Negroes. The greater the admixture of white ancestry the more white, as a rule, does the skin appear. Barnes has shown "that the percentage of Negro pigmentation of the American Negro increases quite rapidly until puberty, with a maximum at the age of 15; decreases rapidly until about the age of 35; and then decreases very slowly the remainder of life." [50] This finding is in essential agreement with the independent findings of Davenport, and of Todd and van Gorder. [51]

The inheritance of skin color is a cumulative process involving the operation of multiple factors, the individual having the largest number of factors usually showing the character developed to the highest degree. In Negro-white crosses the genes for black pigment are not completely dominant over those for lighter color; the first generation is mulatto, or intermediate, in shade. The offspring of mulattoes,

---

[49] Davenport and Steggerda, *Race Crossing in Jamaica,* pp. 423–24.

[50] Barnes, "The Inheritance of Pigmentation in the Skin of the American Negro," *Human Biology,* I (1929), 321–28.

[51] Davenport, *Heredity of Skin Color in Negro-White Crosses;* Todd and van Gorder, "The Quantitative Determination of Black Pigmentation in the Skin of the American Negro," *American Journal of Physical Anthropology,* IV (1921), 239–60.

however, exhibit great variability of skin color, grading from black to white; and it is apparent that in the second generation variability is higher than in the first. This is an effect of multiple-factor inheritance, for, owing to the large number of factors now present, they are segregated in combinations which are more distributively variable than those in the original ancestors. This form of blending inheritance is essentially Mendelian. The evidence thus far suggests that there are at least six pairs of genes conditioning skin color, yielding 26 or 64 possible gene combinations, and at least as many Negro and white phenotypes combined—assuming that the gene pairs have approximately the same effect. In reality a far wider range of phenotypes is observed, which suggests the existence of other modifying genes affecting skin color. Further investigation of a most refined and laborious nature remains to be carried out before the mechanism of the inheritance of skin color is fully understood.[52]

Black children cannot be born to parents one of whom is "pure" white and the other "pure" black. The children of such unions are mulattoes. When a colored infant is born to "white" parents it is proof that both the parents carry Negro genes. Similarly, a Negro female with some white genes cannot bear a white child to a pure Negro.

Black is the dominant hair color among Negroes, although red, dark brown, light brown, and gray-brown hair occurs irregularly; the lighter hair colors are more common among those with half or more white ancestry. The black color of the hair is one of the most dominantly entrenched Negro features. On the other hand, hair form is, interestingly enough, one of the most easily modifiable of characters. While among American Negroes every form of hair from woolly to straight is to be found, it is clear that under hybridization hair form yields most readily to the influence of new genes. This fact was strikingly brought out in the classic study of Fischer[53] on the hybrids of Hottentot-Dutch ancestry in South Africa—one group with dominantly woolly hair, the other with dominantly straight hair. Fischer found that among the Rehobother Bastaards woolly hair occurred in 29 per cent, frizzly or wavy hair in 49 per cent, and straight in 22 per cent.

Davenport and Steggerda found that among Jamaicans woolly

---

[52] Montagu, *Human Heredity,* pp. 202–06.
[53] Fischer, *Die Rehobother Bastards und das Bastardierungsproblem beim Menschen.*

hair occurred in 100 per cent of blacks, in 86.7 per cent of browns, and in 1 per cent of whites. Curly hair occurred in none of the blacks, in 11.4 per cent of browns, and in 30 per cent of whites. Wavy hair did not occur in blacks, but was found in 2 per cent of browns and in 30 per cent of whites; 39.2 per cent of the whites had straight hair.

In Mrs. Day's series of Negro-white families, it is clear that hair form varies with degree of admixture. Hooton, summarizing Mrs. Day's findings, writes: "As far as our data carry us we may conclude that ½ N males, ½ N females, and even ¾ N females may exhibit the entire range of hair curvatures generally recognized, but that, if Mrs. Day's information is valid, distinctively Negroid forms of hair, such as frizzly and woolly, do not appear unless there is at least ⅜ of Negro blood in the individual." [54]

The inheritance of hair form in Negro-white crosses has been studied by Davenport,[55] who found that straight hair is a recessive condition.[56] Wavy or curly hair is a heterogeneous condition, so that wavy plus wavy yields offspring which are straight, wavy, and curly in the proportion 1:2:1. Curly plus curly yields mostly curly; yet 14 per cent of the offspring show straight hair, so that it is apparent that some curly-haired parents carry the gene for straight hair as a recessive.

Straight plus curly produces a good many curly-haired offspring. Post, analyzing Mrs. Day's data, writes:

"Of the total number of 428 offspring, seventy-five have curlier hair than the more curly parent, while only forty-three have straighter hair than the straighter parent. This is all negative evidence for a general dominance of the curlier condition . . .

"The six forms merge into each other. . . . There is no evidence for the emergence of a New American Negro type, in regard to hair form, such as Herskovits has lately described for skeletal proportions." [57]

---

[54] E. A. Hooton, in Day, *A Study of Some Negro-White Families in the United States*, p. 85.

[55] Davenport, "Heredity of Hair Form in Man," *American Naturalist*, XLII (1908), 341.

[56] Six types of hair form are distinguished here: straight, low waves, deep waves, curly, frizzly, and woolly.

[57] R. Post, in Day, *A Study of Some Negro-White Families in the United States*, p. 13.

It may, of course, be argued that the intermediate types of hair form, as well as hair color, exhibited by American Negroes do constitute at least an approach to a new type, for the genetic behavior of hair form is, in the character of its blending, not unlike that of skin color and quite clearly shows many gradations of form, intermediate between the hair forms exhibited by African Negro and white ancestors. Thus, it would seem that Herskovits's general finding concerning the emergence of a new American Negro type holds good also for the character of the hair form.

It is a common belief that the Negro is more glabrous (i.e., destitute of hair—smoother) than whites. This belief is well founded; for, although it is still uncertain whether the Negro possesses fewer hair follicles, it is clear that the development of his body hair, in both thickness and distribution, is considerably less than in the white. Danforth's investigations lead him to believe that in the Negro there has occurred a reduction in the number of hair follicles and that there is also a deficiency in the growth of individual hairs.[58] This would appear to be the most plausible explanation of the relative glabrousness of the American Negro. In an investigation of the facial hair of Negroes and whites Trotter found that there was no difference in the actual number of hairs, but that the average thickness of the facial hairs of the Negroes was less than that of the whites; also, the hairs of Negro women were somewhat shorter than those of white women.[59]

In the Negro, as compared with the white, the general tendency toward reduction in the amount of hair and the character of its distribution have proceeded farther, as is evidenced by the reduction in the number of hair follicles on the fingers, toes,[60] arms, and hands of Negroes.[61]

In the American Negro, as is to be expected, every form of hair distribution and development may be observed; the greater the amount of white admixture the greater the distribution and thickness of hair. These facts are well brought out in Mrs. Day's observations

---

[58] Danforth, "Distribution of Hair on the Digits in Man," *American Journal of Physical Anthropology,* IV (1921), 189–204.

[59] Trotter, "A Study of Facial Hair in White and Negro Races," *Washington University Studies* (Scientific Studies), IX (1922), 273–89.

[60] Danforth, "Distribution of Hair on the Digits in Man," *American Journal of Physical Anthropology,* IV (1921), 189–204.

[61] Davenport and Steggerda, *Race Crossing in Jamaica,* pp. 264–67.

on Negro-white families. From these observations it would appear that facial hair reaches a medium degree of thickness in individuals with ⅜ and less of white ancestry.[62] It is highly probable that the genetic mechanisms here operative are much the same for hair distribution and thickness as for skin color and hair form, with the presence of multiple factors and the consequent segregation of intermediate forms.

On the whole, the American Negro shows a distribution of body hair and an intensity of hair growth intermediate between the condition in the African Negro and the American white.

One of the most popularly entrenched beliefs concerning the Negro is that he possesses a unique and objectionable body odor. During Dollard's investigations in "Southerntown" he encountered this belief, and his references to it are worth reproducing here:

"Among beliefs which profess to show that Negro and white cannot intimately participate in the same civilization is the perennial one that Negroes have a smell extremely disagreeable to white people. This belief is very widely held both in the South and in the North. A local white informant said that Negroes smell, even the cleanest of them. It might not be worse than other human smells, but it was certainly different. It was asserted to be as true of middle-class Negroes as of others, at least upon occasion. Another informant swore that Negroes have such an odor that sometimes white people can hardly stand it. He described it as a 'rusty' smell. This odor was said to be present even though they bathe, but to be somewhat worse in summer. Another white informant described the smell as 'acrid.'" Dollard states that he can detect no difference between the odor of Negroes and that of whites.[63]

Shufeldt remarks that the body odor of the Negro is "sometimes so strong that I have known ladies of our own race brought almost to the stage of emesis when compelled to inhale it for any length of time."[64] No doubt, but the fact is that many whites have been almost equally nauseated by the odor of some of their fellow whites. Members of other ethnic groups find the body odor of whites most objectionable. Thus, the great Japanese anatomist Buntaro Adachi wrote that when he first settled in Europe he found the body odor of

[62] Day, *A Study of Some Negro-White Families in the United States*, p. 86.
[63] Dollard, *Caste and Class in a Southern Town*, pp. 378–79.
[64] Shufeldt, *The Negro a Menace to American Civilization*, p. 33.

Europeans very objectionable—strong, rancid, sometimes sweetish, sometimes bitter. As time drew on he became accustomed to it, and still later found it sexually stimulating.[65] Similar experiences will be found recounted elsewhere.[66] Body odor depends upon a large number of factors. Human sweat is of complex structure and is a compound of the secretion of the sebaceous glands (the fat-secreting glands opening usually in relation to the hair follicles) and the sweat glands proper. Among the known constituents of sweat are water, sodium chloride, phosphates, uric acid, glucose, creatinine, aromatic acids, ethereal sulphates of phenol and skatoxyl, neutral fat, fatty acids, cholesterol, albumin, and iron. Depending upon the amount of these substances present at any one time, the odor of the sweat will vary in the same individual from time to time and under different environmental and dietary conditions. Upon this subject there have been no really adequate studies. All that we at present know is that body odor varies from individual to individual within the same ethnic group and that members of different ethnic groups, and even classes, find the odor of members of other ethnic groups and classes distinctly different and frequently objectionable. Klineberg refers to "an experimental attempt to throw a little further light on this question . . . in an unpublished study by Lawrence, who collected in test tubes a little of the perspiration of White and Colored students who had just been exercising violently in the gymnasium. These test tubes were then given to a number of White subjects with instructions to rank them in order of pleasantness. The results showed no consistent preference for the White samples; the test tube considered the most pleasant and the one considered the most unpleasant were both taken from Whites."[67] Klineberg concludes: "There may be racial differences in body odors, but it is important first to rule out the factors referred to above, particularly the factor of diet, before a final conclusion is reached. It is obvious that cleanliness is also a factor of importance. In any case, the phenomenon of adaptation enters to remove any special unpleasantness arising from the presence of a strange group."[68]

The truth is that sweat in itself is odorless. Shelley, Hurley, and

---

[65] Adachi, "Der Geruch der Europäer," *Globus,* LXXXIII (1903), 14–15.
[66] Klineberg, *Race Differences,* pp. 128–31.
[67] *Ibid.,* p. 131.
[68] *Ibid.*

Nichols have investigated this matter, and shown that pure apocrine sweat as it initially appears on the skin is both sterile and odorless, and that the odor is due to the decomposition effects produced by the action of bacteria.[69]

Morlan conducted an experiment on the perception of body odor in which two Negroes and two whites were the subjects. The judgment of 59 persons in 715 experiments was recorded. The experiment was so set up as to eliminate any possibility of accidental factors or recognition of the subjects. In all there were 157 incorrect answers, and in 368 instances the persons tested stated that they could not tell, while in 190 instances the attribution was incorrect. In short, in 51.4 per cent out of a total of 715 experiments the persons tested were unable to recognize body odor as in any way distinctive, while in 21.9 per cent of instances the attribution was incorrect. In other words, the total number of failures was 73.3 per cent as compared with 26.7 per cent correct attributions. Those who considered themselves good judges did no better than the others.[70]

It is known that diet has an influence upon the odor of sweat, and certainly the frequency of bathing is a factor. Since evidence upon the reactions of unprejudiced whites is not so abundant as it might be, I may record the fact that in my own experience of African and American Negroes I have never observed any particular or general difference in body odor between Negroes and whites. Furthermore, in my own household there have at various times been employed some twelve Negro maids; all of them had plenty of occasion to perspire freely, and all of them served at table. In only one case out of twelve was any odor of perspiration ever perceived by any member of the household. In this case the individual concerned was excessively fat. After the matter of her body odor was discreetly broached, it was never again perceived.

Comparative studies in the physiology and chemistry of Negro and of white sweat do not exist, but there do exist several studies of the sweat glands in Negroes and whites from the anatomical standpoint.

Clark and Lhamon, in a study of the sweat glands of the hands

---

[69] Shelley, Hurley, and Nichols, "Axillary Odor," *Archives of Dermatology and Syphilology,* LXVIII (1953), 430.

[70] Morlan, "An Experiment on the Identification of Body Odor," *Journal of Genetic Psychology,* LXXVII (1950), 257–65.

and feet of Negroes, found that these were more abundantly supplied with exocrine glands [71] than were those of whites.[72]

Glaser, in an investigation of sweat glands in one Bantu Negro and in one European, found that "the regional distribution of the sweat glands in the Negro agrees closely with that usually given for the European. . . . In the great majority of regions compared, however, the Bantu has more sweat glands than the European, and this is probably of considerable value to him in resisting extremes of heat." [73]

Homma, in a study of the apocrine glands [74] of 10 Negroes and 12 whites, found that such glands occurred three times more abundantly in the Negroes than in the whites, and that, while such glands did not occur in the breasts of whites, they were sometimes to be found in the breasts of Negroes.[75]

It is evident, then, that if Negroes possess a greater number of sweat glands than whites, heat regulation under high temperatures would be more efficiently performed in them than in whites, and it is also possible that, if there is any difference in the odor of their sweat, it is probably not a difference in kind, but in degree or intensity, due to the cumulative action of the number of glands involved.

As in the majority of characters in American Negroes, their sweat glands are probably intermediate in number between those of African Negroes and those of whites.

It is a common belief that the penis of the Negro is appreciably larger than that of the white. The view is an old one. Blumenbach (1752–1840), the founder of the science of physical anthropology, referred to this matter as long ago as 1775. He states: "This assertion

---

[71] Exocrine or eccrine glands are distributed over the entire body, emptying their secretions through small ducts through the pores directly onto the skin surface. See Kuno, *Human Perspiration.*

[72] Clark and Lhamon, "Observations on the Sweat Glands of Tropical and Northern Races," *Anatomical Record,* XII (1917), 139–47.

[73] Glaser, "Sweat Glands in the Negro and the European," *American Journal of Physical Anthropology,* XVIII (1934), 371–76.

[74] Apocrine glands are groups of smaller numbers of larger and more complex character than exocrine glands, which are regionally distributed to the armpits, genitoperineal regions, and around the breasts and umbilicus. They open into the sebaceous glands of the hair follicles in the regions named, and when functioning lose part of their cellular protoplasmic substance.

[75] Homma, "On Apocrine Sweat Glands in White and Negro Men and Women," *Johns Hopkins Hospital Bulletin,* XXXVIII (1926), 367–71.

is so far borne out by the remarkable genitory apparatus of an Aethiopian which I have in my anatomical collection. Whether this prerogative be constant and peculiar to the nation I do not know." [76]

Upon this subject there exists no scientific evidence whatever. To my knowledge, no traveler in the past few hundred years or any anthropologist who has worked in Africa has ever remarked upon any difference in the size of the genitalia in Negroes as compared with whites. In any event, the statements of untrained observers would not be of much value. In recent years, however, one traveler and anthropologist, who has made observations in West Africa, has stated that the Negro genitals are not disproportionately larger than those of the white. [77]

Dollard, commenting upon his inquiries into the sexual mores of "Southerntown," writes: "There is a widespread belief that the genitalia of Negro males are larger than those of whites; this was repeatedly stated by white informants. One planter, for example, said he had visual opportunity to confirm the fact; he had gone to one of his cabins, and on entering without warning, found a Negro man preparing for intercourse. Informant expressed surprise at the size of the penis and gave an indication by his arm and clenched fist of its great length and diameter. It was further said that this impression was confirmed at the time of the draft examination of Negroes at the Southerntown Courthouse in 1917. Two physicians from other states have verified this report on the basis of draft-board experience. [78] A Negro

---

[76] Blumenbach, *De generis humani varietate nativa,* trans. by T. Bendyshe, "On the Natural Variety of Mankind," in *The Anthropological Treatises of Johann Friedrich Blumenbach,* p. 68.

[77] Gorer, quoted by Dollard, *Caste and Class in a Southern Town,* p. 161.

[78] During World War II an officer in the Medical Corps of the United States Naval Reserve, who for some five months worked in the main induction center in Mississippi, wrote me (Ashley Montagu) as follows: "I know nothing directly as to the size of the American Negro penis in erection. I have been told that it does not elongate much, but as far as the comparative size of the Mississippi Negro's flaccid penis when judged in relation to Mississippi whites I consider myself an expert. If size is a measure of superiority, and obviously psychologically, at least in Western culture it is, the white in the noble state of Mississippi is definitely inferior to the colored adult male in the general run of that population. To deny this fact is silly. Every physician there remarked about it and was jealous. For my own part I was finally compelled to modify my theories on the overwhelming importance of economics as the basis for the peculiar hostility of the Southern white for

professional, on the other hand, did not believe that Negroes have larger genitalia than whites. He had worked in military camps where he had a chance to see recruits of both races naked, and said there was the usual variation within races, but no uniform difference as between races." [79]

Commenting upon these statements Dollard writes: "One thing seems certain—that the actual differences between Negro and white genitalia cannot be as great as they seem to be to the whites; it is a question of the psychological size being greater than any actual differences could be . . . the notion is heavily functional in reference to the supposed dangers of sexual contact of Negroes with white women." [80]

It is probable that Dollard has here given the correct explanation of the facts, namely, that any difference in size that may exist has, like body odor, been exaggerated, the alleged larger size of the Negro genitalia being for the most part a function of the whites' belief in the undesirability of contact with the Negro.

As an anatomist with many years' experience in American anatomical laboratories, I have in only one instance had occasion to remark any appreciable difference in the size of the flaccid male Negro genitalia as compared with those of the white. Medical students are anxious to confirm their beliefs in this connection, but except for an occasional case which is soon matched with a similar condition in a white in the same laboratory, the evidence is usually disappointing to the student. From my own observations I would be inclined to say that the Negro genitalia are probably relatively no larger than those of the white. Recalling, however, the greater leg length of the Negro, it is possible that the Negro genitalia may be proportionately larger than those of the white, but satisfactory evidence for this is lacking. If there is any difference in size, it is probably so small that the popular exaggerated belief may be dismissed as but another one of the legends which have been built up about the anatomy of the American Negro.

---

the Negro and was led to believe that the roots of it were more probably to be located in the effort on their part to compensate for their sense of inadequacy in that direction." I quote these observations for what they may be considered to be worth.

[79] Dollard, *Caste and Class in a Southern Town*, pp. 160–61. The morbid and revealing interest of many Southern white males in this subject is dramatically described by Griffin in his book *Black Like Me*, pp. 91–99.

[80] *Ibid.*, p. 161.

CONCLUSION

We may conclude this survey, then, with the statement that the American Negro represents an amalgam into which have entered the genes of African Negroes, whites of many nations and social classes, and some American Indians, and that as far as his physical characters are concerned the American Negro represents the successful blending of these three principal elements into a unique biological type. All his characters are perfectly harmonic, and there is every reason to believe that he represents a perfectly satisfactory biological type. His biological future is definitely bright.

Myths are created to fill psychological needs. The need to make the Negro an inferior has given rise to the mythology of his inferior physical characters. The gene differences between Negro and white are very small indeed. Professor Bentley Glass has pointed out: "In all, it is unlikely that there are many more than six pairs of genes in which the white race differs characteristically, in the lay sense, from the black. Whites or blacks, however, unquestionably often differ among themselves by a larger number than this, a fact which reveals our racial prejudices as biologically absurd. It is only the consistency of the difference, not its magnitude, which looms so large in our eyes. Differences between other races are probably even less, and those between such sub-racial groups as 'Nordics' and 'Mediterraneans' are negligible. *The chasm between human races and peoples, where it exists, is psychological and sociological; it is not genetic!*"[81]

---

[81] Glass, *Genes and the Man*, pp. 173-74.

16

Are the Jews a "Race"?

THE JEWS are nearly always referred to in popular parlance as a "race." This is done not only by the so-called "man in the street" but also by many scientists, medical men, philosophers, politicians, historians,[1] and the members of many other professions. When reference is made to the Jewish "race," what is implied is that there exists a clearly defined, though widely scattered, group of people who are physically and behaviorally distinguishable from all other "races"— the "Jewish race."

The so-called "Jewish race" is generally held to be characterized by a combination of physical and behavioral traits which renders any member of it recognizable anywhere on earth. The physical traits are held to be short to middling stature, a long hooked nose, greasy skin, dark complexion, black, often wavy hair, thick lips, flat feet, and a tendency to run to fat in women.

The characteristic behavioral traits are alleged to consist in a rather excessive allotment of the more unattractive social vices: aggressiveness, "loudness," "unscrupulousness," considerable brain power, peculiar gestures, both of the hands and of the face, and a quality of looking and behaving in a "Jewish" manner, hard to define but nevertheless real.

There are many persons who claim to be able to distinguish a Jew from all other people simply by the total appearance which he presents, even when his back is all that is visible to the observer.

It is not only non-Jews who assert these things and who make such

[1] A historian writing in 1950 states that Disraeli "although Jewish by race was a practicing Christian." Thomson, *England in the Nineteenth Century*, p. 107.

claims, but the Jews as a whole have prided themselves on the "fact" that they are God's Chosen People and hence distinguished from all other peoples. Many Jews have insisted that they belong to a distinct "race" of mankind, the "Jewish race." The Jews have, in fact, presented no exception to the general rule that every human group considers itself just a little better than "the others."

Whatever may be generally believed about Jews, and whatever the latter may think of themselves, the facts deserve to be dispassionately presented, together with an interpretation of their significance. Assertions and denials are of little value when they are based on emotion or when they are founded on misinterpreted observation or both. It is only when the actual facts are clearly presented in the light of scientific investigation and correctly interpreted that assertions and denials are in order. Such statements differ from those which are usually made, and are therefore unlikely to appeal to persons who prefer to accept what their emotions dictate rather than be persuaded by scientific demonstration.

What, then, has the anthropologist to say in answer to the question "Are the Jews a 'race' or any other kind of entity?" Do they possess distinguishable physical and behavioral traits? If they do, why do they? To what extent are any of these alleged traits real or inborn, and to what extent, if any, are they acquired?

These are some of the questions to be dealt with in the present chapter.

Do the Jews possess a community of physical characteristics which serves to distinguish them as a distinct ethnic group among the peoples of mankind? To this question the answer of science is an unequivocal "No." This does not mean that the Jews are not recognizable as a distinct group, but it does mean that they are not distinguishable as such upon the basis of physical characters. If they are not distinguishable as a distinct group upon physical grounds, upon what basis, then, are they distinguishable as a group at all? The answer to that question is: primarily, and almost entirely, upon cultural grounds, and upon cultural grounds alone.

We may now proceed to discuss the evidence for these statements.

Our sole authority for the early physical history of the Jews is, at present, the Old Testament. The physical anthropology of this work is far from consistent, but from it the following facts may be pieced together: The ancestors of the early Jews lived on the stretch of land skirting the western bank of the Euphrates. The home of Terah,

Abraham's father, was Ur of the Chaldees, close to the Persian Gulf; here and to the southwest lived numerous Arab tribes, all of whom spoke closely related languages which, after the "brownish" son of Noah, Shem, we customarily term Semitic (Shemitic). The original converts to the religion which Abraham had founded were drawn from several of these tribes. Their physical differences, if any, were probably negligible. But shortly after they had established themselves as a distinct religious group intermixture commenced, first with the Canaanites of the lowlands, with whom they had traded for some time, and then with the Amorites of the highlands of the southwest. The Amorites are supposed to have been distinguished by a high frequency of red hair. The Hivites, Amalekites, Kenites, Egyptians, and the Hittites all mixed with the Jews during this early period of their history, as did many other peoples mentioned in the Old Testament.

There is reason to believe that the peoples mentioned were characterized by somewhat different frequencies of one or more distinctive physical characters. Thus, it is said that the Amorites showed a high frequency of red hair, while the Hittites, who spoke an Indo-Germanic language, presented two types, a tall, heavy-bearded, hook-nosed type and a moderately tall, beardless type, with thick lips, a straight nose with wide nostrils, and "sunken" eyes.

We perceive, then, that already in the earliest period of their development the people whom we now call "the Jews" were a much mixed group, and while for classificatory purposes they might all be designated as Mediterranean in type, there can be no question but that they were at this period far from being a people of "pure" ancestry. Owing to their geographic position and relations we can be fairly certain that the peoples of the East from whom the Jews originated and the many others with whom they subsequently mixed were themselves of much mixed ancestry.

During the period of the Exodus (1220 B.C.) there was further mixture with the peoples with whom they came into contact, principally the types embraced under the term Egyptians and probably, also, some Hamitic peoples. Some 622 crania recovered from a Jewish cemetery at Lachish, dating back to approximately 750 B.C. show marked resemblances to those of the Dynastic Egyptians.[2] This is not

---

[2] Risdon, "A Study of the Cranial and Other Human Remains from Palestine Excavated at Tell Duweir (Lachish)," *Biometrika*, XXXI (1939), 99–166.

to suggest that all Jews at that period resembled Egyptians, but it does suggest something vastly more significant than that, namely, that already, as early as 750 B.C., there existed local groups of Jews who in their physical characters resembled, or were identical with, the population among whom they were living and differed from other groups calling themselves Jews. This is, in fact, exactly the state of affairs we encounter today, and there is every reason to believe that this has been progressively so from the earliest times. In other words, the Jews were never at any time characterized by a community of physical characters, but generally varied according to the populations among whom they lived. This would mean either that they originated from these populations or that they had become physically identified with them as a result of intermixture. We shall see that the latter explanation is the one which most nearly agrees with the facts.

During the Diaspora the Jews have been dispersed to practically every part of the earth and have intermixed with numerous peoples. In the sixth century B.C., during the Babylonian captivity, there was some intermixture with many Mesopotamian peoples. During the Hellenistic period, in the fourth century B.C., Jews followed Alexander the Great into the Hellenistic world, into Egypt, Syria, Asia Minor, Macedonia, to mention a few of the more important regions into which they penetrated and settled. The pattern followed by these Jews was identical with that which the Jews have always followed with such great success: they took over the language of the Greek-speaking populations and in general identified themselves with Hellenistic culture.

In the second century B.C., at the time of the Maccabees, there commenced the movement of the Jews into the Roman world which carried them to the farthest corners of the Roman Empire, especially to Western Europe and particularly to Spain, Italy, France, and the Rhineland of Germany. A large number of Jews settled along the Rhine in the region of Frankfurt, Worms, Cologne, and Trier. The language spoken in that region during the Middle Ages was adopted by the Jews and is preserved, with but little modification, to this day in the form of Yiddish. It is preserved in its purest form practically unchanged to the present time in certain cantons of Switzerland. In its Eastern European form it is spoken by many more Jews than speak Hebrew or any other single language.

During the eleventh century, at the time of the First Crusade, the plunder and massacre of the Jews by Christian knights[3] started a Jewish migration eastward, which was accelerated into a mass migration after the thirteenth century. These Rhineland Jews settled in what is now Galicia, Bukovina, and the southern and western Ukraine. Here they met and merged with the earlier Jewish settlements and adopted as their common language the speech of the Rhineland group, Yiddish. These Jews came to be known as the Ashkenazim (after the Hebrew name for Germany), as distinguished from the Jews of Spanish origin, the Sephardim.

It has been asserted that the modern Sephardim are a much more homogeneous group physically than the Ashkenazim and that they "preserve with reasonable fidelity the racial character of their Palestinian ancestors."[4]

That the Sephardic Jews are less variable in their characters than the Ashkenazim is possible, since they may be slightly less mixed. It is, however, to be doubted that they preserve with any fidelity at all the "racial" character of their Palestinian ancestors. This is greatly to be doubted for the reason that "their Palestinian ancestors" were themselves of different types. Indeed, it is doubtful whether anyone is today in a position to say exactly what was the Palestinian ancestry of the Jews. Certainly, even less can be said concerning the anthropological characters of the groups which entered into that ancestry. At the present time it would be wisest to take the view that if there does exist a significant difference between the Sephardim and the Ashkenazim, then that difference is due to the somewhat different post-Palestinian biological history of the two groups. As we shall see, there is a much greater proportion of blond types among the Ashkenazim than among the Sephardim. It must be recalled that during their residence in Spain, from the beginnings of the eleventh to the end of the fifteenth century, the Sephardim almost certainly underwent some admixture with the Moors and for some three centuries with the non-Moorish populations of Spain and Portugal.

To list the peoples with whom the Jews have at one time or another intermixed would include a large proportion of the populations of the world. This does not mean that the Jews as a whole have undergone such mixture, but—and this is the important point—the different

---

[3] Hay, *The Foot of Pride.*

[4] Coon, "Have the Jews a Racial Identity?" in Graeber and Britt (eds.), *Jews in a Gentile World,* p. 31.

populations of Jews have undergone independent and different kinds and degrees of intermixture with various populations. The result of such varying biological experiences would be, even if the Jews had commenced as a homogeneous group—which they did not—that a certain amount of diversification in physical characters would eventually be produced between local groups of Jews. That this is actually what has occurred is proved by both the historical facts and the analysis of measurable anthropological characters. Thus, in Daghestan in the Caucasus, only 7 per cent of the Jews show light-colored eyes; among German Jews in Baden, however, this percentage rises to 51.2; in the city of Vienna the percentage is 30, in Poland 45 per cent, but among the Samaritans of Jerusalem it is only 11.1 per cent. It is the same with hair color. Among the Samaritans only 3.7 per cent showed blond hair; in Italy the percentage rises to 11.8, in Rumania to 14.7, to 17.9 in Hungary, 20.4 in England, and 29 in Lithuania. In the city of Riga, Latvia, the proportion is 36 per cent. In Jerusalem Jewish Ashkenazi children showed 40 per cent blonds and 30 per cent blue eyes, while the Sephardim showed 10 per cent blonds and even fewer blue eyes.

The census of school children in Germany taken in the nineteenth century, under the direction of Rudolf Virchow, revealed that among 75,000 children 32 per cent had light hair and 46 per cent light eyes.[5] In Austria these figures were 28 and 54 per cent, respectively, and in England 26 and 41 per cent. As Fishberg[6] long ago pointed out, these figures follow the population trends for blondness as a whole, exemplified by the figures for England, Germany, and Riga, whereas in Italy, where the population is predominantly brunet, less than 12 per cent of the Jews are blond, and in the Caucasus, North Africa, and Turkestan the percentage is even less.

Even with respect to that unreliable, but much-beloved child of the

---

[5] Virchow, "Gesammtbericht über die von der deutschen anthropologischen Gesellschaft veranlassten Erhebungen über die Farbe der Haut, der Haare und der Augen der Schulkinder in Deutschland," *Archiv für Anthropologie,* XVI (1886), 275–475.

[6] Fishberg, *The Jews.*

[7] The cephalic index numerically expresses the proportion of the breadth of the head in relation to its length; it is determined by multiplying the maximum breadth of the head by 100 and dividing that sum by the maximum length. The three indices thus yielded are: less than 76 points=longheaded (dolichocephalic), 76 to 80.9 points=medium-headed (mesocephalic), and over 81 points=broadheaded (brachycephalic).

anthropologist, the cephalic index[7] or form of the head, the variation between different local groups of Jews is considerable. Among London Ashkenazim one finds 25.3 per cent of longheads (dolichocephals), 28.3 per cent of moderately roundheads (mesocephals), and 47.4 per cent of round- or broadheads (brachycephals); among

TABLE 4

PERCENTAGE DISTRIBUTION OF EYE COLOR AND HAIR COLOR
AMONG JEWS[a]

(*The figures in parentheses refer to the females*)

REGION OR GROUP	EYES		HAIR			DARK TYPE	FAIR TYPE	MIXED TYPE
	Dark	*Light*	*Dark*	*Fair*	*Red*			
Poland	55.0	45.0	96.8	0.5	2.6	57.9	0.5	41.5
	(56.8)	(43.2)	(86.4)	8.0	(5.6)	(58.5)	(8.5)	(33.0)
Galicia	53.8	46.1	74.0	21.5	4.3	44.0	13.0	43.0
	(60.0)	(40.0)	(76.0)	(20.0)	(4.0)	(51.0)	(16.0)	(33.0)
Ukraine	56.7	43.3	76.4	19.3	4.3	51.3	16.2	31.0
	(61.8)	(38.1)	(83.1)	(14.0)	(2.9)	(68.6)	(6.9)	(24.3)
Southern Russia	64.8	35.2	81.7	14.8	2.4	58.1	10.5	27.9
	(75.6)	(24.4)	(83.0)	(14.6)	(3.5)	(68.3)	(4.9)	(24.4)
Lithuania	65.2	34.8	68.1	29.0	2.0	50.7	13.0	36.2
Rumania	48.7	51.3	83.3	14.7	2.8	47.0	11.0	42.2
Hungary	50.7	49.3	77.1	17.9	5.0	46.0	12.0	42.0
						(62.0)	(5.0)	(33.0)
Baden	48.8	51.2	84.9	12.8	2.3			
England	61.3	38.7	77.6	20.4	2.5			
	(66.8)	(33.2)	(88.1)	(11.9)	(0.0)			
Italy	67.6	32.3	88.2	11.8		60.2	14.7	25.0
Bosnia	69.1	30.9	80.0	18.2	1.8			
North Africa	83.1	16.9	92.2	5.2	2.6	76.4	4.6	19.0
Daghestan	93.0	7.0	97.0	0.5	2.5	97.0		3.0
Georgia	89.0	11.0	93.0	5.0	2.0	82.0	3.0	15.0
Turkestan	85.0	15.0	98.0	2.0		85.0	2.0	13.0
Samaritans	88.9	11.1	96.3	3.7	0.0			
	(88.9)	(11.1)	(92.6)	0.0	(7.4)			
Karaites	74.0	26.0	94.0	2.0	4.0	70.0	6.0	24.0
Yemen	100.0		100.0			100.0		

South Russian Jews these figures are, respectively, 1, 18, and 81 per cent; for London Sephardim these figures are 17 per cent dolicho-cephalic and 34 per cent brachycephalic; Galician and Lithuanian Jews yield a proportion of 85 per cent brachycephals and only 3.8 per cent dolichocephals.

If, as is customarily done, the mean or average shape of the head is given, an incorrect idea is obtained of the actual conditions prevailing among the Jews so far as the shape of head is concerned. It is the percentage distribution of the various head shapes in such a popula-tion which gives us a true account of these conditions. These per-centage distributions show that head shape, or cephalic index, like all other characters, is variable among the Jews as a whole, the head shape of the Jews in various countries varying substantially from one to another, as is demonstrated in the following table.

TABLE 5

PERCENTAGE DISTRIBUTION OF HEAD SHAPE (CEPHALIC INDEX)
IN JEWS OF DIFFERENT REGIONS[a]

Cephalic Index	Daghestan Caucasus	Europe	North Africa	Yemen Arabia
Hyperdolichocephalic (–76)		2.89	25.97	71.80
Dolichocephalic (76–77)		7.36	24.67	14.10
Subdolichocephalic (78–79)	4.70	15.51	19.48	7.69
Mesocephalic (80–81)	6.10	25.78	13.00	2.56
Subbrachycephalic (82–83)	17.37	24.01	9.09	3.85
Brachycephalic (84–85)	23.94	15.97	6.49	
Hyperbrachycephalic (86–)	47.89	8.47	1.30	
Number of observations	2.3	2,641	77	78

[a] From Kautsky, *Are the Jews a Race?* The definitions of the cephalic index vary slightly from those generally accepted, but not sufficiently to affect the discussion.

Table 5 shows that Caucasian Jews have predominantly round heads, while those in North Africa, particularly those in Arabia, are predominantly longheaded and those in Europe are predominantly of intermediate type.

Much more significant characters than those so far mentioned are the blood groups A, B, AB, and O. The blood groups remain constant throughout life, they appear to have a very low mutation rate, and they are inherited according to the laws of Mendel. The proportions in which these blood groups are found (actually the frequency of the genes) in different populations should tell us to what extent those populations resemble each other in respect, at least, to their gene frequencies for the blood groups. If, now, the blood groups of Jews from different regions are compared with one another, some interesting facts are seen to emerge. The distribution of these blood groups is shown in the following four tables (from Brutzkus). For the purposes of comparison the percentages for the surrounding Gentile populations (italicized) are also given.

TABLE 6

BLOOD GROUPS OF JEWS IN THE MEDITERRANEAN REGION

Town or Country	Number of Persons	A	B	AB	O
Monastir (Macedonia)	500	33.0	23.2	5.0	38.8
Morocco	642	35.9	19.9	7.3	36.9
Tunis	200	31.0	15.0	12.5	41.0
Aleppo (Syria)	173	34.0	20.0	8.0	38.0
Aleppo (Arabs)	*933*	*37.0*	*21.0*	*6.0*	*36.0*
Georgia	1,236	43.93	19.01	10.76	26.29
Persia	116	46.5	25.0	8.6	19.9
Georgians	*2,177*	*37.11*	*10.93*	*4.82*	*46.6*
Yemen	1,000	26.1	16.1	1.8	56.0
Palestine (Arabs)	*347*	*39.7*	*20.4*	*7.4*	*32.5*

The figures in Table 6 show that, with the exception of the Georgian and Persian Jews, and strangely enough the Jews from Yemen, in their blood group distributions the Jews of the Mediterranean region bear a close resemblance to the Arab populations. The Jews and Arabs of Aleppo are much alike in this respect, while Georgian Jews and non-Jews are much more unlike. Very different are the blood group distributions of the Jews in the Caucasus, the Crimea, and Turkestan.

From Table 7 it will be seen that the percentages for blood group B are significantly higher than they are for Jews of the Mediterranean region listed in Table 6. The Jews of the Caucasus, Crimea, and

TABLE 7

BLOOD GROUPS AMONG THE JEWS IN THE CAUCASUS, CRIMEA, AND TURKESTAN

Region or People	Number of Persons	A	B	AB	O
Daghestan	87	26.6	24.1	9.1	40.2
Samarkand	616	29.2	30.5	7.9	32.3
Crimea	500	34.4	32.6	12.2	20.8
Khirgiz	914	23.96	31.4	7.87	36.76

Turkestan have apparently absorbed, sometime in their history, an appreciable number of persons possessing a substantial proportion of blood group B. It so happens that these regions were once inhabited by the Chazars, a Turco-Mongolian people, a large proportion of whom adopted the Jewish faith and intermarried with Jews. Since the Turco-Mongolian region exhibits high frequencies of blood group B, it is likely that the Chazars were similarly characterized, and that through them some, at least, of the Jews of these regions acquired some of their B genes.

TABLE 8

BLOOD GROUPS AMONG THE JEWS OF WESTERN EUROPE

Town	Number of Persons	A	B	AB	O
Berlin	230	41.1	11.9	4.9	42.1
Berlin	2,500	44.0	15.0	6.0	35.0
Amsterdam	705	39.4	13.4	4.5	42.6
Amsterdam	6,679	41.7	8.6	3.0	46.8

The high frequency of blood group A among the Jews from Berlin and Amsterdam (Table 8) is striking, as is the resemblance of the blood group distributions to those of the non-Jews, particularly in

Berlin. The suggestion is that there has been an appreciable amount of admixture between Jews and non-Jews in these towns.[8]

TABLE 9

BLOOD GROUPS AMONG THE JEWS OF EASTERN EUROPE

Country	Number of Persons	A	B	AB	O
Russia	3,333	41.7	19.6	6.5	32.2
Russia	10,151	36.7	21.9	7.5	33.9
Poland	8.8	41.5	17.4	8.0	33.1
Poland	11,488	37.8	20.8	8.9	32.5
Rumania	1,135	39.0	17.5	5.3	38.2
Rumania	1,521	43.3	15.6	7.4	33.7

Sufficient, I hope, has been said concerning the origins of the Jews and of the variability of only a small selection of their physical characters to show how mixed and how variable the Jews are in both their ancestry and their physical characters. As Siemens has concluded: "A study of the main characteristics of the indigenous stocks of various regions and the corresponding characteristics of the Jews that have lived among them in these regions indicates that the Jews are of heterogeneous types each of which conforms to a greater or smaller extent to the indigenous physical types."[9] From the standpoint of scientific classification, from the standpoint of physical anthropology, and from the standpoint of zoology there is no such thing as a Jewish physical type, and there is not, nor was there ever, anything even remotely resembling a Jewish "race" or ethnic group.

Are the Jews, then, constituted of a number of different ethnic groups distinguishable from other non-Jewish ethnic groups? The answer is "No." There are certainly many different types of Jews, but these, in general, do not sufficiently differ from the populations among whom they live to justify their being distinguished from those populations on physical grounds and classified as distinct ethnic

[8] See Mourant, *The Distribution of the Human Blood Groups*, pp. 70–74.
[9] Siemens, "Anthropometric Effects of Recorded Cases of Miscegenation among Certain Caucasian Sub-Groups," *Ohio Journal of Science*, L (1950), 45–52.

groups. On physical grounds it is quite impossible to distinguish Jews from most of the native populations among whom they live in the Middle East, in the Orient, and in many other regions. Dr. Magnus Hirschfeld, an acute observer and himself a Jew, writes of his difficulty in distinguishing Jews from non-Jews in Palestine, "for in Palestine," he writes, "there is no way of telling at first glance whether a person is a Christian, a Jew, or a Mohammedan." "Very seldom—much more seldom, anyway, than in Carlsbad or Marienbad—one sees the characteristic 'Struck' [10] heads or the Oriental beauties as they were painted in my youth by Sichel. The so-called 'Jewish nose' too, supposedly an Aramaic-Arab characteristic, is hardly more frequent than the pug nose. Noses of 'western' or 'northern' form predominate (to use Gunther's nomenclature), and the formation, too, of lips, hair, eyes and hands is hardly different from the average European types. One even sees, especially among the children, a surprisingly large number of blonde and blue-eyed types. In a kindergarten I counted 32 blondes among 54 children, that is, more than 50 per cent." [11]

Writing of the Jews of Tunis, Sir Harry Johnston remarked upon the absence of strongly marked racial features among them and the rarity with which one encountered a Jew who suggested a Semitic origin. [12] Sir E. Dennison Ross, the distinguished orientalist, writing of his stay in Tiflis, Georgia, says, "In this town I was very much struck by the similarity, both in appearance and character, of the Greeks, Jews, and Armenians." [13]

Certainly anyone who has lived for any length of time in Italy will know that it is utterly impossible to distinguish a Jew from an Italian in that country. The same is not, however, true in all lands, for in England, in Germany, and in America it is certainly possible, with some degree of accuracy, to pick out many persons who are Jews as

---

[10] Hermann Struck, Jewish artist who specialized in rendering the heads of Jewish orthodox "types."

[11] Hirschfeld, *Men and Women,* pp. 277–78. Hirschfeld adds: "not pure, but mixed, races are a matter of course biologically. How, then, should there be 'pure' races among the whites when we consider that every individual possesses and unites in himself a line of paternal and maternal ancestors embracing thousands, perhaps even hundreds of thousands of generations? How extraordinarily various must have been the mixture of genes over so long a period!"

[12] Johnston, *The Story of My Life,* pp. 66–72.

[13] Ross, *Both Ends of the Candle,* p. 72.

distinguished from non-Jews of all types. Is the fact that one can do so due to the physical characters of these persons, characters which distinguish them from the rest of the population? Let us see.

A proportion of Jews retain an aggregation of Mediterranean physical traits. In any population not exhibiting such an aggregation of physical traits, some persons would be easily recognizable as Jews by virtue of this difference. But this does not mean that such physical traits are peculiar to all or most Jews, for, in fact, a large proportion of Jews do not possess such traits. Nor does it mean that some Jews alone possess the aggregate of physical traits referred to, for many of the non-Jewish populations of the Near and Middle East as well as of the Mediterranean exhibit such traits in much higher frequencies than do Jews.

Furthermore, some Jews exhibit a certain quality of looking "Jewish," but again this quality is not peculiar to Jews, for it is the "look" which most of the peoples of the Near and Middle East possess. In the Occident persons of such origin are often taken for Jews. This Jewish-looking quality occurring in any population not generally characterized by it renders it possible to recognize some persons as being Jews. Even so, one will often go wrong and mistakenly identify as Jews persons of non-Jewish origin, such as many Italians, Greeks, Turks, Arabs, Berbers, and related peoples. The quality of looking Jewish is not due so much to any inherited characters of the persons in question as to certain culturally acquired habits of expression, facial, vocal, muscular, and mental. Such habits do, to an impressive extent, influence the appearance of the person and in large part determine the impression he makes upon others. Whether such persons will be identifiable as "Jews" will depend upon the character of the population among which they live.

Without question a certain proportion of persons of Jewish cultural background exhibit a complex of physical traits which represent the residual expression of their remote Near Eastern ancestry. This is the type indistinguishable from that represented by millions of non-Jews of the Near and Middle East. In the Occident it is not difficult to recognize such persons as Jews because they do differ from the general population sufficiently to suggest their origin. That origin is not, in fact, Jewish but Eastern.

The fact is that "the" Jews are neither a "race" nor an ethnic group nor yet a number of ethnic groups—no more so, indeed, than are

Catholics, Protestants, or Moslems. It is, in fact, as incorrect to speak of a "Jewish race" or ethnic group as it would be to speak of a Catholic, Protestant, or Moslem "race" or ethnic group. What, then, does the term "Jew" mean? Strictly speaking, a person is a Jew by virtue of his adherence to the Jewish religion. If he is not a member of some organized form of Judaism, then he is not a Jew.

There is, however, another sense in which a person who does not subscribe to the tenets of the Jewish faith may nevertheless be correctly described as exhibiting Jewish traits, in just the same way as we say of a person that he looks or behaves like a Frenchman, or a German, or a member of any other national group. The Jews are not a nation, but, interestingly enough, they have preserved cultural traits, almost everywhere, which we usually associate with differences in national culture; these traits, therefore, have a quasi-national character. The Jews, wherever they have been, have clung tenaciously to their ancient beliefs and ways of life, more so than any other Western people of whom we have any knowledge, and they have generally preserved a certain community of cultural traits. These traits are cultural, not biological ones. Any person who is born into, or brought up in, a Jewish cultural environment will acquire the traits of behavior and certain personality traits peculiar to that culture. These are the traits which make many Jews socially "visible" in many of the communities in which they live. These traits, taken collectively, differ sufficiently from those which prevail in the communities in which Jews generally live to render them at once distinguishable from practically all other members of each of these communities.

It is extremely difficult to define the "quality of looking Jewish," even though it is doubtful whether anyone could be found who would deny that such a quality exists. This quality is exhibited not only in the facial expression but in the whole expression of the body—in its movements and in its gesticulations. No attempt to define this quality will be made here, because it defies definition; but that it exists in many Jews and that it is culturally determined there can be little doubt. The quality is completely lost by persons whose recent ancestors have abandoned Jewish culture for several generations and who have themselves been raised in a non-Jewish culture. It is even lost, or is never developed, in Jews who have been educated predominantly in a non-Jewish cultural environment. Jews such as the latter are Jews by religion alone; culturally, they belong to the culture in which they have been raised and educated, be it English, French, German, Italian, or what not.

What makes most persons or communities of persons visible or distinguishable as Jews is neither their physical appearance nor the fact of their adherence to the religion of Judaism, but certain cultural traits which they have acquired in a Jewish cultural environment.

We have, then, a rather interesting situation: A person is never a Jew by virtue of belonging to some specific physical type, nor is a person necessarily recognizable as a Jew because he subscribes to the tenets of the Jewish religion; he is a Jew by religion, but in every other way he may be culturally non-Jewish. Finally, only those persons are recognizable as Jewish who exhibit certain behavioral traits commonly associated with Jews, yet such persons may not subscribe to the Jewish religion, but to some other religion or none at all.

We see, then, that actually it is membership in Jewish culture which makes a person a Jew, and nothing else, not even his adherence to Judaism.

It is possible to distinguish many Jews from members of other cultural groups for the same reason that it is possible to distinguish Englishmen from such groups, or Americans, Frenchmen, Italians, and Germans. Every cultural group differs by virtue of its difference in culture, that is, in its way of life, from every other cultural group, and each cultural group molds the behavior of every one of its members according to its own pattern. Members of one cultural group do not readily fit into the pattern of another. Because of the complexities which characterize each separate pattern of culture, persons who have been brought up in one culture cannot and should not be expected to make a perfect adjustment to a different pattern of culture—however closely related the latter may be. Even when persons are anxious to free themselves from one culture and adopt, and become part of, another, such persons rarely, if ever, succeed in making the complete change; to some extent they always remain culturally disoriented. Once a cultural pattern has been woven, it is generally not possible to unravel it and weave a completely new one. The reason for this is that habits of behavior formed in early life become, in a real sense, part of one's "second" nature; it is notoriously difficult to disentangle oneself from such habits in later life.

This, of course, explains why persons of Jewish cultural background or persons of any other cultural background, try as they may, frequently fail to free themselves completely from the conditioning effects of that background.

What, in the case of persons who are recognizable as Jews, are these conditioning effects which render them distinctive from other cultural groups? Before we attempt an answer to this question it must be emphasized that not all persons who have been brought up in a Jewish cultural environment exhibit Jewish cultural traits. There are many varieties and degrees of Jewish culture, some being much less intense than others, and a large proportion of them are modified by the culture in which the family or community happens to have lived for some generations. In addition to this, some individuals take rather more readily to the Gentile culture outside the home than they do to that within the home or local community, while others emancipate themselves early from the domestic cultural environment.

It will be generally agreed that those persons who are readily identifiable as Jews most frequently originate from the lower socioeconomic classes of their community. As in all lower socioeconomic classes, the conditions of life are not conducive to the development of gentle manners and refined thoughts or ways of expressing them. In fact, the contrary is likely to be the case. Good breeding is something one does not expect from any but those who have enjoyed the necessary opportunities. Jews of the lower socioeconomic classes are no better than the members of the comparable classes of any other culture, and for the same reasons: the struggle to keep body and soul together has been a full-time job, while the opportunities for developing into a well-bred person have been rare indeed.

What distinguishes the conduct of persons who are recognizable as Jews from the behavior which characterizes the members of other groups is, of course, the addition of a certain cultural quality or flavor to that behavior. This quality is of the same kind as that which expresses itself in the differences in behavior which generally distinguish the members of different classes within the same society. Thus, persons who have lived the greater part of their early lives in a lower socioeconomic environment generally exhibit a certain coarseness and wildness of expression in their features. They habitually feel and think in certain culturally common ways, and such emotions and thoughts register themselves in the index which is provided by the thirty-two muscles of expression of the face.

Just as there is such a thing as an English, a German, a French, an

Italian, and even an American cast of features, so there is such a thing as a Jewish cast of face. This cast of face is often erroneously assumed to be biologically determined, but the fact is that it is culturally determined in precisely the manner which has been indicated.

Add to the culturally determined cast of face traditionally determined gesticulations of the face and body, character of speech, together with certain similarly culturally determined preferences for color combinations, style, and total ensemble of clothes, and we have a powerful association of traits which readily enables one to distinguish certain Jewish persons from non-Jews. That all these traits are culturally determined is readily proved by the fact that every last trace of them may be completely lost in a single generation following the adoption of a non-Jewish culture. This is, perhaps, most strikingly seen in certain Anglo-Jewish and American-Jewish families.

There are few traits which are inherently objectionable, but certain differences in behavior exhibited by some Jews have been characterized as such by those who feel compelled to do so. Many of the traits which non-Jews find objectionable in Jews are the very traits upon which some of the latter pride themselves. Aggressiveness and the habit of gesticulation with the upper extremities, for example.

Centuries of dispossession, massacre, oppression, frustration, and discrimination have forced upon many Jews the ineluctable development of a certain amount of aggressiveness or else the inevitability of perishing. Aggressiveness, under certain conditions, is a quality of considerable survival value, a form of adjustment. It is fortunate for the world that the Jews have been able to preserve themselves from the worst that it could do by responding with the necessary aggressiveness. That those who have forced so many Jews to develop this quality should find it objectionable is in perfect keeping with the usual sad logic by which the wrongheaded conduct themselves in these matters. Oppression and frustration produce aggressiveness. It is a normal tendency of the human organism when it is frustrated, when it is made the object of aggression, to respond with counteraggression.[14] It may be pointed out that all drives or urges are aggressive, and in fact aggression has been described as that essential factor which provides a well-integrated personality with its necessary drive.

When oppression and discrimination against the Jews shall have ceased, their aggressiveness, or what remains of it, will vanish entirely.

---

[14] See Dollard *et al., Frustration and Aggression.*

But as long as that oppression and discrimination continue, they will need their aggressiveness in order to hold their own in the world. From the standpoint of the scientist objectively attempting to evaluate its quality within the framework in which it functions, the aggressiveness of many Jews is a highly desirable quality, since it enables them to survive in a hostile world. With the disappearance of this hostility, the necessity for aggressiveness will disappear. But for those who maintain this hostility to object to the aggressiveness which they have forced upon Jews is something less than reasonable. Arthur Koestler has stated this beautifully. The Jews, he makes one of his characters reflect, are "not an accident of race, but simply man's condition carried to its extreme—a branch of the species touched on the raw. Exiled in Egypt, in Babylon, and now over the whole globe, exposed to strange and hostile surroundings, they had to develop peculiar traits; they had no time or chance to grow that hide of complacency, of a specious security, which makes man insensitive to and forgetful of the tragic essence of his condition. They were the natural target of all malcontents, because they were so exasperatingly and abnormally human . . .

"Made homeless in space, they had to expand into new dimensions, as the blind develop hearing and touch. The loss of the spatial dimension transformed this branch of the species as it would have transformed any other nation on earth, Jupiter or Mars. It turned their vision inwards. It made them cunning and grew them claws to cling on with as they were swept by the wind through the countries that were not theirs. It increased their spiritual arrogance: deprived of Space, they believed themselves chosen for eternity in Time. It increased the protective adaptability of their surface, and petrified their inner core. Constant friction polished their many facets: reduced to drift-sand, they had to glitter if they wanted to avoid being trodden on. Living in bondage, cringing became second nature to their pride. Their natural selector was the whip: it whipped the life out of the feeble and whipped the spasm of ambition into the fit. In all fields of living, to get an equal chance they had to start with a plus. Condemned to live in extremes, they were in every respect like other people, only more so." [15]

Gesticulation is an Eastern trait, and no doubt a persisting cultural

---

[15] Koestler, *Thieves in the Night*, pp. 355–56. Permission of The Macmillan Co.

derivative of the Eastern ancestry of much of Jewish culture. The gesticulations of many Jews are often called vulgar by peoples who are
not given to expressing themselves in any manner other than by speech
"unadorned." Such a judgment is, however, purely subjective. Many
Jews regard their habits of gesticulation as a kind of auxiliary language, without which they are tongue-tied, and those who have
studied these gestures find them very expressive indeed. Nevertheless,
those who indulge in them are at once rendered identifiable as Jews,
even though non-Jews may acquire the same habits of gesticulation
by association with Jews.

Interestingly enough, the gestures customarily used by many Jews
have been asserted to be "racially" determined. Nothing could be
further from the truth. Scientific investigation of the gestural behavior
of Eastern Jews and Southern Italians living in New York City shows
that the more members of each of these groups become assimilated
into the so-called "Americanized" community the more do they lose
the gestural traits associated with the original group.[16] Gesture has
no connection whatever with biological factors, but merely represents
a mode of expression conditioned by cultural factors.

We see, then, that it is, indeed, not a difficult matter to distinguish
many Jews by means of certain traits which they exhibit; but it should
also be clear that those traits are all *culturally* determined and have no
connection whatever with inborn biological factors. Neither on physical nor on mental grounds can the Jews be distinguished as an ethnic
group. With his usual bright genius Sir Thomas Browne put the
matter neatly some three centuries ago. "Upon consult of reason,"
he writes, "there will be found no easie assurance to fasten a material
or temperamental propriety upon any nation; there being scarce any
condition (but what depends upon clime) which is not exhausted or
obscured from the commixture of introvenient nations either by commerce or conquest; much more will it be difficult to make out this
affection in the *Jews*; whose race, however pretended to be pure, must
needs have suffered inseparable commixtures with nations of all sorts;
not only in regard of their proselytes, but their universal dispersion;
some being posted from several parts of the earth, others quite lost,
and swallowed up in those nations where they planted." [17]

---

[16] Efron, *Gesture and Environment;* see also La Barre, "The Cultural Basis of
Emotions and Gestures," *Journal of Personality,* XVI (1947), 49–68.
[17] Browne, *Pseudodoxia Epidemica,* Book IV, Chapter X.

Reference may here be made to the oft-repeated assertion that the Jews have a greater amount of brain power than other peoples. This assertion is not usually made in order to flatter Jews, but is rather urged as yet another count in their disfavor, because, it is held, owing to their superior brain power others are thereby placed at a disadvantage in competition with them.

Science knows of no evidence which would substantiate the claim that Jews or any other people have better brains than any other. This is not to say that such a difference may not exist; it may, but if it does, science has been unable to demonstrate it. The business acumen, the scholastic and the interpretative musical abilities of Jews have been specially cultivated. The life of the merchant has been forced upon Jews under the most unfavorable circumstances; under such conditions they have in each generation been forced to develop a sharpness of wit which would enable them to survive. Scholarship has been a revered tradition among Jews for many centuries; furthermore, it has, in the modern world, often been the one means the Jew has had of raising himself socially or of escaping from the depressing conditions of life in the ghetto. It is a fact that in order to make his way in the world the Jew has had to offer a great deal more than anyone else. He had to be like other people, "only more so." [18]

It may be that owing to the great variety of intermixture which Jews have undergone, their considerable physical variability tends also to be exhibited in their mental capacities, that there may be a somewhat greater frequency of mentally well-endowed individuals among them. Whether this is so or not we cannot tell. In any event it would be of no great moment if we could, because it is not so much biological as cultural factors which, other things being more or less equal, determine the nature of a mind. As Boas has written: "Our conclusion is that the claim to biologically determined mental qualities of races is not tenable. Much less have we a right to speak of biologically determined superiority of one race over another. Every race contains so many genetically distinct strains, and the social behavior is so entirely dependent upon the life experience to which every individual is exposed, that individuals of the same type when exposed to different surroundings will react quite differently, while individuals of different

---

[18] The Negro, on the other hand, has, in the past, been forced to the opposite extreme. In order to succeed at all he must, as a rule, do worse than anyone else. He mustn't matter. See Kardiner and Ovesey, *The Mark of Oppression.*

types when exposed to the same environment may react the same way."[19]

The facts, then, lead to the following conclusions: Owing to the original mixed ancestry of the Jews and their subsequent history of intermixture with every people among whom they have lived and continue to live, the Jews of different regions are neither genetically nor physically equivalent. In each country the Jews closely resemble the general population in their physical characters, but many Jews may differ from that population in behavioral characters because they have been primarily educated in a Jewish cultural environment rather than in that of the general population. As Huxley and Haddon have said: "The word *Jew* is valid more as a socio-religious or pseudo-national description than as an ethnic term in any genetic sense. Many 'Jewish' characteristics are without doubt much more the product of Jewish tradition and upbringing, and especially of reaction against external pressure and persecution, than of heredity."[20]

Jews would constitute a national group if they subscribed to the principle of Jewish nationality. Some Jews do, but these are the minority and not the majority. The majority are nationals of the country in which they were born or live. Some Jews, outside Israel, do subscribe to the principle of Jewish or Israeli nationality (not, in fact, the same things), but these are a minority, not the majority. Hearnshaw has spoken of nationality as "that principle compounded of past traditions, present interests and future aspirations which gives to a people a sense of organic unity and separates it from the rest of mankind." In this sense a proportion of Jews can be regarded as quasi-national, but this is a cultural rather than a national relationship for most persons calling themselves Jews.

It would be preferable to call the Jews a quasi-national rather than a pseudo-national group, for there is nothing "pseudo" about their nationalistic cultural traits, even though they may not be definitely recognized as a nation neatly delimited by definite geographic boundaries.[21] It is by virtue of the traits of this quasi-Jewish national culture

---

[19] Boas, "Racial Purity," *Asia*, XL (1940), 234.

[20] Huxley and Haddon, *We Europeans*, pp. 73–74.

[21] Steinberg has suggested that the Jews may be recognized as a "minority nationality in Central and Eastern Europe, an emerging nation in Palestine, and a religio-cultural group in Western democratic lands." *A Partisan Guide to the Jewish Problem*. p. 151. For other attempted definitions see Herskovits,

that a Jewish community may be said to exist and that any person exhibiting these traits may be recognized as a Jew, whether he is an adherent of the Jewish religion or not. Such traits are not inborn, but acquired, and they have nothing whatever to do with biological or so-called "racial" conditions. They are conditioned by culture alone.

The Israeli people or nation should not be confused with the quasi-national Jews of the Diaspora. A large proportion of non-Jews of Arab-Islamic affiliation are citizens of the Israeli nation, while by far the majority of Jews are citizens, and will remain citizens, of other countries.

There could, undoubtedly, be no better demonstration of the fact that the Jews are not a "race" or ethnic group than an inspection of the people of the Israeli nation. The variety of physical types represented among the Israeli Jews probably exceeds that to be found in almost any other land.

A Jewish physical type has been neither preserved nor transmitted down to the present day, because such a type never existed; if such a type had existed it would long ago have been dissolved as a result of the subsequent intermixture of Jews with other peoples. What the Jews have preserved and transmitted have been neither physical nor mental "racial" traits, but religious and cultural traditions and modes of conduct.

The final conclusion is, then, that the Jews are not and never have been a "race" or ethnic group, but they are and always have been a sociological entity best described as a "quasi-national" group or people.

"Who Are the Jews?" in Finkelstein (ed.), *The Jews: Their History, Culture, and Religion*, II, pp. 1151–71.

17

"Race" and Democracy

IN THE PRESENT CONDITION of domestic and world affairs we are, all of us, daily confronted with many conflicting, contradictory, and often novel viewpoints. It must be our task, seriously undertaken, to evaluate these ideas and viewpoints for ourselves, so that we may arrive at a just decision concerning them which will enable us to act effectively and for the best interest of everyone concerned. This chapter is written from the standpoint of those who believe that democracy is the best form of government for a free and intelligent people—a form of government in which every citizen has, or may have, an effective voice in regulating the manner in which he and his fellows shall be governed.

If it be agreed that democracy is the form of government which prevails in this country and that among us live citizens who are members of different ethnic groups, it is a just and proper inquiry and in the interests of us all to ask whether there are any physical and mental qualities peculiar to any of these groups which our social order needs to consider in the government of this land. Today, more than ever, this question needs to be asked and the evidence sympathetically discussed, for we are today facing one of those recurring periods in the history of international relations in which payment is being exacted for our own mistakes as well as for those of earlier generations.

Many of those mistakes are a matter of recent history. It will serve us not at all to lament them; they have been made and have rebounded upon us. The monster that has been let loose upon the world is to a large extent of our own making, and whether we are willing to face the fact or not we are, all of us, individually and collectively, responsible for the ghastly form which he has assumed. Moreover, something of each of us has gone into the making of this Frankenstein, whose name is racism. If we are to combat this formidable problem successfully, we must become fully aware of the means by which we may do so. World War II, at home and abroad, was as much a war of ideas as of arms—ideas which were being made to infiltrate the mind in such a manner that the victim was, for the most part, unaware of what was happening until it was too late.

Let it be recalled that World War II was the first in which ideas were dropped from the skies, over the radio waves as well as from airplanes, before the bombs themselves began to wreak their inhuman havoc. Among these ideas, explicitly as well as in disguised form, racism played a prominent part. Linking the Jews with whatever it was desired to discredit was the first step in the process of the conquest and confusion of thought. It is an old and effective device used by unscrupulous politicians for distracting the attention of the people from vital issues and from their own nefarious activities. It was no less a monster than Hitler, who stated that racial propaganda was the most powerfully disruptive idea at the service of fascism. Hitler remarked to Rauschning: "My Jews are a valuable hostage given to me by the democracies. Anti-Semitic propaganda in all countries is an almost indispensable medium for the extension of our political campaign. You will see how little time we shall need in order to upset the ideas and the criteria of the whole world, simply and purely by attacking Judaism."[1] It is a matter of recent history that in Europe the Nazis were able to impose a purely mythological dogma, first upon the Jews and then upon the Poles, a dogma which deprived all those who were not so-called "Aryans" of their civil rights and of the right to earn a living. The Poles found themselves being beaten with their own stick, for their treatment of the Jews in prewar days was based upon the same prejudices and discriminations the Germans put into effect against them.[2] We have seen, and we see today, that what may at first be practiced on a local scale may spread until it is practiced

---

[1] Rauschning, *The Voice of Destruction*, p. 236. See also Massing, *Rehearsal for Destruction;* Poliakov, *Harvest of Hate;* Tenenbaum, *Race and Reich;* Trachtenberg, *The Devil and the Jews.*

[2] It is regrettable to have to record that the late Polish government in exile, its army, and official representatives maintained these prejudices unchanged. During the occupation of their country by the Germans the Poles, generally,

nationally, and what is practiced nationally may spread until it becomes international. One nation learns from another. It is for us to decide whether it is the spirit of the racist or the spirit of democracy, of freedom and brotherhood, which is to become both national and international.

If men have acted upon ideas and beliefs which have brought the world to its present sorry state, then surely it should be clear to everyone in his proper senses that something is seriously wrong with such ideas and beliefs. And is there anywhere anyone who can for a moment entertain a doubt upon that score? If humanity is to be saved— and it is no less a matter than that—every one of us must make the greatest endeavor in his power to clarify his thoughts upon this most urgent of all problems with which we, as human beings, are today faced. We have too long taken things for granted and have lived too easily off our prejudices. If it is our privilege and our right to live and work upon this earth, then we must once more clearly recognize that with that privilege and that right is inseparably linked the obligation to make this earth an increasingly better and happier place for all who shall live on it. Toward that end it is particularly necessary at this time to be alive to the obligations of social inequality.

In the United States of America, as Thomas Jefferson put it, "this government, the best hope of man," we have every opportunity open

---

assisted the enemy in the task of maltreating and murdering the Jews. As one Pole put it, "Fortune has come to us through Hitler. He is preparing for us a Poland without Jews." For a fully documented presentation of the facts see Lestchinsky, "The Jew in Ruined Europe," *Chicago Jewish Forum*, IV (1945), 10–16. There were, however, some noble exceptions; see Dabek-Szyszko, "The Great Bor Lie," *The Protestant*, VI (1946), 12–31. Following the liberation the elimination of the Jews in Poland seems to have met with the approval of the majority of Poles. See Levin (ed.), "Journal of Kibbutz Buchenwald," *Commentary*, I (1946), 31–39. In July, 1946, a frightful anti-Semitic pogrom in the Polish village of Kielce cost the lives of forty-one Jews. The Catholic Church in Poland, even after the war, continued to play the leading role in the encouragement and maintenance of anti-Semitism. See Warsaw Correspondent, "Jews and the Catholic Church in Poland," *Jewish Chronicle* (London), 25 June 1948, p. 11. In February, 1957, Sydney Gruson, in a special communique from Warsaw to the New York *Times* (February 17, 1957) reported that Jews were leaving Poland in great numbers owing to "the raving anti-Semitism" prevalent in that country. "All concerned have conceded that terror was being used until recently against Jews, particularly in small towns."

to us to make our lives a blessing to ourselves and to all the generations which will follow us—in this great land first, and perhaps later,
by our example, in all the rest of the world. Let it not be said that
democracy is a form of government which most Americans are not
yet good enough to deserve.

Europe, the Europe from which we all escaped, whether we came
on the *Mayflower* or on a cargo vessel, shows us today where we shall
end if we think that the shape of the nose or the color of the skin has
anything to do with human values and culture. The lights in Europe
were almost all put out, one by one; extinguished by the evil breath of
bigoted and perverted men. Let us do everything in our power to
secure the lights from being dimmed here, so that we continue increasingly to live in enlightenment and to know and enjoy the benefits
of a free society, benefits which will ever increase and will—soon, let
us hope—extend to the uttermost limits of the earth.

How may we achieve this? The answer is in two words: "enlightened action." Action without a thoroughly sound basis in thought,
that is, analyzed fact, to support it is worthless, as is the soundest
thought which is not realized in action. The first is dangerous, the
second sterile. Thought without action and action without thought
eventually lead to the same disastrous results.

In the preceding pages we have examined the concept of "race"
in the light of its historical development, and we have analyzed it in
terms of the most recent and soundest scientific evidence. We have
seen how erroneous is the general conception of "race"—a conception
which presupposes the existence of different groups of mankind, each
believed to possess inborn physical and mental traits that are reflected
in differences in national outlook, culture, social behavior, and so on.

We have seen that far too great significance has been attributed to
both the physical and the mental differences existing in some degree
between different ethnic groups. Within certain broad limits we can
demonstrate the physical differences, and we can observe those of
culture and behavior. But the one thing we cannot do is to prove or
demonstrate that differences in behavior and culture have anything
to do with innate or inherited qualities.

Certainly there appear to be differences in temperament, intellectual
attitudes, and cultural behavior between ethnic groups; but there is
no reason to believe that these differences are inborn. As we have seen,
for the most part they seem to be due to differences in cultural condi-

tions, different social backgrounds, and differences in economic conditions. The acquired nature of these differences should be strongly enough indicated to us in the United States, where these differences have been given a chance to emerge into a fairly uniform character, and there has emerged, as a result, a typical American temperament or psychology, contrasting sharply with the British, French, German, and Italian psychology or temperament.

We have seen that the physical differences which exist between the varieties of mankind cannot be intelligently discussed in terms of physical or cultural superiority to one another. There are no superior or inferior groups by birth. If there are any inborn mental differences associated with the physical differences which distinguish different ethnic groups, then science has been unable to discover them. Physical differences are purely external and are only superficially associated with cultural differences existing or imputed. Yet these external differences provide a convenient peg upon which to hang all sorts of imagined internal differences, moral, intellectual, mental, and emotional. In this way physical differences become the basis for social discrimination and the creation of social inequalities. But science is aware of no such association between external and internal characters, except, of course, such as are socially produced.

In our own society such differences of behavior and character as seem to exist between ethnic groups are due principally to inequalities in the opportunities for social and economic betterment which have been afforded them, not to unalterable inborn or hereditary differences. No ethnic group has a monopoly of good or bad hereditary qualities. The existence of any ethnic group at the present time is proof of the fact that it possesses a majority of desirable qualities, otherwise it could not have survived to the present time.

Democracy, like charity, begins at home. Give every ethnic group within our democracy an equal social opportunity, and it may be predicted that one will find between minds only such differences as now exist between individuals of the same ethnic group who have enjoyed equal cultural opportunities. Every human being, whatever his ethnic affiliation, differs from every other in his make-up and has had a somewhat different inheritance and different opportunities. Would not this be a very dull world were we all poured to the same mould? As things are, the great reservoir of diversity upon which we can draw will always serve to enliven and enrich our interest in life.

There need be no fear that a leveling process will ensue if all people, without discrimination, were afforded equal opportunities. Education increases differences—it does not diminish them. We may here recall the words of the great educational psychologist Professor E. L. Thorndike: "To the real work of man,—the increase of achievement through improvement of the environment,—the influence of heredity offers no barrier."

The important differences are not differences in "racial" averages, but between persons; and it is because of the existence of individual differences, which have little or nothing to do with "race," that a true democracy must aim to devote its attention to individual differences regardless of whether the individual has a narrow nose or a broad one. A democracy must recognize differences and make every possible allowance for them—the differences which individuals exhibit, not as members of different ethnic groups but as individual citizens, individuals differing in innumerable ways and capable of making individualized contributions of all sorts to our common culture. It is for this reason that democracy must be actively concerned with the task of affording every individual, regardless of group affiliation, adequate opportunities for self-development, so that the best that every individual has it within him to give shall be given, both for his own happiness and for that of his fellows. We may here recall the words of a great American, Charles Sumner: "The true greatness of nations is in those qualities which constitute the greatness of the individual." In a speech made in the U.S. Senate February 6, 1866, pleading for the granting of civil rights to the freedmen, Sumner said: "The populations of the earth—embracing Caucasians, Mongolians, Malays, Africans, and Americans—is about thirteen hundred million, of whom only three hundred and seventy-five million are 'white men,' or little more than one-fourth, so that in claiming exclusive rights for 'white men,' you degrade nearly three-quarters of the human family, made in the 'image of God' and declared to be of 'one blood' while you sanction a case offensive to religion, and oligarchy inconsistent with Republican government, and a monopoly which has the whole world as its footstool.

"Against this assumption, I protest with mind, soul, and heart. It is false in religion, false to statesmanship, and false in economy. . . . You cannot deny these rights without impiety. And so has God linked the material welfare with national duty, you cannot deny these rights without peril to the Republic."

The freedman's civil rights were written into the law, but the freedman has yet to be permitted those civil rights in his everyday life, over the length and breadth of the land.

It was Woodrow Wilson who said: "America is not anything if it consists of each of us. It is something only if it consists of all of us; and it can consist of all of us only as our spirits are banded together in a common enterprise. That common enterprise is the enterprise of liberty and justice and right."

There are no minority groups in America, except those that bigots and racists create. America is a nation made up of the members of almost every ethnic group and every religion, all of which have contributed toward its development. All of us are either the descendants of immigrants or ourselves recent immigrants, and those who have voluntarily chosen to be Americans have often had occasion to remark that they had rather be foreign-born Americans than American-born foreigners. The important thing is to be an American, without being narrowly nationalistic, and to grant all Americans the right to their Americanism, which implies freedom of religion, freedom of speech, and freedom of opportunity. "As I would not be a *slave,* so I would not be a *master.* This expresses my idea of democracy. . . . Whatever differs from this, to the extent of the difference, is no democracy . . ." Those are the simple words of Abraham Lincoln.

Many Americans, when they speak of democracy, make a pretense of a creed in which they do not actually believe. "One nation indivisible, under God, with liberty and justice for all." For the Negro? For Mexican Americans? For the American Indian? Not to mention other "minority" groups. The truth is that many Americans are quite alienated from the creeds that, with incantation and with ritual, on ceremonial occasions, they identify with the essence of Americanism. But these are merely ceremonial credos, the smoke of incense offered up before an empty shrine, for there is nothing in those credos in which they, in fact, believe. On their treatment of the American Negro most Americans stand indicted before the bar of humanity. As Secretary of State Dean Rusk, himself from the State of Georgia, wrote to Attorney General Kennedy on May 29, 1961: "The efforts of the United States Government in international affairs to build the kind of world we want to live in . . . cannot be divorced from our ability to achieve these same purposes for all the people of our own country. The principle of racial equality and nondiscrimination are imperatives of the American society with its many racial strains. In the degree to which we ourselves practice these principles our voice will carry conviction . . . in the conduct of our foreign relations. . . . American actions which fall short of Constitutional standards safeguarding individual freedom and dignity prejudice our position before the world."

Indeed, racism is American society's most exposed weakness. It is America's greatest domestic failure, and the worst of its international handicaps. As Professor Harold R. Isaacs has said, racism "is so highly visible that when hundreds of millions of people all around the world look in our direction they often seem to be able to see little else. . . . The world's image of Americans as white racists is threatening to blot out the image of Americans as builders of the dream of the freest and most open society ever organized by man. Worse, it is blurring the image and sapping the strength of the very idea of the open society itself." [3]

Racism has damaged the reputation of Americans as the defenders of individual rights, and has provided the detractors of America with all the material they need to see to it that the image sticks. Racism is no longer a domestic issue, it has become a deeply involved problem of international relations, and a decisive element in the newly developing nations' opinion of the United States. When a Nigerian diplomat was refused service in a Charlottesville, Virginia, restaurant in December, 1960, the National Council of Nigeria and the Cameroons issued a statement calling the United States "a country devoid of respect for human dignity, a country with completely blank racial policy, a country which still lives in the dark ages, has no claim to leadership of free men." [4]

Incidents of this sort, not to mention Little Rock[5] and Mississippi,

---

[3] Isaacs, "American Race Relations and the United States Image in World Affairs," *Human Relations,* X (1962), 266–80; *Idem, The New World of Negro Americans.*

[4] Debrah, "The Effect of the Existence of Segregation in the U.S. on the American Image in Africa," U.S. National Commission for UNESCO (Press Release, Nat. Conf. 8/18, October 25, 1961).

[5] Bates, *The Long Shadow of Little Rock.*

have done more damage to the prestige and standing of the United States in the eyes of the whole world than all the billions of dollars we are pouring into Foreign Aid can ever hope to repair. One Governor Faubus or one Governor Barnett is worth more in propaganda value to the Russians than anything they themselves could supply. But not content with our domestic failures, we export them abroad. In December, 1962, traveling in a United States Army Air Force plane, at the expense of the American taxpayer, Senator Ellender, "Democrat," of the State of Louisiana, delivered himself of the most depreciatory remarks concerning the abilities of Africans to govern themselves. At a news conference held in Southern Rhodesia Senator Ellender announced to the press that "The average African is incapable of leadership except through the assistance of Europeans." [6]

What can Africans think of the United States when its "democratic" senators representing the American people utter such insulting racist nonsense? What they think is clear and unequivocal.

America's historic future, its very survival as a great power in the world, depends upon its solution of the race problem. It is on that issue that the United States will ultimately stand or fall as a power in the world. The equality of man to the rights of development, fulfillment, and citizenship is today no longer a pious wish—it is a practical political necessity, and a condition of civilized survival.

The image the United States presents to the world is not an abstraction, but the extension of the conduct of its citizens. Every American represents America, and it is his individual conduct that is held responsible for racism in America. Whether responsible or not for racism, every American, as an American, must make himself responsible for the elimination of racism, for racism is inhuman, ethically wrong, and constitutionally intolerable.

Stressing superficial differences between people only helps to maintain an illusion in our minds that there may be more fundamental differences behind them. What we, as informed and enlightened citizens living under a democratic form of government, ought to do is to stress the fundamental kinship of all mankind; to stress the likenesses that we all bear to one another; to recognize the essential unity of all mankind in the very differences which individuals of all ethnic groups display; and thus build that genuine democracy which is

---

[6] *Time,* December 14, 1962, p. 22.

based on a unity of spirit in a diversity of minds. If we would preserve our unique differences, we must acknowledge our similarities. For "as we learn to see the common humanity showing through the accidental and finite differences in men we come to a practical recognition of human equality and learn to have a concern and regard for all mankind." [7] The fact that we are human beings is infinitely more important than all the peculiarities which may distinguish human beings from one another.

Every political system is capable of some improvement, and our democracy is no exception. We stand to profit immediately by giving up acting on "racial" mythology—the "racial" mythology that lurks in the minds of so many of us and contributes so much to social friction. We cannot, however, change the conditions of social friction merely by changing our minds. Changing our minds often amounts to no more than rearranging our prejudices. As members of an unregimented thinking democracy, we should study these things in order to keep them from adding to social friction, realizing that we have been and are being snobs and that there will be a price to pay if we go on being snobs. Let us by acting upon such facts and their interpretation as have been presented in the pages of this book afford the benefits of our democracy to all who live in it, so that we may truly "promote the general welfare and secure the blessings of liberty to ourselves and our posterity." This is the principle which is enshrined in the Constitution which created the government of the United States.

American democracy, at least in theory, is built upon the fundamental principle that all people should enjoy the same prerogatives and privileges because, by and large, they all possess the potentialities which would enable them to benefit by them, individually and mutually, and this is the first and greatest of the principles laid down in the Declaration of Independence, a document which represents the noblest and truest declaration of the principles of human liberty ever penned. Science and humane thought support this principle to the full, and it has been well called the genetic basis for democracy. The premise of racism, on the other hand, constitutes a negation of the very principle upon which the American Commonwealth is

---

[7] Lindsay, *The Good and the Clever*, p. 18.

founded. The test of democracy in the United States must be measured by the degree to which it succeeds in applying the principles of the Declaration of Independence to the lives of all Americans. Democracy means cooperative living. It is a way of life in which men and women of different complexions, creeds, cultural origins, and cutoms can live together with mutual respect, understanding, and cooperation.

The flaring of latent "racial" enmities in times of economic stress is an association of events which has never been more painfully evident than it is today. Everywhere in the world under conditions of economic stress "race" prejudice has become a powerful weapon with which so-called "minority" groups have been attacked. Physical and cultural differences are seized upon and made the basis for group antagonism and discrimination. Trivial things, such as differences in manners, polish, social backgrounds, religious beliefs, and so forth, which if sympathetically understood would be points of interest and value, become the bases of distrust. Just as a child runs to its mother as a familiar refuge when in difficulties, so most of us run to our own group when we feel insecure, and we fancy that anyone not of our own group is a bogeyman and the cause of all our troubles. In a democracy there should be no place for such immature conduct; nor should there be for the conditions which give rise to it, namely, improper education and economic insecurity. We can remedy these conditions. We can improve education and social and economic conditions so that all men may share in them equally. The power lies within our own hands; let us, then, use it.

We are the result of the mixing of many different ethnic groups; every one of us is a much-mixed alloy, having all the added strength and qualities which the alloy possesses as compared with the unalloyed metal. Let us use that strength for the common good, so that the many may become truly one.

Equality is the condition of freedom. It is a fundamental tenet of democracy that it must balance the interests of all its component groups and citizens. As we have seen, there is nothing in the nature of any group, ethnic or otherwise, which gives it less weight in the balance of democracy than any other. That being the case, we must recognize and act upon this first principle set out in the Declaration of Independence "that all men are created equal, that they are endowed by their Creator with certain unalienable Rights, that among these are

Life, Liberty, and the pursuit of Happiness. That to secure these rights, Governments are instituted among Men, deriving their just powers from the consent of the governed."

After almost two centuries science joins hands with humanity to ask Americans whether they will accept the challenge of those words.

18

What Is the Solution?

THE PURPOSE OF this book has been to clarify the reader's thinking upon the much-vexed and usually tendentiously discussed problem of "race," to induce the reader to rethink his basic convictions regarding human relations, and to present the whole problem in such a way as to encourage him to draw his own conclusions concerning the kind of solution or solutions that would be most effective in solving the "race" problem.

In the preceding chapters we have discussed and considered some of the "causes" of the "race" problem. It would seem evident that the removal of the conditions which give rise to these causes would suggest itself as the most obvious approach to the solution of the problem. If we eliminate these conditions, we shall eliminate the effects which they produce.

We saw that the term "race" itself, as it is generally applied to man, is scientifically without justification, and that as commonly used the term corresponds to nothing in reality. We saw that the word is predominantly an emotionally loaded one, and we were able to trace something of its rise and development in what has invariably been a background or matrix of strong feeling and prejudiced thought. Men may pretend that they are masters of reason when they are in fact creatures of emotion. It was Oliver Goldsmith who wrote:

> Logicians have but ill defin'd
> As rational the human kind;
> Reason, they say, belongs to man,
> But let them prove it if they can.

Reason and intellect play a minor role in the lives of men, and what part they do play is often confused and fragmented. Symonds, in a study on the methods by which teachers solve personal problems[1] found that "very few of the larger problems of life are adjusted to through reason. The intellect is used rarely by persons in meeting the larger problems and issues of life and few individuals are able to use their reasoning powers except in limited situations. The large part of adjustment is carried on through the impulses, emotions," and similar mechanisms.[2]

As Oscar Wilde so wryly remarked: "I wonder who it was defined man as a rational animal. It was the most premature definition ever given. Man is many things but he is not rational." Or as another poet, Walter de la Mare, put it, *"raw homo,* that is, with little admixture of *sapiens."*

Sapience here lies in frankly facing the fact that most people are emotional creatures who use their minds mostly in order to support their prejudices. Prejudice is a passion with a logic all its own. It is of little use attempting to correct this logic by demonstrating its falsity, for it is not the logic which is the cause of the prejudice, but the prejudice which is the cause of the false logic. Hence, we would be more effectively employed in trying to understand the sources of this prejudice than in hectoring the insecure logicians. All of us have prejudices of some sort. The important thing is to recognize that we do, and do something about freeing ourselves from them, or if that is not possible, controlling them.

It is said that "The truth shall make ye free." But most men wish neither to know the truth nor to be free.[3] Most men wish to know the kind of things that will support them in the culture of which they are a part. Whatever contributes to that end is "true." That is their pragmatic test of truth. It is all too readily understandable. Men live by the values they learn from their culture. What teachers in the classroom and instructors in the lecture hall may tell them has its importance, but what matters most is what actually goes on in the world. We may preach equality, but if we practice discrimination the hypocritical lesson will not fail to be learned. What is done, *not* what

---

[1] Symonds, "How Teachers Solve Personal Problems," *Journal of Educational Research,* II (1941), 80–93.

[2] Symonds, *The Dynamics of Human Adjustment,* pp. xii–xiii.

[3] Fromm, *Escape from Freedom;* Montagu, "Escape from Freedom," *Psychiatry,* V (1942), 122–29; Montagu, *Man in Process;* Montagu, *The Humanization of Man.*

is said, is the reality in which most men believe. A culture lives what it believes; that is, it acts out what it really believes in, it does not live by what it aspires to be. Men will fight to the death for what they believe, but not for the ideals in which they have no faith. These they will combat if they conflict with their own conception of reality. For the support of such conceptions men do not generally require the sanction of scientifically established facts. Emotions, prejudices, and metaphysics are usually quite sufficient. As Stephen Spender has remarked: "Very few people in the world's history have died for the sake of 'being definite,' thinking clearly, and behaving morally without the background of a belief in any metaphysical system." As we have already seen, "race" is the metaphysical system which for most men constitutes such a conception of reality. The child picks up attitudes long before he becomes familiar with the facts. It is difficult to convince a child that there is no such thing as "race," nor can one successfully explain the facts to him, however simply and clearly one may present them, when outside the classroom, on the street, at home, everywhere about him, he sees that "race" is a "real" thing. To make him see that this "real" thing has been arbitrarily created would be a reasonably simple matter in the hands of a good teacher, but whatever he did would be largely undone by the world outside the classroom unless conditions outside the classroom were favorable, which, as we know, they generally are not.

I would not for this reason lightly regard the teaching of the facts about "race" in the schools; on the other hand, I recommend such teaching unequivocally and unreservedly.[4] It should, however, be made clear here that we must not expect too much from such attempts at education in the schools, for the so-called "education" received at school is only a small part of that larger education which men receive from direct contact with the world. It is the world men live in, not the school, and what the world teaches that are to them real. What the school teaches is largely unreal and theoretical. The three *r*'s are

---

[4] It has been shown, for example, that college graduates are, on the whole, better informed about the facts of "race" and more understanding in the matter of ethnic relations than high school graduates; the latter, in turn, rank higher in these respects than grammar school graduates. Here, then, is good evidence of the value of *general* education in producing better intergroup understanding. See Allport, "Is Intergroup Education Possible?" *Harvard Educational Review*, XV (1945), 83–86.

in many instances the only concrete things with which it leaves them. The fourth, and most important of the *r*'s is omitted, *relations,* human relations.

This is the sad and tragic state to which we have come. The dissociation between what is taught in the schools and what is taught by real life has become so glaring that the schools and all who are associated with them have fallen into something like contempt, since as measured by the standard of successful achievement in the "real world" they do not measure up at all. "That's all right for a school child" is a common saying, or "That's academic."

Children learn early that "race" prejudice, unlike other antisocial behavior, is socially sanctioned and has the approval of "respectable" people.[5]

It is, or should be, clear, then, that education in the schools is not enough, since what is taught in the schools is not what men believe, and men will not act upon what they do not believe. As the seventeenth-century Portuguese philosopher Francisco Sanchez put it, "ideas taught do not have greater power than they receive from those who are taught." What, then, must we do to persuade men to implement the right ideas with the power of their convictions? To present to them the right ideas is only half the task; we must also provide them with the proper supports for such ideas and eliminate the conditions which render the support of such ideas difficult. If we can remove those conditions and substitute others for them, we shall have made possible a substantial change in the beliefs of men and in many of the notions upon which they customarily act.

Do we know what those conditions are? I think we do, at least a goodly number of them. We have seen that frustration and aggression are linked factors which play an important role in preparing the individual personality for "racial" hostility. But we also saw that neither frustration nor aggression leads to "racial" hostility unless the conditions are such as to favor such a development. These conditions are always artificially constructed in economic, political, and social frameworks wherein "racial" hostility can be used to advantage by the individual or by the group within that framework.

[5] Allen *et al.,* "Social Awareness in a City High School," *Intercultural Educational News,* VIII (1946), 1–7; Radke and Trager, "Children's Perceptions of the Social Roles of Negroes and Whites," *Journal of Psychology,* XXIX (1950), 1–33; Trager and Yarrow, *They Learn What They Live.*

Clearly, any culture or part of a culture which finds it necessary to create and maintain hostilities between different groups of men, instead of encouraging their social development by mutual exchange and cooperation of interests to the advantage of all, is sick. For the great principle of biological as well as of social development is cooperation, not antagonism.

We have already seen that modern science has demonstrated that there is strong reason to believe that cooperation and altruism have played more important roles in the evolution of animal species, but especially of man, than have the egoistic forces in nature. A healthy competition is desirable in any society; but it must be a competition "with," not a competition "against," it must be a competition to cooperate, to cooperate in the interest not alone of the individual or his particular group but in the interest of all society, and not only of society as a whole but of all men everywhere. No man can be free until all his fellow men are free. Race prejudice arises from man's failure to make use of his own potentialities, particularly his powers to relate himself to other beings, to establish human ties. Those who exploit their society for their own interest, whether they are aware of it or not, are working against the interest of their society. They produce imbalances, top-heaviness, disoperative rather than cooperative conditions. Obviously, where self-interest is the dominant motive of the individuals in a society, the society will be characterized by a fundamental spirit of disorganization. In such a society the individual thinks of himself first, of society last. He will so order his conduct as to attain his ends as quickly as possible without any concern for the consequences to society. If Negroes or members of any other ethnic or so-called "minority" group can be utilized, to their disadvantage, in the attainment of those ends, there are pitifully few individuals in our culture who would hesitate not to use them so—the Declaration of Independence, the Bill of Rights, the teaching of the churches, of the schools, and common human decency notwithstanding.

Who is to blame for this sorry condition? Surely not the common man! When he leaves school and enters the workaday world and attempts to behave in a humane manner he soon discovers that he is not likely to prosper. In order to survive he finds it necessary to adapt himself to the conditions of life as he finds them—which he usually does. In doing so he fails both himself and his society, for, let us ask ourselves, to what is it that we adapt ourselves? Without enumerating the unhappy catalogue, we may answer at once: to conditions as we find them. We accept and adapt ourselves to evil as if it were a good, to the principle of expediency rather than that of integrity; to the principle of competition rather than cooperation. Are these responses to the challenges of being human a reflection of a failure of nerve, of courage? I do not think so. On the other hand, I believe that most men accept the world for what it is, believing that it is so ordered by some immutable power and that things are as they are because that is the way they are, and little, if anything, can be done to change them. "You can't change human nature" is the common expression of this viewpoint.

If what I have said is true, then our only hope lies in education of the right sort. If we can succeed in reorganizing our system of education from top to bottom, making our principal purpose the cultivation of human beings living in one great cooperative enterprise with other human beings, we shall have gone a long way toward achieving a new society.

Our educational systems have not, in fact, been educational systems at all; they are really systems of instruction. We instruct, we do not educate; and otherwise we leave the individual to shift as well he may for himself. We leave our children with information, *not* with knowledge; we teach them to act before we teach them to reflect. Instruction in reading, writing, and arithmetic does not constitute a sufficient preparation for living with complex human beings in a rather complex world. In order to live happily and efficiently in such a world it is necessary to understand not only the nature of human beings but also how they came to be as we now find them, both culturally and physically. Surely our first and last task in education should be to inspire our growing citizens with a full understanding and appreciation of humanity; in what it means to be human.[6] The facts, the spiritual teachings, and the examples are all ready to our hand. What is to prevent us from weaving them into the pattern of the lives which we have in our making? School boards, vested interests, and corrupt politicians are strong forces in our society; but stronger forces than they have been moved in the past and will be moved again. There are no irresistible forces.

---

[6] See Montagu, *On Being Human;* Montagu, *The Direction of Human Development;* Montagu, *Man in Process;* Montagu, *The Humanization of Men.*

It is fatuous to assert that human beings live in the type of society they deserve. The fact is that most human beings have little to do with the making of the society in which they live. They are brought up in it and generally accept it more or less unquestioningly. They may suffer to some extent themselves and be the cause of suffering in others; but they accept this kind of suffering as inevitable—in the nature of things. Their social consciousnesses are structured in terms of their culture.

How, then, under such conditions, can we ever hope to solve the "race" problem? Obviously, by altering those conditions to such an extent as to produce a profound awareness in every person of his proper place in society, to make him aware of the fact that he must become an active, not a passive, instrument in the government of his society and that government can be, and must be, for the benefit of all the people without discrimination of color, class, or creed.

One cannot teach human beings these things merely by uttering them. They can only be made part of an attitude of mind if they are understood at an early age as part of a whole integrated system of education in humanity, in human relations.

The facts of life assume a meaning only when they are related to action in living. The meaning of a word lies in the action it produces. We can teach children to believe in humanity, and we can teach them to act upon what they believe. We can teach them the truth about the present character of our society, and equip them to play their part in improving it, instead of subtly priming them to support the status quo.

To teach children the facts about the meaning of the many varieties of mankind is alone insufficient; as I have said, such teaching can achieve little unless it becomes part of a planned, integrated, complete experience in the meaning and significance of humanity.

There have been few attempts to teach children to become human beings, and yet that is what our schools should principally be doing. Our schools must be converted into institutes for the teaching of the art and science of human relations, learning the art of being a human being, and the reasons why it is necessary to be one. "Race" problems are essentially problems in human relations, and "race" problems are but one of the many indications of our failure in human relations. The necessary change can be brought about by the educators of this and other lands. It is the educators of the young who are the true, unacknowledged legislators of the world. The opportunity beckons to them to bring into existence, by their example and by their teaching, a new world of humanity. Surely it is unnecessary for our educators to wait until they are forced into action by the pressure of public opinion. It is educators who produce the trained incapacity for humane living for which the parents have usually well and truly laid the foundations. It is the educators, and the parents, who are capable of changing all this, of making truly humane beings of the wards in their charge. The enterprise must be a joint one, between parents and teachers. But where the parents have failed the teacher should not also fail. Parents of the coming generations must be taught to love their children, to endow them with that sense of inner security which will fortify them against all exterior assaults upon their integrity, and by loving them thus teach them to love all others. But this is where teachers must take the lead. It is this which they must teach those who are to become parents and those who are already parents. We shall have neither peace nor harmony in the world until we have made human beings with peace and harmony in themselves. It has been estimated that it costs about $150,000 to kill a man in modern warfare; we could make an almost perfect human being for considerably less. Would it not be worth trying?

How shall we try? What are the specifications for the blueprint for action? What the educators must do is, I think, obvious: they must become aware of their strategic advantage, and they must, alone or in cooperation, take it upon themselves to reorganize the education of the young along the lines I have indicated; to teach humanity first and to regard all other education as subordinate to this. "The best place to think through and practice intelligent human relations is in the classroom. The best laboratory for human engineering is in the school room where democracy has its best opportunity and its greatest challenge." [7]

As for a blueprint for action, each teacher must work that out for himself in adjustment to the local situation which he knows best. Approaches to the solution of the "race" problem must be made at all levels, but ultimately it is the individual teacher upon whom our reliance must be placed. Good teachers are more important than

---

[7] Bishop, "Democracy Demands Co-operative Living," *Education,* LXVIII (1946), 12–18.

anything they teach. An integrated program in human relations throughout the school system is indispensably necessary, a program to include teachers as well as pupils, but it does not have to start that way. It can commence with a small group of teachers, and failing such a group, with but a single one. Let such a one say to himself: "I am only one; but I am one. I cannot do everything; but I can do something. What I can do I ought to do; and, by the grace of God, *I will*."

The UNESCO Statements on Race

TWO STATEMENTS ON RACE were issued by UNESCO. The first was largely the work of a group of social scientists, the second was the product of a group of physical anthropologists and geneticists. The first Statement was published on July 18, 1950, under the title "The UNESCO Statement by Experts on Race Problems," and the second was published July 15, 1952, under the title "Statement on the Nature of Race and Race Differences—by Physical Anthropologists and Geneticists, September 1952." In conversation one would refer to the first as "The Statement on Race" and to the second as "Statement on the Nature of Race." As the reader will perceive, there is marked agreement between the social and the natural scientists.

Most of the members on the first committee would, I believe, now replace the term "Division" in the first Statement with the term "Major Group" from the second Statement.

UNESCO STATEMENT ON RACE—BY SOCIAL SCIENTISTS, JULY 1950

1. Scientists have reached general agreement in recognizing that mankind is one: that all men belong to the same species, *Homo sapiens*. It is further generaly agreed among scientists that all men are probably derived from the same common stock; and that such differences as exist between different groups of mankind are due to the operation of evolutionary factors of differentiation such as isolation, the drift and random fixation of the material particles which control heredity (the genes), changes in the structure of these particles, hybridization, and natural selection. In these ways groups have arisen

361

of varying stability and degree of differentiation which have been classified in different ways for different purposes.

2. From the biological standpoint, the species *Homo sapiens* is made up of a number of populations, each one of which differs from the others in the frequency of one or more genes. Such genes, responsible for the hereditary differences between men, are always few when compared to the whole genetic constitution of man and to the vast number of genes common to all human beings regardless of the population to which they belong. This means that the likenesses among men are far greater than their differences.

3. A race, from the biological standpoint, may therefore be defined as one of the group of populations constituting the species *Homo sapiens*. These populations are capable of interbreeding with one another but, by virtue of the isolating barriers which in the past kept them more or less separated, exhibit certain physical differences as a result of their somewhat different biological histories. These represent variations, as it were, on a common theme.

4. In short, the term "race" designates a group or population characterized by some concentrations, relative as to frequency and distribution, of hereditary particles (genes) or physical characters, which appear, fluctuate, and often disappear in the course of time by reason of geographic and/or cultural isolation. The varying manifestations of these traits in different populations are perceived in different ways by each group. What is perceived is largely preconceived, so that each group arbitrarily tends to misinterpret the variability which occurs as a fundamental difference which separates that group from all others.

5. These are the scientific facts. Unfortunately, however, when most people use the term "race" they do not do so in the sense above defined. To most people, a race is any group of people whom they choose to describe as a race. Thus, many national, religious, geographic, linguistic or cultural groups have, in such loose usage, been called "race," when obviously Americans are not a race, nor are Englishmen, nor Frenchmen, nor any other national group. Catholics, Protestants, Moslems, and Jews are not races, nor are groups who speak English or any other language thereby definable as a race, people who live in Iceland or England or India are not races; nor are people who are culturally Turkish or Chinese, or the like thereby describable as races.

6. National, religious, geographic, linguistic and cultural groups

do not necessarily coincide with racial groups; and the cultural traits of such groups have no demonstrated genetic connection with racial traits. Because serious errors of this kind are habitually committed when the term "race" is used in popular parlance, it would be better when speaking of human races to drop the term "race" altogether and speak of *ethnic groups*.

7. Now what has the scientist to say about the groups of mankind which may be recognized at the present time? Human races can be and have been differently classified by different anthropologists, but at the present time most anthropologists agree in classifying the greater part of present-day mankind into three major divisions, as follows:

The Mongoloid Division
The Negroid Division
The Caucasoid Division

The biological processes which the classifier has here embalmed, as it were, are dynamic, not static. These divisions were not the same in the past as they are at present, and there is every reason to believe that they will change in the future.

8. Many sub-groups or ethnic groups within these divisions have been described. There is no general agreement upon their number, and in any event most ethnic groups have not yet been either studied or described by the physical anthropologists.

9. Whatever classification the anthropologist makes of man, he never includes mental characteristics as part of those classifications. It is now generally recognized that intelligence tests do not in themselves enable us to differentiate safely between what is due to innate capacity and what is the result of environmental influences, training and education. Wherever it has been possible to make allowances for differences in environmental opportunities, the tests have shown essential similarity in mental characters among all human groups. In short, given similar degrees of cultural opportunity to realize their potentialities, the average achievement of the members of each ethnic group is about the same. The scientific investigations of recent years fully support the dictum of Confucius (551–478 B.C.) "Men's natures are alike; it is their habits that carry them far apart."

10. The scientific material available to us at present does not justify the conclusion that inherited genetic differences are a major factor in producing the differences between the cultures and cultural achievements of different peoples or groups. It does indicate, how-

ever, that the history of the cultural experience which each group
has undergone is the major factor in explaining such differences. The
one trait which above all others has been at a premium in the evolution of men's mental characters has been educability, plasticity. This
is a trait which all human beings possess. It is, indeed, a species character of *Homo sapiens*.

11. So far as temperament is concerned, there is no definite evidence that there exist inborn differences between human groups.
There is evidence that whatever group differences of the kind there
might be are greatly over-ridden by the individual differences, and
by the differences springing from environmental factors.

12. As for personality and character, these may be considered
raceless. In every human group a rich variety of personality and
character types will be found, and there is no reason for believing
that any human group is richer than any other in these respects.

13. With respect to race-mixture, the evidence points unequivocally to the fact that this has been going on from the earliest times.
Indeed, one of the chief processes of race-formation and race-extinc-
tion or absorption is by means of hybridization between races or
ethnic groups. Furthermore, no convincing evidence has been ad-
duced that race-mixture of itself produces biologically bad effects.
Statements that human hybrids frequently show undesirable traits,
both physically and mentally, physical disharmonies and mental degeneracies, are not supported by the facts. There is, therefore, no
biological justification for prohibiting intermarriage between persons
of different ethnic groups.

14. The biological fact of race and the myth of "race" should be
distinguished, for all practical social purposes "race" is not so much
a biological phenomenon as a social myth. The myth of "race" has
created an enormous amount of human and social damage. In recent
years it has taken a heavy toll in human lives and caused untold
suffering. It still prevents the normal development of millions of
human beings and deprives civilization of the effective co-operation
of productive minds. The biological differences between ethnic groups
should be disregarded from the standpoint of social acceptance and
social action. The unity of mankind from both the biological and
social viewpoints is the main thing. To recognize this and to act
accordingly is the first requirement of modern man. It is but to
recognize what a great biologist wrote in 1875: "As man advances in

civilization, and small tribes are united into larger communities, the simplest reason would tell each individual that he ought to extend his social instincts and sympathies to all the members of the same nation, though personally unknown to him. This point being once reached, there is only an artificial barrier to prevent his sympathies extending to the men of all nations and races." These are the words of Charles Darwin in *The Descent of Man* (2nd ed., 1875, pp. 187–188). And, indeed, the whole of human history shows that a co-operative spirit is not only natural to men, but more deeply rooted than any self-seeking tendencies. If this were not so we should not see the growth of integration and organization of his communities which the centuries and the millennia plainly exhibit.

15. We now have to consider the bearing of these statements on the problem of human equality. It must be asserted with the utmost emphasis that equality as an ethical principle in no way depends upon the assertion that human beings are in fact equal in endowment. Obviously individuals in all ethnic groups vary greatly among themselves in endowment. Nevertheless, the characteristics in which human groups differ from one another are often exaggerated and used as a basis for questioning the validity of equality in the ethical sense. For this purpose we have thought it worth while to set out in a formal manner what is at present scientifically established concerning individual and group differences.

(1) In matters of race, the only characteristics which anthropologists can effectively use as a basis for classifications are physical and physiological.

(2) According to present knowledge there is no proof that the groups of mankind differ in their innate mental characteristics, whether in respect to intelligence or temperament. The scientific evidence indicates that the range of mental capacities in all ethnic groups is much the same.

(3) Historical and sociological studies support the view that genetic differences are not of importance in determining the social and cultural differences between different groups of *Homo sapiens,* and that the social and cultural *changes* in different groups have, in the main, been independent of *changes* in inborn constitution. Vast social changes have occurred which were not in any way connected with changes in racial type.

(4) There is no evidence that race mixture as such produces bad

results from the biological point of view. The social results of race mixture whether for good or ill are to be traced to social factors.

(5) All normal human beings are capable of learning to share in a common life, to understand the nature of mutual service and reciprocity, and to respect social obligations and contracts. Such biological differences as exist between members of different ethnic groups have no relevance to problems of social and political organization, moral life and communication between human beings.

Lastly, biological studies lend support to the ethic of universal brotherhood; for man is born with drives toward co-operation, and unless those drives are satisfied, men and nations alike fall ill. Man is born a social being who can reach his fullest development only through interaction with his fellows. The denial at any point of this social bond between men and man brings with it disintegration. In this sense, every man is his brother's keeper. For every man is a piece of the continent, a part of the main, because he is involved in mankind.

Original statement drafted at Unesco House, Paris, by the following experts:

Professor Ernest Beaglehole, *New Zealand*.
Professor Juan Comas, *Mexico*.
Professor L. A. Costa Pinto, *Brazil*.
Professor Franklin Frazier, *United States*.
Professor Morris Ginsberg, *United Kingdom*.
Dr. Humayun Kabir, *India*.
Professor Claude Levi-Strauss, *France*.
Professor Ashley Montagu, *United States* (Rapporteur).

Text revised by Professor Ashley Montagu, after criticisms submitted by Professors Hadley Cantril, E. G. Conklin, Gunnar Dahlberg, Theodosius Dobzhansky, L. C. Dunn, Donald Hager, Julian S. Huxley, Otto Klineberg, Wilbert Moore, H. J. Muller, Gunnar Myrdal, Joseph Needham.

STATEMENT ON THE NATURE OF RACE AND RACE DIFFERENCES BY PHYSICAL ANTHROPOLOGISTS AND GENETICISTS
SEPTEMBER 1952

1. Scientists are generally agreed that all men living today belong to a single species, *Homo sapiens,* and are derived from a common

stock, even though there is some dispute as to when and how different human groups diverged from this common stock.

The concept of race is unanimously regarded by anthropologists as a classificatory device providing a zoological frame within which the various groups of mankind may be arranged and by means of which studies of evolutionary processes can be facilitated. In its anthropological sense, the word "race" should be reserved for groups of mankind possessing well-developed and primarily heritable physical differences from other groups. Many populations can be so classified but, because of the complexity of human history, there are also many populations which cannot easily be fitted into a racial classification.

2. Some of the physical differences between human groups are due to differences in hereditary constitution and some to differences in the environments in which they have been brought up. In most cases, both influences have been at work. The science of genetics suggests that the hereditary differences among populations of a single species are the results of the action of two sets of processes. On the one hand, the genetic composition of isolated populations is constantly but gradually being altered by natural selection and by occasional changes (mutations) in the material particles (genes) which control heredity. Populations are also affected by fortuitous changes in gene frequency and by marriage customs. On the other hand, crossing is constantly breaking down the differentiations so set up. The new mixed populations, in so far as they, in turn, become isolated, are subject to the same processes, and these may lead to further changes. Existing races are merely the result, considered at a particular moment in time, of the total effect of such processes on the human species. The hereditary characters to be used in the classification of human groups, the limits of their variation within these groups, and thus the extent of the classificatory sub-divisions adopted may legitimately differ according to the scientific purpose in view.

3. National, religious, geographical, linguistic and cultural groups do not necessarily coincide with racial groups; and the cultural traits of such groups have no demonstrated connection with racial traits. Americans are not a race, nor are Frenchmen, nor Germans; nor *ipso facto* is any other national group. Moslems and Jews are no more races than are Roman Catholics and Protestants; nor are people who live in Iceland or Britain or India, or who speak English or any other language, or who are culturally Turkish or Chinese and the like,

thereby describable as races. The use of the term "race" in speaking of such groups may be a serious error, but is one which is habitually committed.

4. Human races can be, and have been classified in different ways by different anthropologists. Most of them agree in classifying the greater part of existing mankind into at least three large units, which may be called major groups (in French *grand races,* in German *Hauptrassen*). Such a classification does not depend on any single physical character, nor does, for example, skin colour by itself necessarily distinguish one major group from another. Furthermore, so far as it has been possible to analyze them, the differences in physical structure which distinguish one major group from another give no support to popular notions that any general "superiority" or "inferiority" which are sometimes implied in referring to these groups.

Broadly speaking, individuals belonging to different major groups of mankind are distinguishable by virtue of their physical characters, but individual members, or small groups, belonging to different races within the same major group are usually not so distinguishable. Even the major groups grade into each other, and the physical traits by which they and the races within them are characterized overlap considerably. With respect to most, if not all, measurable characters, the differences among individuals belonging to the same race are greater than the differences that occur between the observed averages for two or more races within the same major group.

5. Most anthropologists do not include mental characteristics in their classification of human races. Studies within a single race have shown that both innate capacity and environmental opportunity determine the results of tests of intelligence and temperament, though their relative importance is disputed.

When intelligence tests, even non-verbal, are made on a group of non-literate people, their scores are usually lower than those of more civilized people. It has been recorded that different groups of the same race occupying similarly high levels of civilization may yield considerable differences in intelligence tests. When, however, the two groups have been brought up from childhood in similar environments, the differences are usually very slight. Moreover, there is good evidence that, given similar opportunities, the average performance (that is to say, the performance of the individual who is representative because he is surpassed by as many as he surpasses), and the variation round it, do not differ appreciably from one race to another.

Even those psychologists who claim to have found the greatest differences in intelligence between groups of different racial origin, and have contended that they are hereditary, always report that some members of the group of inferior performance surpass not merely the lowest ranking member of the superior group, but also the average of its members. In any case, it has never been possible to separate members of two groups on the basis of mental capacity, as they can often be separated on a basis of religion, skin colour, hair form or language. It is possible, though not proved, that some types of innate capacity for intellectual and emotional responses are commoner in one human group than in another, but it is certain that, within a single group, innate capacities vary as much as, if not more than, they do between different groups.

The study of the heredity of psychological characteristics is beset with difficulties. We know that certain mental diseases and defects are transmitted from one generation to the next, but we are less familiar with the part played by heredity in the mental life of normal individuals. The normal individual, irrespective of race, is essentially educable. It follows that his intellectual and moral life is largely conditioned by his training and by his physical and social environment.

It often happens that a national group may appear to be characterized by particular psychological attributes. The superficial view would be that this is due to race. Scientifically, however, we realize that any common psychological attribute is more likely to be due to a common historical and social background, and that such attributes may obscure the fact that, within different populations consisting of many human types, one will find approximately the same range of temperament and intelligence.

6. The scientific material available to us at present does not justify the conclusion that inherited genetic differences are a major factor in producing the differences between the cultures and cultural achievements of different peoples or groups. It does indicate, on the contrary, that a major factor in explaining such differences is the cultural experience which each group has undergone.

7. There is no evidence for the existence of so-called "pure" races. Skeletal remains provide the basis of our limited knowledge about earlier races. In regard to race mixture, the evidence points to the fact that human hybridization has been going on for an indefinite

but considerable time. Indeed, one of the processes of race formation and race extinction or absorption is by means of hybridization between races. As there is no reliable evidence that disadvantageous effects are produced thereby, no biological justification exists for prohibiting intermarriage between persons of different races.

8. We now have to consider the bearing of these statements on the problem of human equality. We wish to emphasize that equality of opportunity and equality in law in no way depend, as ethical principles, upon the assertion that human beings are in fact equal in endowment.

9. We have thought it worth while to set out in a formal manner what is at present scientifically established concerning individual and group differences.

(1) In matters of race, the only characteristics which anthropologists have so far been able to use effectively as a basis for classification are physical (anatomical and physiological).

(2) Available scientific knowledge provides no basis for believing that the groups of mankind differ in their innate capacity for intellectual and emotional development.

(3) Some biological differences between human beings within a single race may be as great or greater than the same biological differences between races.

(4) Vast social changes have occurred that have not been connected in any way with changes in racial type. Historical and sociological studies thus support the view that genetic differences are of little significance in determining the social and cultural differences between different groups of men.

(5) There is no evidence that race mixture produces disadvantageous results from a biological point of view. The social results of race mixture whether for good or ill, can generally be traced to social factors.

(Text drafted, at Unesco House, Paris, on June 8, 1951, by: Professor R. A. M. Bergman, Royal Tropical Institute, Netherlands Anthropological Society, Amsterdam; Professor Gunnar Dahlberg, Director, State Institute for Human Genetics and Race Biology, University of Uppsala; Professor L. C. Dunn, Department of Zoology, Columbia University, New York; Professor J. B. S. Haldane, Head, Department of Biometry, University College, London; Professor

M. F. Ashley Montagu, Chairman, Department of Anthropology, Rutgers University, New Brunswick, N. J.; Dr. A. E. Mourant, Director, Blood Group Reference Laboratory, Lister Institute, London; Professor Hans Nachtsheim, Director, Institut für Genetik, Freie Universität, Berlin; Dr. Eugène Schreider, Directeur adjoint du Laboratoire d'Anthropologie Physique de l'Ecole des Hautes Etudes, Paris; Professor Harry L. Shapiro, Chairman, Department of Anthropology, American Museum of Natural History, New York; Dr. J. C. Trevor, Faculty of Archaeology and Anthropology, University of Cambridge; Dr. Henri V. Vallois, Professeur au Muséum d'Histoire Naturelle, Directeur du Musée de l'Homme, Paris; Professor S. Zuckerman, Head, Department of Anatomy, Medical School, University of Birmingham. Professor Th. Dobzhansky, Department of Zoology, Columbia University, New York, and Dr. Julian Huxley contributed to the final wording.)

"Ethnic Group" and "Race"

I N THE UNESCO STATEMENT on Race, paragraph 6 reads as follows:
"National, religious, geographic, linguistic and cultural groups do
not necessarily coincide with racial groups; and the cultural traits of
such groups have no demonstrated genetic connection with racial
traits. Because serious errors of this kind are habitually committed
when the term 'race' is used in popular parlance, it would be better
when speaking of human races to drop the term 'race' altogether and
speak of *ethnic groups.*"

The principal objection to the term "race" with reference to man
is that it takes for granted as solved problems which are far from being
so, and tends to close the mind to problems to which it should always
remain open. If, with ritual fidelity, one goes on repeating long enough
that "the Nordics" are a race or that "the Armenoids" are, or that "the
Jews" are, or that races may be determined by their blood group gene
frequencies, we shall have already determined what a "race" is. Since
there are today quite a number of physical anthropologists who question the validity of the term "race" when applied to man, and some
biologists who question its value when applied to some non-human
groups of animals,[1] the following discussion will not appear as hetero-
dox as it has been until very recently.

In 1936 Huxley and Haddon repudiated the term "race" in favor
of "ethnic group,"[2] and recently Calman has recommended that the
term "variety" should be avoided altogether and suggested that "Other
terms such as 'geographical race,' 'form,' 'phase,' and so forth, may be

---

[1] Livingstone, "On the Non-Existence of Human Races," *Current Anthropology*, III (1962), 279–81.
[2] Huxley and Haddon, *We Europeans*, pp. 82–83.

useful in particular instances but are better not used until some measure of agreement is reached as to their precise meaning."[3] Kalmus writes: "A very important term which was originally used in systematics is 'race.' Nowadays, however, its use is avoided as far as possible in genetics."[4] In a more recent work Kalmus writes, "It is customary to discuss the local varieties of humanity in terms of 'race.' However, it is unnecessary to use this greatly debased word, since it is easy to describe populations without it."[5] G. S. Carter, in his book on *Animal Evolution,* writes that the terms " 'race,' 'variety,' and 'form' are used so loosely and in so many senses that it is advisable to avoid using them as infraspecific categories."[6] Professor Ernst Hanhart denies that there are any "true races" in man,[7] and Professor L. S. Penrose, in a review of Dunn and Dobzhansky's little book *Heredity, Race and Society,* writes that he is unable to "see the necessity for the rather apologetic retention of the obsolete term 'race,' when what is meant is simply a given population differentiated by some social, geographical or genetical character, or . . . merely by a gene frequency peculiarity. The use of the almost mystical concept of race makes the presentation of the facts about the geographical and linguistic groups . . . unnecessarily complicated."[8] Dr. J. P. Garlick, reviewing two books on "race," writes, "The use of 'race' as a taxonomic unit for man seems out-of-date, if not irrational."[9]

In spite of these strictures many biologists will continue to use the term, and if they can use it in an adequately defined manner so that their meaning can be clearly understood by other scientists, erroneous though that usage may be, it will be all the more easy for the critic to direct attention to the sources of the error. It cannot be too frequently emphasized that definitions are not to be achieved at the beginning of an inquiry but only at the end of one. Such inquiries have not yet been completed to the satisfaction of most scientists who have paid considered attention to the subject of "race." The term, therefore, at best is at the present time not really allowable on any score in man.

---

[3] Calman, *The Classification of Animals,* p. 14.
[4] Kalmus, *Genetics,* p. 45.
[5] Kalmus, *Variation and Heredity,* p. 30.
[6] Carter, *Animal Evolution,* p. 163.
[7] Hanhart, "Infectious Diseases," in A. Sorsby (ed.), *Clinical Genetics,* p. 545.
[8] Penrose, in *Annals of Eugenics,* XVII (1952), 252–53.
[9] Garlick, in *Annals of Human Genetics,* XXV (1961), 169–70.

One may or may not be of the opinion that the term "race" ought to be dropped altogether from the vocabulary, because it is so prematurely defined and confusing and because biologists and other scientists are frequently guilty of using it incorrectly, and that therefore it would be better if they did not lend the aura of their authority to the use of so confusing a word. The term "subspecies" has been used as the equivalent of the term "race," but this suffers from the same disadvantages, and has been as misused as its equivalent.[10] The term "race" is so embarrassed by confused and mystical meanings, and has so many blots upon its escutcheon, that a discouragement of its use would constitute an encouragement to clearer thinking.

In opposition to this view a number of objections have been expressed. One doesn't change anything by changing names. It's an artful dodge. A subterfuge. Why not meet the problem head-on? If, in popular usage, the term "race" has been befogged and befouled, why not cleanse it of the smog and foulness and restore it to its pristine condition? Re-education should be attempted by establishing the true meaning of "race," not by denying its existence. The "race" problem is not merely a matter of faulty semantics. One cannot combat racism by enclosing the word in quotes. It is not the word that requires changing but people's ideas about it. It is a common failing to argue from the abuse of an idea to its total exclusion. And so on.

It was Francis Bacon who remarked that truth grows more readily out of error than it does out of confusion. The time may come when it may be possible for most men to use the term "race" in a legitimate scientific sense, with clarity and with reason. But that time is not yet. It does not appear to be generally realized that while high walls do not a prison make, scientific terms are capable of doing so. Until people are soundly educated to understand the muddlement of ideas which is represented by such terms as "race" they will continue to believe in absurdities. And as Voltaire so acutely remarked, "As long as people believe in absurdities they will continue to commit atrocities." Words are what men breathe into them. Men have a strong tendency to use words and phrases which cloak the unknown in the undefined or undefinable. As Housman put it, "calling in ambiguity of language to promote confusion of thought."[11] The race problem is

[10] Hall, "Zoological Subspecies of Man at the Peace Table," *Journal of Mammalogy*, XXVII (1946), 358–64.
[11] Housman, *The Name and Nature of Poetry*, p. 31.

certainly not a matter of faulty semantics, but the faulty semantics implicit in the common conception of "race" equally certainly contributes to the exacerbation of that problem.

The layman's conception of "race" is so confused and emotionally muddled that any attempt to modify it would seem to be met by the greatest obstacle of all, the term "race" itself. This is another reason why the attempt to retain the term "race" in popular parlance must fail. The term is a trigger word; utter it and a whole series of emotionally conditioned responses follow. The phrase "ethnic group" suffers from no such defect. If we are to clarify the minds of those who think in terms of "race" we must cease using the word primarily because in the layman's mind the term defines conditions which do not in fact exist. There is no such thing as the kind of "race" in which the layman believes. If we are to re-educate him in a sound conception of the meaning of that population or somatological or genetic group which we prefer to designate by the general and noncommittal phrase *ethnic group*, then it would seem far more reasonable to convey to him the temporariness of the situation with a general rather than with a particular term. This is particularly desirable when it is sought to remove a prevailing erroneous conception and substitute one that clarifies without solidifying. Professor Henry Sigerist has well said that "it is never sound to continue the use of terminology with which the minds of millions of people have been poisoned even when the old terms are given new meanings." [12] And Professor George Gaylord Simpson has written, "A word for which everyone has a different definition, usually unstated, ceases to serve the function of communication and its use results in futile arguments about nothing. There is also a sort of Gresham's Law for words; redefine them as we will, their worst or most extreme meaning is almost certain to remain current and to tend to drive out the meaning we might prefer." [13] Bertrand Russell has suggested that for words that have strong emotional overtones we should substitute in our arguments the letters of the alphabet.

The biologist who has been largely concerned with the study of animal populations will be likely to take an oversimplified view of the problems here involved and to dismiss such attempts at re-education of the layman as unsatisfactory. By substituting one term

---

[12] Sigerist, *A History of Medicine*, p. 101.
[13] Simpson, *The Major Features of Evolution*, p. 268.

for another, he will say, one solves nothing. It is quite as possible to feel "ethnic group prejudice" as it is to feel "race prejudice." Perhaps. But this kind of comment indicates that the real point has been missed. The phrase "ethnic group" is *not* a substitute for the term "race." The grounds upon which it is suggested constitute a fundamental difference in viewpoint which significantly differentiates what the phrase stands for from what the term stands for. It is not a question of changing names, and there is no question of resorting to devices or artful dodges—the imputation would be silly. If what the phrase "ethnic group" means is clearly understood and accepted, "ethnic group prejudice" would hardly require to be taken seriously. There have been some who have felt that the use of the phrase "ethnic group" was an avoidance of the main issue. On the other hand, most students of human nature would take the view that such a usage constitutes a more realistic and more promising approach to the problem of lay thinking on this subject than the method of attempting to put new meaning into the old bottle of "race." I agree with Korzybski that "because of the great semantic influence of the structure of language on the masses of mankind, leading, as it does, through lack of better understanding and *evaluation* to *speculation on terms*, it seems advisable to abandon completely terms which imply to the *many* the suggested elementalism, although these terms are used in a proper non-elementalistic way by the few."[14]

The ground on which the phrase "ethnic group" is principally suggested is that it is easier to re-educate people by introducing a new conception with a new distinctive term, particularly, I repeat, when it is desired to remove a prevailing erroneous conception and introduce a new and more correct one. Those who do not understand that the greatest obstacle to the process of re-education would be the retention of the old term "race," a term which enshrines the errors it is desired to remove, do not understand the deep implicit meanings which this word has inescapably come to possess for so many of its users. The question may, then, be asked: Will the phrase "ethnic group" be sufficient to cause such persons to alter their ideas? The answer is for some "No," for others, "It will help"; and for still others, "Yes." No one should be so naive as to suppose that by this means alone one is going to solve the "race" problem! The suggestions here made are

---

[14] Korzybski, *Science and Sanity*, p. 31.

calculated to help; they can do no more at best. Each time one uses the term "race" most individuals believe they understand what is meant, when in fact the chances are that what they understand by the term is largely false. "Race" is something so familiar that in speaking of it one takes one's private meaning completely for granted and one never thinks to question it. On the other hand, when one uses the phrase "ethnic group" wherever "race" would have been used, the question is generally asked: "What do you mean by 'ethnic group'?" And that at once affords the opportunity to discuss the facts and explain their meaning as well as the falsities of the prevailing conception of "race." This, it seems to me, is one of the greatest educational advantages of the phrase "ethnic group" over the term "race." Another advantage of the phrase is that it leaves all question of definition open, it refers specifically to human populations which are believed to exhibit a certain degree, amount, or frequency of undetermined physical likenesses or homogeneity. An ethnic group has already been described as one of a number of populations, which populations together comprise the species *Homo sapiens*, and which individually maintain their differences, physical and cultural, by means of isolating mechanisms such as geographic and social barriers. These differences vary as the power of the geographic and social barriers vary. Where these barriers are of high power, such ethnic groups will tend to remain distinct from each other geographically or ecologically.

English and English write as follows, "Ethnic group is an intentionally vague or general term used to avoid some of the difficulties of *race*. The ethnic group may be a nation, a people (such as the Jews), a language group (the Dakota Indians), a sociologically defined so-called race (the American Negro), or a group bound together in a coherent cultural entity by a religion (the Amish)."[15] To which one may add that the group may be characterized by a certain unity of genetic or physical traits.

Yet another advantage of the phrase "ethnic group" is that it avoids the reductionist or "nothing but" fallacy, that is to say, the notion that men are nothing but the resultant of their biological heredity, that they are what they are because of their genes. The phrase "ethnic group" is calculated to provide the necessary corrective to this errone-

---

[15] English and English, *A Comprehensive Dictionary of Psychological and Psychoanalytical Terms*, p. 189.

ous viewpoint by eliminating the question-begging emphases of the biologistic bias on purely physical factors and differences, and demanding that the question of definition be left open until the necessary scientific research and answers are available. The emphasis is shifted to the fact that man is a uniquely cultural creature as well as a physical organism, and that under the influence of human culture the plasticity of man, both mentally and physically, is greatly increased—indeed, to such an extent as to lead anthropologists to the creation of races upon the basis of physical traits which were subsequently discovered to be due to cultural factors, as, for example, the head forms of the so-called Armenoid and Dinaric "races."

Here, too, reply may be made to those who may object that the phrase "ethnic group" is too reminiscent of the cultural. But this is precisely why the phrase is so well found. The Greek word *ethnos* originally meant a number of people living together, and subsequently came to be used in the sense of a tribe, group, nation, or people. In modern times the term "ethnic" has occasionally been used to refer to a group identified by ties both of race and of nationality. This is pretty much what the phrase "ethnic group" ought to be taken to mean in the sense given in our description of an "ethnic group."

If it be said that what the student of man's variety is interested in is the way in which human groups came to be what they are, and that for this reason it is the biological facts and mechanisms in which he must be chiefly interested, the answer must be made that anyone who believes this must be disabused of his belief as quickly as possible. For it must be emphasized again that man is not merely a physical organism but a *human* being who as a member of a cultural group has been greatly influenced by his culture. Human populations have had a remarkable assortment of marriage or breeding regulations, for instance, varying standards of sexual selection, different kinds of social barriers, mobility, and similar variables, all of which have probably played an appreciable part in the evolution of ethnic differences. These are the very kinds of factors which are most neglected by those who come to the study of man with a biologistic bias. It would for such students of man, especially those who come in from the nonhuman biological fields, as well as for the layman, be a great advantage to be required to look at the problem of human variety from the viewpoint of the "ethnic group" rather than from that of "race." Where man is concerned the biologist, like the layman, needs to add a cultural dimension to his horizons. This is what the phrase "ethnic group" will help him to do.

The conception of an "ethnic group" is quite different from that which is associated with the term "race." The phrase "ethnic group" represents a different way of looking at populations, an open, non-question-begging way, a tentative, noncommittal, experimental way, based on the new understanding which the sciences of genetics and anthropology have made possible. A term is discontinued, retired, but another is not merely substituted for it; rather a new conception of human populations is introduced replacing the old one, which is now dropped, and a term or phrase suitable to this new conception is suggested. The old conception is *not* retained and a new name given to it, but a new conception is introduced under its own name. That is a very different thing from a mere change in names. It is important to be quite clear upon this point, for the *new conception* embraced in the phrase "ethnic group" renders the possibility of the development of "ethnic group prejudice" quite impossible, for as soon as the nature of this conception is understood it cancels the possibility of any such development. It is a noncontaminating neutral concept.

Perhaps the greatest advantage of the phrase "ethnic group" is that it is noncommittal and somewhat flexible. It may be applied to any group concerning which physical and cultural traits are so identified that it is given a certain distinctiveness which appears to separate it from other groups. The phrase may also be used as embracing the definition of race in the biological sense, and particularly groups which are less clearly defined, which may or may not be races and hence should not be called races in the absence of the necessary scientific demonstration. All that we say when we use the phrase "ethnic group" is that here is a group of people who physically, and perhaps in other additional ways, may be regarded as a more or less distinct group. Until we know what it really is, and until we understand thoroughly what we are talking about with respect to this and all other groups, let us call all such groups "ethnic groups." In other words, the concept of "ethnic group" implies a question mark, *not* a period. It implies that many questions remain to be asked, and that many answers will have to be given before we can say precisely what any particular ethnic group represents.

To conclude and summarize: The advantages of the phrase "ethnic group" are: first, while emphasizing the fact that one is dealing with a distinguishable group, this noncommittal phrase leaves the whole question of the precise status of the group on physical and other grounds open for further discussion and research; second, it recognizes the fact that it is a group which has been subject to the action of cultural influences; and third, it eliminates all obfuscating emotional implications.

As for the suggested dropping or the restricted or suspended use of the term "race," there are many parallels for this in science. Possibly the most striking one in recent years is the dropping of the term "instinct" by psychologists for similar reasons to those which make the term "race" undesirable.[16] Similarly, in anthropology the term "savage" has been completely dropped, while the term "primitive" as referring to living peoples is largely being abandoned in favor of the term "nonliterate" for much the same reason, namely, the inaccuracy of the earlier terms, and hence their unsuitability. In biology the term "unit character," as erroneously referring to single genes as determining single characters or traits, has been forever banished from the scientific vocabulary. Retardative concepts like "phlogiston" of eighteenth-century chemistry have been dropped never to be readopted. It may be that the terms "instinct" and "race" may someday be shown to have more than a merely verbal validity of common usage, but this is very unlikely, and it would be more in accordance with the scientific spirit to declare a moratorium on the use of the term "race."

The phrase "ethnic group" serves as a challenge to thought and as a stimulus to rethink the foundations of one's beliefs. It encourages the passage from ignorant certainty to thoughtful uncertainty. For the layman, as for others, the term "race" closes the door on his understanding; the phrase "ethnic group" opens it.

---

[16] See Bernard, *Instinct: A Study in Social Psychology.*

The Fallacy of the "Primitive"

FROM THE rather self-conscious heights of our own state of equivocal civilization and of that of the community to which we belong, we men of the latest period of human development have traditionally taken the view that whatever has preceded us was by so much the less advanced. Since we are the latest bearers of human development we reason, therefore, that we are the most fully developed. This rather ortholinear view of development is widely held, and it is, of course, widely believed to be in harmony with the evolutionary facts.

The truth is that evolutionary processes do not proceed in straight lines but are more accurately observed to assume a reticulate form. And so it has been in the evolution of man, both physically and culturally. So entrenched, however, have our beliefs become concerning the ortholinear evolution of man that our conceptions of "progress," "development," and "evolution" have rendered the assumption automatic that what developed later in time must therefore be more "advanced" and more "evolved" than that which developed earlier. From this the "logical" inference followed that what was less developed must be earlier than that which was more developed, and therefore the earlier was the more "primitive" and the later the more "advanced." Furthermore, since straight-line evolution is taken for granted by so many, it followed that the more advanced developed from the less advanced, from the "primitive," and that the former was "superior" to the latter.

Since evolution from the less advanced to the more advanced or from the simpler to the complex (not quite the same thing) is a fact beyond dispute (although the reverse has sometimes occurred in evolution), it has been easy to fall into the habit of assuming that the later developed is not only the more evolved but also the better. "Better" is, of course, a value judgment, and value judgments are a quagmire in which one may get hopelessly mired. And this seems to be the condition into which civilized man has fallen, with respect to those whom he chooses to call "primitive."

We speak of "primitive" peoples—the nonliterate peoples of the earth. What do we mean when we use the term? We mean that such peoples are, in comparison with ourselves, undeveloped; in many respects that is true. For example, it would be true of reading and writing, of technological progress, and in various cultures it would be more or less true of certain aspects of moral and institutional development. But it is very necessary to point out that, in certain respects, such cultures are more highly developed than are most civilized cultures. By the standards of values in these matters prevailing in civilized societies, "primitive" cultures are "better" than civilized cultures.

For example, Eskimos and Australian aborigines, to take two of the so-called most "primitive" cultures known to anthropologists, are very much more generous, loving, and cooperative than are most of the members of civilized societies. By the standard of our own values in these matters, Eskimos and Australian aborigines are better than we are. Members of these "primitive" cultures are honest, dependable, cheerful, and courageous, in all these respects to a degree which comparatively few civilized men manage to be. Who is more developed in these respects? Those who pay lip-service to these qualities or those who live them out in their lives?

An additional assumption widely made is that "primitive" peoples are "nearer" and more closely resemble prehistoric man than the so-called "more advanced" peoples. This, too, is a questionable assumption. The fact is that nonliterate peoples have as long a history as civilized ones. Despite references to "living fossils," no human population can, even by the most violent torsion of the imagination, be considered to be a fossil. All human societies change. The rate of change undoubtedly varies, some being slower than others, but changes must occur. They occur in language, religion, custom, and technology, and the changes will be considerably influenced by the varying experiences which each society undergoes. Those that are isolated from the mainstream of cultural change will change slowly; those that are exposed to the fertilizing effects of cultural interchange with other peoples will change rapidly. But even in the absence of such cultural stimulation, the very nature of cultural life involves more or less continuous adjustment to and encouragement of change to meet the requirements of changing conditions. We can, therefore, be certain that no culture, as we know it today, is as it was in prehistoric times. It may even be that some of the so-called "primitive" cultures are much less like those of prehistoric times than some that appear to be more advanced. It cannot be questioned that, in some respects, some nonliterate cultures are closer to the conditions as they prevailed in prehistoric times than are civilized cultures. This, however, does not mean that they are so in all, or even most, respects.

Each culture in the course of time makes the progress necessary to enable its members to live as comfortably as possible in the environment in which the culture functions. The environment generally sets certain limits beyond which it is impossible for the culture to develop unless radical changes are introduced from the outside. Metal tools, for example, will not be developed in an environment in which metal ores are unknown. As I have already said, cultures differ from one another in the history of the experiences they have undergone and, therefore, in the kind of development they have realized. This does not mean that any culture, i.e., the human beings through whom the culture is expressed, is—given the same history of conditions—incapable of realizing or achieving the same degree of development as any other culture, but merely that most cultures have not had the same or similar opportunities to do so, and largely for that reason differ culturally from one another.

Too often we identify "primitive man" with contemporary nonliterate peoples when the only legitimate use of the phrase "primitive man" is when it is applied to prehistoric man. But even here there are dangers in the use of terms which are so loaded with erroneous ideas. Primitive man, that is, prehistoric man, is too often thought of as a beetle-browed monster, with little brain, a bull neck, knock-knees, and a nasty habit of dragging his womenfolk around by their hair. Sad to say, all these ideas were perpetrated upon an innocent public by leading scientists of their day. Beetle-brows there undoubtedly were, but it should have been explained that behind those beetle-brows beat a brain of considerable power and, as in the case of Neanderthal man, larger in size than our noble own! The monster, the bull neck, the knock-knees, and the hair-dragging of women are all figments of the imaginations of those who wished to see these things the way they thought they ought to be. But the true scientist endeavors to see things the way they are, not the way they ought to be or what is considered desirable.

One of the consequences of the belief that primitive man was so much less developed than ourselves is the failure to understand that prehistoric man of 15,000 years ago was in some aspects of his life capable of achievements which have scarcely been surpassed by men since. An outstanding example of this is prehistoric art, especially the art of the Upper Old Stone Age. When this was first discovered at the beginning of the century, it was at first attributed to modern artists who, for some reason, had crept into a natural crypt and decorated its ceiling in the manner of Michelangelo in the Sistine Chapel. But, as other discoveries were made in the dark recesses of caverns and caves under conditions which pointed to an extreme antiquity, the weight of evidence could no longer be resisted, and prehistoric man was finally acknowledged as the creator of these wonderful works of art, paintings, sculptures, and engravings. As Sir Herbert Read has said, "The best paintings in the Altamira, Niaux, and Lascaux caves exhibit a degree of skill which is not less than that of a Pisanello or a Picasso." Anyone who has seen the originals or even reproductions will agree that this is no overstatement. In addition to the technical skill displayed by the artists, their work exhibits a vitality and expression which has seldom been equalled in any age.

Be that as it may, in the works of art of prehistoric men who lived between 15,000 and 30,000 years ago, we have the clearest evidence that these men, as artists, were as accomplished as any who have lived since. When it is remembered that these works were not really executed as works of art but as magico-religious rituals calculated to yield success in the hunt, that the conditions under which these works were created were usually of the most difficult kind, high up on walls and ceilings, often with the artist lying on his back, and doing his work by the uncertain light of a smoky oil flame, the achievement becomes all the more remarkable. There can be little doubt that individuals capable of such skills were endowed with an intelligence potentially no less great than that possessed by contemporary civilized man. Because the term "primitive" not only tends to obscure that fact, but also militates against the possibility of understanding the true significance of the facts, it will readily be understood why, if the term is used at all, it should be used with the greatest caution.

Primitive man as prehistoric man is most certainly a reality, and the more we learn to understand him, the better we understand ourselves. But to identify existing nonliterate peoples with prehistoric man is an egregious error when it is not an expedient fiction, a fiction which is rather bathetically calculated to provide a lift for the faltering ego. In the rapidly developing world in which we live, in which the undeveloped regions of the world will witness their most spectacular advances in the areas of human development, it is of the first order of importance that the civilized peoples of the world understand and act upon these facts.[1]

---

[1] For further valuable discussions of this subject see Dozier, "The Concepts of 'Primitive' and 'Native' in Anthropology," in *Yearbook of Anthropology 1955*, pp. 187–202; and Berndt, "The Concept of the Primitive," *Sociologus*, X (1960), 50–69.

Race, Science, and Politics:
Ex-Representative Andrew J. May and
"The Races of Mankind"

The following piece of history is preserved for the record because it presents an actual case in which a venal politician was able to suppress and prevent the distribution of a highly instructive and valuable booklet to our armed forces during World War II.

ON MONDAY, March 6, 1944, the American public learned through an Associated Press report, that the House Military Affairs Committee "had closed the books today on a secret investigation of Army plans to distribute 55,000 copies of a pamphlet on racial equality, but kept an eye on a government warehouse to make certain that the books stay there."

The pamphlet referred to is entitled *The Races of Mankind*. It was prepared by Professor Ruth Benedict and Dr. Gene Weltfish, of the Department of Anthropology of Columbia University, under the supervision of a committee of the American Association of Scientific Workers, and is published by the Public Affairs Committee, Inc., of New York City, a nonprofit organization financed in part by the Alfred P. Sloan Foundation.

The pamphlet concisely and clearly states the facts concerning the "races" and ethnic groups of mankind as science has come to know them. Written, as it is, by one of the world's most distinguished anthropologists, Dr. Ruth Benedict, and by a younger anthropologist of much experience in the field, in study, and in teaching, this delightfully illustrated booklet constitutes a sound and reliable summary of the facts about "race." One could hardly imagine a more ingenuous statement of the facts.

It therefore came as a shock, if not as a surprise, to the colleagues of the authors of the pamphlet, in this country and abroad, to learn of the action of the House Military Affairs Committee.

The chairman of the committee, Representative Andrew J. May, of Kentucky, charged that the pamphlet described Northern Negroes as superior in intelligence to Southern white men.

It does nothing of the sort. No such statement or anything approaching such a statement is to be found in the pamphlet or in any of the writings of the authors. This would, indeed, be racism in reverse.

Specifically, Mr. May appears to have objected, according to the report, to "a claim in the book that surveys indicated the average Negro in New York, Connecticut and Massachusetts was the intellectual equal of the average white resident of Kentucky, Arkansas and Mississippi."

The reference to Connecticut and Massachusetts may be regarded as a slip, for these states are not mentioned in the pamphlet; the states actually mentioned are New York, Illinois, and Ohio. This is of no moment. What is of moment, is that the claim to which Mr. May objects is based on data which have been a matter of official record for a period of twenty-three years.[1]

These data were gathered by Colonel Robert M. Yerkes of the United States Army, and several groups of Army investigators during World War I. The facts thus gathered were compiled and analyzed by these Army men, and were released for publication by the United States Army under the title *Psychological Examining in the United States Army* as Memoir XV of the National Academy of Sciences, and printed and published by the United States Government Printing Office in Washington in 1921.

It seems strange that statements based on the facts gathered in 1917–1918 by the United States Army and printed in 1921 by the United States Government Printing Office should, in 1944, be found objectionable by a House Military Affairs Committee. The 1921 volume contains only such officially authorized statements as the Army released. Among these were numerous tables showing the results of the tests made on both white and Negro recruits. The facts in which Mr. May might have been interested are shown in Tables 205 and 206 on pages 690 and 691 of the report. These tables enable one to make a com-

---

[1] Mr. May, so zealous a guardian of his country's morals was at this very time accepting bribes from munitions makers. For this "error" Mr. May was subsequently tried, found guilty, and imprisoned.

parison of all Army Alpha scores, that is scores made by literate recruits, for white and Negro recruits from different states. Such a comparison has been made by Lorimer and Osborn in their *Dynamics of Population*.[2]

In order to make them more comprehensive, there are included in the ratings the scores of men who were also given Beta or individual examinations, but the scores of those who were initially classed as illiterate are excluded.

It is for this reason that the scores given by Klineberg in his *Race Differences*,[3] and in the pamphlet by Benedict and Weltfish, which are based on the Alpha tests alone, differ from those given by Lorimer and Osborn. But both series of figures tell the same story.

The scores listed in Table 10 are shown in order of white intelligence rank. It will be seen that there is an interesting relation between the order of white and the order of Negro intelligence rank.

From these figures it is clear that the literate Negroes from Ohio not only surpassed the literate Negroes from the South but also achieved a median score above the median scores of the literate whites from eight Southern states; that the literate Negroes from Illinois surpassed the literate whites from five Southern states, that the literate Negroes from Indiana surpassed the literate whites from four Southern states; while for all Northern Negroes reported the median Alpha score surpassed the median Alpha score for the whites of eight Southern states combined. The median Alpha score for Northern Negroes was 40.4 while the median Alpha score for Southern whites was 40.3.

It is evident that when Drs. Benedict and Weltfish compared the median scores of Southern whites from three states with those of Northern Negroes from an equal number of states they were actually understating the facts.[4]

How are the facts to be interpreted? I do not think they can be better interpreted than in the words of Drs. Benedict and Weltfish, and they are therefore quoted here. The Army intelligence tests, they

---

[2] Lorimer and Osborn, *Dynamics of Population*, p. 140, Table 46.

[3] Klineberg, *Race Differences*, p. 182, Table 23.

[4] To what extent they were doing so may be determined by references to pages 229–31 of this volume, and to Montagu, "The Intelligence of Northern Negroes and Southern Whites in the First World War," *American Journal of Psychology*, LXVIII (1945), 161–88.

TABLE 10

MEDIAN ALPHA SCORES OF WHITE AND NEGRO RECRUITS, UNITED STATES ARMY, FIVE NORTHERN STATES AND EIGHT SOUTH CENTRAL STATES[a]

	Median Alpha Score, White Recruits	Median Alpha Score, Negro Recruits
Five Northern States:		
Ohio	62.2	45.3
Pennsylvania	62.0	34.7
Illinois	61.6	42.2
New York	58.3	38.6
Indiana	55.9	41.5
Eight South Central States:		
Tennessee	44.0	29.7
Texas	43.4	12.1
Oklahoma	42.9	31.4
Kentucky	41.5	23.9
Alabama	41.3	19.9
Mississippi	37.6	10.2
Louisiana	36.1	13.4
Arkansas	35.6	16.1

[a] Medians computed from the data in Yerkes (ed.), "Psychological Examining in the United States Army," *Memoirs of the National Academy of Sciences,* XV (1921), 690 and 691, Tables 205 and 206. Adapted from Lorimer and Osborn, *Dynamics of Population,* p. 140, Table 46.

write, "showed that Negroes made a lower score on intelligence tests than whites. But the tests also showed that Northerners, *black and white,* had higher scores than Southerners, *black and white.* Everyone knows that Southerners are inborn equals of Northerners, but in 1917 many southern states' per capita expenditures for schools were only fractions of those in northern states, and housing and diet and income were far below average too.[5] Since the vast majority of Negroes lived in the South, their score on the intelligence test was a score they got not only as Negroes, but as Americans who had grown up under

[5] See pp. 229–31 of this volume.

poor conditions in the South. Scientists therefore compared the scores of Southern whites and Northern Negroes.

"Negroes with better luck after they were born got higher scores than whites with less luck. The white race did badly where economic conditions were bad and schooling was not provided, and Negroes living under better conditions surpassed them. The differences did not arise because people were from the North or South, or because they were white or black, but because of differences in income, education, cultural advantages, and other opportunities." [6]

After the preceding paragraphs were written a Congressional sub-committee issued a report on *The Races of Mankind* charging, according to the *Times-Herald,* Washington, D. C., of Friday, April 28, 1944, that "all the techniques—more or less subtly presented—of Communist propaganda" are utilized in this booklet.

The subcommittee, headed by Representative Durham, of North Carolina, is described as "investigating the 'infiltration' into the Army and its training programs of teachings of philosophies 'inimical to the interests of the people and the Government.'" The committee finds that "the statements attributed to science or scientists were vague and 'range all the way from half-truths through innuendoes to downright inaccuracies.'"

"The report said that while the theme of the booklet was 'that the races of mankind are all brothers,' it failed to take into account that 'even brothers in the same family may differ mentally, physically, socially or morally.'"

"It charged the illustrations were 'crude, grotesque and frivolous, entirely incongruous with the text of a real scientific treatise,' and added 'Adam and Eve are depicted with navels.'"

"It said the authors start their 'thinly-disguised sophistries' as anthropologists, 'but drop anthropology for politics, sociology, labor unionization and similar subjects employed by propagandists of communism.'"

"The report said that 'the most controversial statement' in the book was a World War I comparison of 'Southern whites from States having small educational appropriations with Northern Negroes from states having much larger budgets to the detriment of the former.'"

"Obviously the States were selected," the subcommittee asserts, "for

---

[6] Benedict and Weltfish, *The Races of Mankind,* pp. 17–18.

this tabulation with an intention to create false or misleading impressions."

From the comments here quoted from the newspaper account of the report of the House Military Affairs subcommittee it seems fairly clear that the members of the subcommittee disapproved of the booklet entitled *The Races of Mankind*. This was unfortunate because the principal comparison to which the subcommittee objected was much more strongly and extensively substantiated by the independent earlier analysis of Lorimer and Osborn, and has since been even more fully corroborated by me.[7]

While Drs. Benedict and Weltfish cite the evidence for three Northern and three Southern states, Lorimer and Osborn give the findings for five Northern and eight Southern states. Lorimer and Osborn's interpretation of the figures reproduced in the table is about the same as that given by Drs. Benedict and Weltfish.

The fact that there was a failure to suggest that Lorimer and Osborn were in the pay of Moscow when they published the figures, which are so much more startling than those in *The Races of Mankind*, was doubtless due to the subcommittee's ignorance of them. One of the authors of the book in which this "subversive" group of figures was published, Frederick Osborn, was at the time when the subcommittee's report was made public a general in the United States Army—evidently another Trojan Horse harbored in our midst, the first having been Colonel Robert M. Yerkes, who was responsible for the original testing.

With regard to the committee's finding that "the statements attributed to science or scientists were vague and 'range all the way from half-truths through innuendoes to downright inaccuracies,' " it would have been more helpful if some of these charges had been supported by examples. As matters stand it can only be said that most scientists living in lands where freedom of speech is not forbidden would subscribe to practically everything contained within the covers of the booklet without reservation.

Some of the legends to the illustrations might have been revised, but this is a matter of opinion. The booklet was intended for the layman; it is not a scientific treatise, and sharpness of statement is not always possible in works intended for the layman. The illustrations

---

[7] See pp. 229–31.

are delightful and to the point. They are gay, as they should be, but not in the least frivolous.

What relevance, except to confuse the issue, the statement that even brothers in the same family may differ mentally, physically, socially, and morally has for the statement that the "races" of mankind are all brothers it is difficult to see. Of course, every human being differs from every other; and it is as a human being, not as a member of a particular family, group, or "race," that he should be considered. That is precisely the point. It is not "races" that differ in these qualities but persons, and a person should not be made to suffer because he happens to belong to a "race" or cultural group which does not meet with the approval of those who follow and approve the white supremacy doctrines of the South.

As an anatomist I can see the point of the subcommittee's objection to the representation of Adam and Eve with navels. This was undoubtedly an error on the part of the artist, who is probably more conversant with the practice of Christianity and the religion of Christ than with the omphalical niceties of political exegetical criticism—in which the House Military Affairs Committee seems to be so expert.

Neither politics nor labor unionization is referred to, discussed, or in any way implied in the pamphlet in any sense other than that illustrative of the manner in which better relations have been developed between different ethnic groups. The statement that "the States were selected for this tabulation with an intention to create false or misleading impressions" can only be regarded as a disingenuous libel.

The Springfield Community-School Plan in Education for Democracy and Cooperation

"RACISM" IS A DISEASE. It is a malfunctioning of the mind which endangers human relations, a psychically contagious disease due to the infection of the predisposed mind by false, pathological, ideas which produce hostility toward other groups and their members. In much the same way as organs become diseased as the result of the action of infective agents, so minds become diseased as the result of the action of wrong or pathogenic ideas. The epidemiology of pathological ideas deserves more attention than it has received.[1] In August, 1939, the National Conference of Christians and Jews, having carefully studied the disease, concluded that it was impossible to eradicate "race" prejudice by counter propaganda. What, clearly, was required, was the development of an immunity to the disease. Such immunity could, it was felt, best be secured in a systematic manner by providing children and adults with the necessary protective education. It was suggested to the Conference that it induce the school system of some representative community to develop educational means for immunizing children and adults against "racism."

In October, 1939, the Conference proposed to Dr. John Granrud, superintendent of schools in Springfield, Massachusetts, that his school system should be the first to try the experiment. With great foresight and sympathetic understanding Dr. Granrud immediately accepted this suggestion and appointed a committee of nine, representing all educational levels in the school system, including super-

---

[1] See Golin, "How Deadly the Thought," *Journal of the American Medical Association,* CLXXI (1959), 148–54; also the editorial in the same issue, "Epidemiology of the Future," 154.

visors, principals, and classroom teachers, to study the problems involved in organizing the program. A thorough study, lasting some six months, of the problems involved led the committee to the following conclusions:

1. Many of the prejudices, biases, and undemocratic attitudes evident among the children are reflections of forces and factors outside the school, such as the home, the street, the club, and sometimes even the church. The program for democracy should not, therefore, be designed solely for the child in the schools, but should reach the parents and the adult world which condition the child's environment and thinking.

2. One of the major weaknesses of the previous attempts to inculcate democratic ideas is the fact that the teaching has been too idealized. Youngsters were given to understand that we in this country had already achieved a perfect democracy. This teaching and idealization did not coincide with the realities of the youngsters' experiences. They soon became disillusioned, because their own observations invalidated the idealizations. Children were taught, for example, that this is a land of equal opportunity and that in this country people are not discriminated against because of race, religion, or creed. But the Negro girl knew very well that even though she was an excellent stenographer there was little possibility of securing a position as a stenographer; and the boy with a foreign-sounding name knew that his chances for securing a good position were not so good as those of his classmates who had the right kind of American name. The committee decided, therefore, that issues should be faced squarely; that, while a positive and affirmative position on democratic ideals would be taken, it should be emphasized that we had not yet achieved the perfect democracy which is our goal; that the weaknesses in our democratic processes should be pointed out; and that how these weaknesses could be corrected and how our democratic processes could be strengthened should be discussed realistically.

3. In order to eradicate blind and intolerant attitudes it is imperative that pupils understand all the constituent elements of our population, the historical backgrounds of these elements, and their contributions to American life.

4. Finally, it is essential that democratic ideals be presented to students in a dynamic fashion calculated to fire their enthusiasm and

to inspire their devotion to democracy as the best means of achieving the good life for all our peoples.[2]

Here, then, were some practical aids by which to frame the program. The program was, from the outset, based on the assumption that "race" prejudice can be prevented and that mass phobias, manias, and hysterias—infectious diseases of the mind—can be controlled as infectious diseases of the body have been controlled.

The method followed is much the same as that followed in the control of any disease. The plan is to apply the same scientific-humane principles which in a lifetime have all but conquered smallpox and typhoid, which since 1900 have reduced the deaths from tuberculosis from 200 per 100,000 to less than 40. Once the germ has been isolated, a mass education campaign teaches not only the terrible cost of the plague but also the breeding places of the germs and the scientific way of eliminating them.

Various tests were applied to the children in the Springfield public schools in order to determine the distribution of the breeding places of these germs, to determine the attitudes of the children toward Jews, Negroes, the foreign-born, and various religious groups. The tests revealed the fact that most of the prejudiced attitudes of children come from parents or other adults and from adult institutions. Special emphasis has therefore been placed on reaching the grownups.

Before the program was put into operation the children were also given a number of objective tests, especially constructed for the purpose, for "open-mindedness," "ability to distinguish between fact and opinion," "ability to analyze conflicting statements," "critical evaluation," and "support of generalizations." The data thus obtained was helpful in formulating the unit study in public opinion and how it is influenced, drawn up under the expert guidance of Dr. Clyde R. Miller, at that time associate professor of education at Teachers College, Columbia University; it also provided a basis by means of which the progress of the children could be measured. Following the public opinion unit study, the teachers discuss with children and adults how public opinion is formed, how to distinguish fact from opinion, what prejudices are, how they are, how they are developed, and how to deal with them and avoid them.

---

[2] Halligan, "A Community's Total War against Prejudice," *Journal of Educational Sociology*, XVI (1943), 374–80.

The teaching and activities are adapted to every level in the school system, and the emphasis throughout is upon cooperation, upon doing things together, on living and learning together.

HOW THE PLAN IS SET UP

In order to carry out this program two directing bodies were set up; one to function in the schools, called the Committee on Education for Democracy. This committee is appointed by the superintendent of schools and is representative of all educational levels in the schools, including supervisors, principals, and classroom teachers. The task of this committee is to study and advise on the problems involved in the organization and functioning of the program in the schools.

The other is a community committee for directing the community-wide program. It is broadly representative. Its membership includes leading clergymen of various faiths, representatives of different organizations in the business community, the publishers of the newspapers, labor leaders, representatives of the social agencies, spokesmen of young people's organizations, the wife of a Negro minister, leading figures in civic and club activities, the superintendent of schools, and the director of adult education, who serves as secretary.

HOW THE PLAN FUNCTIONS

As the pupil advances through the school system, he is first given in the elementary grades an understanding of "living and working together," and he develops from the outset a comprehension of some of the fundamental concepts of democracy. Each child is encouraged to make his contribution to the group. He learns what other peoples have contributed to our civilization, and he gets a first sense of the interdependence of nations.

When he reaches the junior high school level, he is given an opportunity to develop an appreciation of the rich heritage of America. He is encouraged to build a sympathetic attitude toward all racial and nationality groups through an understanding of their cultural patterns. Specifically, he obtains knowledge of the contributions of the various nationalities to the growth not only of the United States but also of Springfield.

Senior high school students are provided with opportunities for self-government; they analyze current problems, studying both the strengths and the weaknesses of our democratic processes in order to determine how the latter can be corrected and democracy strengthened. They learn how to analyze and evaluate their own prejudices and biases and how to reach conclusions objectively.

Tests given at the end of each year have shown substantial progress at all levels in the school system.

ADULT EDUCATION

The community sponsors free public forums in school buildings and has introduced controversial subjects, competent authorities taking opposing positions. A film forum series covers many topics, including the problems of "racial," religious, and economic groups. The discussions following the films are led by experts and are focused on *local problems*. Average attendance of public forums is 1,000. A series of ten "film forums" drew an average attendance of 800.

The New England type of town meeting was revived when nonpartisan political meetings were sponsored in public school buildings in each of the wards. Opposing candidates speak from the same platform. People who have not been in a school building for years renew their contact with the school system. One political rally drew an audience of 5,000.

OUTSIDE THE SCHOOL

In cooperation with the Council of Social Agencies an investigation of the conditions of domestic workers employed in private homes was undertaken, and standards for fair working conditions in household employment were established. Representatives of all the major women's clubs in the city subscribed to these standards. In cooperation with the Council an investigation of the social and economic conditions of the Negro population in Springfield has been completed, with a view to improving those conditions. Through the School Placement Bureau slow but steady progress has been made in breaking down discrimination in employment. Training of Negroes for skilled occupations has been developed, and there are now a number of Negro teachers in the school system of Springfield, all appointments being made strictly on the basis of merit.

THOSE WHO LEAD ALSO LEARN

Special training courses for teachers and community leaders are given at Springfield College, with emphasis upon contemporary problems and the new tasks they impose on education.

Through newspapers, radio, meetings of all sorts, and civic groups, and through study courses given in parent-teacher meetings, the work is carried to the entire community.

SPRINGFIELD, MASSACHUSETTS

Springfield is an average American city. The population is about 180,000. About 40 per cent of the residents are of old Yankee stock, and the rest are largely of Russian, Polish, Greek, Italian, Irish, and French-Canadian extraction, with the usual Jewish and Negro "minority" groups. Some 60 per cent are Roman Catholic.

At the time the plan was put into operation "conflicts and tensions in Springfield were typical of those in other communities. Coughlinites were fairly strong. Anti-Semitism was fairly pronounced. Opportunities for Negroes were probably fewer than in most similar communities." [3]

Furthermore, Springfield is a rather conservative community and had to be introduced gradually to the changes in the system. Nevertheless, Springfield had several advantages. It enjoyed two exceptionally fine, civic-spirited newspapers. Its school system was known for its excellence, and its superintendent, Dr. Granrud, followed a course of practical democracy in appointing teachers. The school personnel was therefore representative of all groups, and the people had confidence in their schools.

The community has cooperated with the schools in Springfield to make the program a success. In this instance it was the teachers who led the community, but without the encouragement, by cooperation, of the community the efforts of the schools could scarcely have succeeded as well as they have.

The children have made substantial progress in learning to think critically, and a large proportion have made considerable progress

---

[3] Miller, "Community Wages Total War on Prejudice," *The Nation's Schools,* XXXIII (1944), 16–18.

toward overcoming their prejudices as a result of the self-analysis and open discussion conducted in class. Mutual understanding of one another has been brought to many adults through the adult educational program. But Springfield is not yet Utopia. "We have only made a start in the great task before us," Dr. Granrud has said. "But I am profoundly convinced that significant progress has already been achieved, and as our experience and skill grow, even greater advances will be made in developing the type of citizenry which will not only strive toward but which will achieve greater promise implicit in the democratic way."

The experiment in education for democracy which has been so successfully initiated and tried in Springfield will, it is hoped, be tried in hundreds of other communities throughout the United States. Already the representatives of the school systems of a number of large cities have the Springfield Plan under study for adoption in their own school systems. Pittsburgh put the plan into action in January, 1944.

Each community will, of course, adapt the plan to meet its own peculiar conditions. Every community which has undertaken to carry out the plan will willingly assist other communities to launch it successfully in their own cities.

There can be little doubt that the Springfield Plan is a most promising practical scheme for the combating of "race" prejudice and the education of Americans for a living democracy. Prejudices must be prevented from developing. To eradicate the infection, we must begin in the nurseries, on the playgrounds, and in the schools. This Springfield has done. Its example must be widely imitated, not alone in the United States, but throughout the world wherever people of different physical types or religious faiths meet. In this way man's most dangerous myth, the fallacy of "race," can be overcome and relegated to the refuse heap of man's past follies.

The Term "Miscegenation"

THE TERM "MISCEGENATION" provides a remarkable exhibit in the natural history of nonsense. The term today is used in a pejorative sense as referring to "race mixture." The prefix "mis" (from the Latin *misces,* "mix") has probably contributed its share to the misunderstanding of the nature of "race" mixture. Words that begin with the prefix "mis" suggest a "mistake," "misuse," "mislead," and similar erroneous ideas implying wrong conduct.

The word "miscegenation" was invented as a hoax, and published in an anonymous pamphlet at New York in 1864, with the title *Miscegenation: The Theory of the Blending of the Races, Applied to the White Man and Negro.* The pamphlet was almost certainly the joint product of two members of the New York *World* staff, David Goodman Croly, an editor, and George Wakeman, one of the reporters. The purpose of the authors was to raise the "race" issue in aggravated form in the 1864 presidential campaign by attributing to the abolitionist Republicans and the Republican party the views set forth in *Miscegenation.* The pamphlet was intended to commit the Republican leaders to "the conclusions to which they are brought by their own principles," without any hope of success but in the expectation that their folly would be made all the more clear to them in granting the Negro the franchise. The brief introduction sets the tone of the whole pamphlet.

"The word is spoken at last. It is Miscegenation—the blending of the various races of men—the practical recognition of all the children of the common father. While the sublime inspirations of Christianity have taught this doctrine, Christians so-called have ignored it in denying social equality to the colored man; while democracy is founded upon the idea that all men are equal, democrats have shrunk from the logic of their own creed, and refused to fraternize with the people of all nations; while science has demonstrated that the inter-marriage of diverse races is indispensable to a progressive humanity, its votaries, in this country at least, have never had the courage to apply that rule to the relations of the white and colored races. But Christianity, democracy, and science are stronger than the timidity, prejudice, and pride of short-sighted men; and they teach that a people, to become great, must become composite. This involves what is vulgarly known as amalgamation, and those who dread that name, and the thought and fact it implies, are warned against reading these pages."

The word "miscegenation" is defined by the authors as follows: *"Miscegenation*—from the Latin *Miscere,* to mix, and *Genus,* race, is used to denote the abstract idea of the mixture of two or more races."

Thus, the word "miscegenation" was invented by the satirists to replace the vulgar term "amalgamation," as not being sufficiently elevated or distinguished.[1] Indeed, the word does carry with it a sort of authoritative aura, implying, however, a certain lack of respect-ability.[2] The word should be replaced by ordinary English words such as "intermixture," "mixture," "admixture," and "intermarriage."

---

[1] The pamphlet is the subject of an excellent little book, Bloch, *Miscegenation, Melaleukation, and Mr. Lincoln's Dog.*

[2] This is well illustrated by a remark recently made by former President Harry S. Truman. When asked whether he thought "racial" intermarriages would become widespread in the United States, he answered, "I hope not. I don't believe in it. What's that word about four feet long? Miscegenation?" New York *Times,* September 12, 1963.

A Reappraisal of the Constitutionality of "Miscegenation" Statutes[*]

by Andrew D. Weinberger [†]

TODAY, nineteen States of the Union by statute forbid marriages on racial grounds.[1] These statutes are neither uniform in the racial groups against whom the ban is applicable, nor in defining membership in the various ethnic groups. Thus, while in Mississippi

---

[*] © by Cornell University 1957 assigned to the author. Revised to November 1, 1963, from the original publication in 42 *Cornell Law Quarterly* 208 (1957) and republication in *Law Review Digest* (January–February 1957), *Revue de Droit International pour le Moyen-Orient* (Juin 1957), *Revista de la Facultad de Derecho de Mexico* (Julio–Septiembre 1957), *Journal of Negro Education* (Fall 1957), *Law Review of the University of Sto. Tomas* (Manila, November–December 1957) and *Journal of the National Medical Association* (May 1959).

[†] Andrew D. Weinberger, D. Hum., LL. D. Member of the New York Bar. Visiting Lecturer or Professor, New York University Graduate School of Public Administration and Social Service (1953–1956), National University of Mexico (1959–1960), and Toyo University, Tokyo (1961–1962). Author of *Freedom and Protection: The Bill of Rights* (San Francisco, Chandler Pub., 1962).

[1] Ala. Const. § 102; Ala. Code tit. 14, § 360 (1958); Ark. Stat. § 55–104 (1947); Del. Code Ann. tit. 13, § 101 (1953); Fla. Const. art. XVI, § 24; Fla. Stat. § 741.11 (1961); Ga. Code Ann. § 53–106 (1933); Ind. Ann. Stat. § 44–104 (Burns, 1952); Ky. Rev. Stat. § 402.020 (1953); La. Civ. Code art. 94 (Dart., 1945); Md. Ann. Code art. 27, § 398 (1957); Miss. Const. art 14, § 263; Miss Code Ann. § 459 (1942); Mo. Rev. Stat. § 451.020 (1959); N.C. Const. art. XIV, § 8; N.C. Gen. Stat. § 51–3 (1953); Okla. Stat. tit. 43, § 12 (1961); S.C. Const. art. 3, § 34; S.C. Code § 20–7 (1952); Tenn. Const. art. 11, § 14; Tenn. Code Ann. § 36–402 (1956); Tex. Rev. Civ. Stat. art. 4607 (1948);

white-Mongolian marriages are illegal and void,[2] in North Carolina they are permitted.[3] In Arkansas, where white-Negro marriages are void, a Negro is defined as "any person who has in her or his veins any negro blood whatever."[4] In Florida, one ceases to be a Negro when he has less than "one-eighth of . . . African or negro blood";[5] and in Oklahoma, anyone not of "African descent" is miraculously transmuted into a member of the white race.[6]

The racial groups[7] affected by such statutes include Mongolians,[8] Malays,[9] Chinese,[10] Japanese,[11] American Indians,[12] Cherokees,[13]

Va. Code Ann. § 20–54 (1953); W. Va. Code Ann. § 4701 (1) (1961); Wyo. Stat. § 20–18 (1957).

This contrasts with seventeen States, in 1954, having statutes requiring segregation in education. Brown v. Board of Education, 347 U.S. 483 (1954); 349 U.S. 294 (1955). See also Comments, 32 Calif. L. Rev. 269 (1944); 20 So. Calif. L. Rev. 80 (1946).

There is no federal policy against intermarriage. None of the islands or possessions has such statutes. Apparently Guam at one time had such prohibitions, but these were abolished in 1951. (Public Law 19, First Guam Legislature.)

Those States which at one time had anti-miscegenation statutes, together with the date of repeal are: Arizona, 1962; California, 1959; Colorado, 1957; Idaho, 1959; Iowa, 1851; Kansas, 1857; Maine, 1883; Massachusetts, 1840; Michigan, 1883; Montana, 1953; Nebraska, 1963; Nevada, 1959; New Mexico, 1866; North Dakota, 1955; Ohio, 1877; Oregon, 1951; Rhode Island, 1881; South Dakota, 1957; Utah, 1963; Washington, 1867. (The repeals by Kansas, New Mexico, and Washington occurred while they were Territories.)

[2] Mississippi Code Ann. § 459 (1942).

[3] North Carolina Constitution, N.C. Gen. Stat. *supra* note 1.

[4] Ark. Stat. *supra* note 1.

[5] Fla. Stat. *supra* note 1.

[6] The Oklahoma Constitution, art. XXIII, § 11 provides:

Wherever in this Constitution and laws of this State the word or words "colored" or "colored race," "negro" or "negro race" are used the same shall be construed to mean or apply to all persons of African descent. The term "white race" shall include all other persons.

[7] Ethnic groups would be a more correct description as these are not each a separate race.

[8] Georgia, Mississippi, Missouri, and Wyoming.

[9] Maryland and Wyoming.

[10] Georgia.

[11] Georgia.

[12] North Carolina and South Carolina.

[13] North Carolina.

Mestizos,[14] and Halfbreeds.[15] The sole racial group (other than white persons) affected by all nineteen statutes is the Negro.[16]

The courts of last resort of eleven States[17] have upheld anti-miscegenation statutes and the statutes of the other eight States have been enforced in the lower courts. Legislative prohibition of marriage between the races was declared unconstitutional by courts in California in 1948,[18] in Nevada in 1959,[19] and in Arizona in 1959.[20] Subsequently each of these States repealed their laws prohibiting interracial marriage.

The United States Supreme Court accepted jurisdiction, in 1955, in a case from Virginia which squarely raised the question whether a statute proscribing the marriage of the Chinese appellant to a white woman was violative of the equal protection clause of the Fourteenth

---

[14] South Carolina and Tennessee.

[15] South Carolina.

[16] There was no such prohibition at common law. 1 Bishop, Marriage, Divorce, and Separation 308 (1873); Madden, Persons and Domestic Relations 35 (1931).

Early in the development of the colonies severe penalties were enacted for sexual intercourse between members of different racial groups. As early as 1661, Maryland provided by statute that English women having children fathered by Negro slaves were to be slaves of the Negro's master. In Virginia, the white parent was banished from the colony, and in North Carolina, along with the child, was placed in servitude. Reuter, Race Mixture 78 (1931).

[17] Green v. Alabama, 58 Ala. 190 (1877); Dodson v. State, 61 Ark. 57, 31 S.W. 977 (1895); McLaughlin v. Florida, 153 So. 2d 1 (1963); Scott v. Georgia, 39 Ga. 321 (1869); State v. Gibson, 36 Ind. 389 (1871); Miller v. Lucks, 203 Miss. 824, 36 So. 2d 140 (1948); State v. Jackson, 80 Mo. 175 (1883); State v. Kennedy, 76 N.C. 251 (1877); Eggers v. Olson, 104 Okla. 297, 231 Pac. 483 (1924); Lonas v. State, 50 Tenn. 287 (1871); Naim v. Naim, 197 Va. 80, 87 S.E.2d 749, remanded, 350 U.S. 891 (1955), aff'd, 197 Va. 734, 90 S.E.2d 849, app. dismissed, 350 U.S. 985 (1956).

[18] Perez v. Sharpe, 32 Cal. 2d 711, 198 P.2d 17 (1948). The California Supreme Court, by a four to three decision, sitting as a court of the first instance (at that time actions against a public official were initiated in the Supreme Court) granted mandamus against a County Clerk who refused to issue a marriage license to petitioners, one of whom was Negro and the other white, holding the statute violative of the Fourteenth Amendment. For a discussion of this case see Notes, 1 Stan. L. Rev. 289 (1949); 58 Yale L.J. 472 (1949).

[19] Bridges v. Brown, Nevada District Court, Reno (December 10, 1958, not reported).

[20] Ogama v. O'Neill, Arizona Superior Court, Tucson (December 23, 1959, not reported).

Amendment. The Court decided the record was incomplete as to the domicile of the parties and remanded it to the Virginia Supreme Court to be returned to the trial court so that additional evidence could be taken.[21]

Thereupon, that court, presumptuously, held that the record clearly showed that the plaintiff was a resident of Virginia; the defendant a non-resident, and that both parties had been married in North Carolina for the purpose of circumventing the Virginia anti-miscegenation statute. Therefore, the court concluded, the case was decided upon a complete record and there was no procedure to remand the case to the trial court to take further evidence and, in complete contravention of the Supreme Court's determination, affirmed its own decision.[22] Nevertheless, upon application to the Supreme Court to recall the remand or to argue *de novo,* the Court held that the second judgment of the Virginia court left the case devoid of a properly presented Federal question and denied the application.[23]

Of all discriminations practiced against Negroes, Orientals, Indians, and other ethnic minorities, the prohibition against intermarriage is the one which the minority groups are least interested in abolishing. Myrdal lists a "White Man's Rank Order of Discriminations"[24] as an organizing principle in his study. His order of importance of types of discrimination, that is, the order in which white believers in segregation object to integration, is:

1. Intermarriage.
2. Barriers against dancing, bathing, eating and social intercourse generally.

---

[21] Naim v. Naim, 350 U.S. 891 (1955). The opinion per curiam reads: The inadequacy of the record as to the relationship of the parties to the Commonwealth of Virginia at the time of the marriage in North Carolina and upon their return to Virginia, and the failure of the parties to bring here all questions relevant to the disposition of the case, prevents the constitutional issue of the validity of the Virginia statute on miscegenation tendered here being considered "in clean cut and concrete form, unclouded" by such problems. Rescue Army v. Municipal Court, 331 U.S. 549, 584. The judgment is vacated and the case remanded to the Supreme Court of Appeals in order that the case may be returned to the Circuit Court of the City of Portsmouth for action not inconsistent with this opinion.

[22] 197 Va. 734, 90 S.E.2d 849 (1956).

[23] 350 U.S. 985 (1956).

[24] Myrdal, *An American Dilemma,* p. 60.

 3. Segregation in schools, churches and transportation.

 4. Political disenfranchisement.

 5. Discrimination in law courts, by the police and other public servants.

 6. Discrimination in housing, employment, credit and public relief.

The non-white's rank order of objectionable attitudes is parallel but *precisely inverse* to that of the white segregationist.[25]

The tremendous struggle of recent years in and out of the courts for racial equality has been to abolish discrimination and segregation in employment, housing, education, voting and the use of public facilities. In the mass of litigation, publications, and demonstrations sponsored by the National Association for the Advancement of Colored People, and other civil rights organizations, there has been no effort whatever favoring intermarriage. As a prominent Negro writer said:

> One barrier to a closer drawing together of the white and Negro races in America has been the misconception on the part of many whites that the Negro desires amalgamation. . . .
> Speaking as a Negro, I know that most Negroes do not desire sexual relationships with white women. . . . Negro men resent the mingling of white men and Negro women as much as white men fear miscegenation of white women and Negro men.[26]

Yet the ethnic minorities understandably find statutes repugnant which classify them as inferior and unfit to marry persons they may choose.[27] As DuBois said:

> But the impudent and vicious demand that all colored folk shall write themselves down as brutes by a general assertion of their unfitness to marry other decent folk, is a nightmare.[28]

Substantial injury to more tangible interests is, moreover, often a factor to be weighed. In addition to the prohibition of marriage, criminal penalties are often prescribed,[29] and by statute the offspring

---

[25] *Ibid.* at pp. 60, 61.

[26] Logan, *A Negro's Faith in America*, p. 27

[27] Myrdal, *op. cit. supra* note 24 at pp. 64, 65; DuBois, Crisis 106 (Editorial 1920).

[28] DuBois, *ibid.*

[29] Ala. Code tit. 14, § 360 (1958) (felony); Ark. Stat. § 55–105 (1947) (misdemeanor); Del. Code Ann. tit. 13, § 102 (1953) (misdemeanor); Fla. Stat.

of such marriages are declared illegitimate.[30] Other social situations[31] such as violation of the vagrancy statutes,[32] the marital privilege available to a defendant in a criminal prosecution,[33] and the right to receive property bequeathed by will,[34] or passing under the laws of intestacy,[35] are thereby affected. The Criminal Court of Baltimore, in 1957, held unconstitutional as discriminatory against white persons and women, a 1715 law which provided for punishment of a white woman who had a child by a Negro, and contained no penalty for the father. The omission of penalty against the Negro father is a demonstration of the economic base in slavery of the anti-miscegenation statutes.[36]

Despite the differences in holdings between the States, in 1954 the United States Supreme Court refused certiorari in a case in

§ 741.12 (1961) (felony); Ga. Code Ann. § 53–9903 (felony); Ind. Ann. Stat. § 10–4222 (Burns, 1952) (felony); Ky. Rev. Stat. § 402–990 (felony); La. Crim. Code art 740–79 (Dart., 1945) (felony); Md. Ann. Code art. 27, § 513 (1957) (felony for white woman "to be got with child by a negro or mulatto") but see *infra* note 36 and its text; Miss. Code Ann. § 2339 (1942) (felony); Mo. Rev. Stat. § 563.240 (1959) (felony); N.C. Gen. Stat. § 14–181 (1953) (misdemeanor but sentence may be up to ten years); Okla. Stat. tit. 43, § 13 (felony); S.C. Code § 20–7 (1952) (misdemeanor); Tenn. Code Ann. § 36–403 (1956) (felony); Tex. Pen. Code Ann. art. 492 (1952) (felony); Va. Code Ann. § 20–59 (1953) (felony); W. Va. Code Ann. § 4697 (1961) (white person may be fined not more than $100 and imprisoned up to one year; no penalties against Negro); Wyo. Stat. § 20–19 (1957) (misdemeanor).

[30] E.g., Fla. Stat. *supra* note 1. In all states having prohibitory statutes, with the exception of West Virginia, a miscegenistic marriage is void and therefore the offspring would be illegitimate. In West Virginia the marriage is valid until such time as a court declares it a nullity. Therefore, seemingly, in West Virginia the children of the marriage born before a decree of nullity are legitimate.

[31] See Comments, 32 Calif. L. Rev. 269 (1944); 20 So. Calif. L. Rev. 80 (1946).

[32] Jackson v. Denver, 109 Colo. 196, 124 P.2d 240 (1942). The defense to a charge of vagrancy (which included meretricious cohabitation) was marriage. The court held that the marriage was void because of the racial differences of the spouses and, therefore, the defense was untenable. (It should be noted that Colorado repealed its prohibitory statute in 1957.)

[33] State v. Pass, 59 Ariz. 16, 121 P.2d 882 (1942). (Although Arizona repealed its prohibitory statute in 1962, the rationale of the case would be applicable in States with anti-miscegenation statutes.)

[34] Miller v. Lucks, *supra* note 17.

[35] Eggers v. Olson, *supra* note 17.

[36] State v. Howard, Daily Record, Baltimore (April 22, 1957).

which the constitutionality of the Alabama statute was directly raised.[37] However, a year later the Court accepted jurisdiction in the *Naim* case, and though it was thwarted from making a constitutional determination by procedural defects, it is reasonable to believe that at the next opportunity the Court will pass on this question.

It is accordingly timely to reappraise the constitutionality of the miscegenation statutes and their concept of a "mongrel breed of citizens." [38]

RACIAL CLASSIFICATION AND THE RIGHT TO MARRY

The right to marry is a civil right and it is, therefore, within the purview of the equal protection clause. In *Meyer v. Nebraska*,[39] the Court said:

> While this court has not attempted to define with exactness the liberty thus guaranteed [by the Fourteenth Amendment], the term has received much consideration, and some of the included things have been definitely stated. Without doubt, it denotes not merely freedom from bodily restraint, but also the right of the individual to . . . marry, establish a home and bring up children. . . .

Judge Traynor in the *Perez* case described the nature of the right to marry and the constitutional protection afforded it in even more eloquent terms.

> Marriage . . . is something more than a civil contract subject to regulation by the state; it is a fundamental right of free men. There can be no prohibition of marriage except for an important social objective and by reasonable means. . . .
> Legislation infringing such rights must be based upon more than prejudice and must be free from oppressive discrimination to comply with the constitutional requirements of due process and equal protection of the laws.[40]

---

[37] Jackson v. State, 37 Ala. App. 519, 72 So. 2d 114 cert. denied sub nom., Jackson v. Alabama, 348 U.S. 888 (1954).

[38] Naim v. Naim, 197 Va. 80, 90, 87 S.E.2d 749, 756 (1955). For a critical discussion of this case see 1 Howard L. Rev. 84 (1955).

[39] 262 U.S. 390, 399 (1923), See also Skinner v. Oklahoma, 316 U.S. 535, 541 (1942).

[40] Perez v. Sharpe, 32 Cal. 2d. 711, 714–15, 198 P.2d 17, 18–19 (1948).

To this concept of marriage as a civil right there should then be applied the prohibitions, as previously defined by the Court, against classification by race. Consider first *Strauder v. West Virginia*[41] in which the Court said:

> ... all persons, whether colored or white, shall stand equal before the laws of the States and, in regard to the colored race, for whose protection the Amendment was primarily designed, that no discrimination shall be made against them by laws because of their color. . . .[42]

In *Edwards v. California*,[43] Mr. Justice Jackson said that race was "constitutionally an irrelevance."[44] And while the doctrine of "separate but equal" is no longer accepted, *Plessy v. Ferguson*[45] is still authority for the proposition that "The object of the [Fourteenth] amendment was undoubtedly to enforce the absolute equality of the two races before the law. . . ."[46]

Consistently in area after area the Court has held that race may not be a means of legislative classification.

A Louisville, Kentucky, ordinance which established white and colored residential zones was tested against the equal protection clause in 1917 and held void.[47] Racial restrictive land covenants were held judicially unenforceable in 1948.[48] In *Brown v. Board of Education*,[49] the Court required that public schools be desegregated, holding that separation itself was a denial of equality.

The Court has held that the States are prohibited by the Fourteenth Amendment from using race as a test in licensing laundries[50] and commercial fishermen.[51]

The only exception to this long line of decisions, one after another denouncing racial classification in legislation, is the military restric-

---

[41] 100 U.S. 303 (1880).
[42] *Id.* at 307.
[43] 314 U.S. 160 (1941).
[44] *Id.* at 185.
[45] 163 U.S. 537 (1896).
[46] *Id.* at 544.
[47] Buchanan v. Warley, 245 U.S. 60 (1917).
[48] Shelley v. Kraemer, 334 U.S. 1 (1948).
[49] 347 U.S. 483 (1954); 349 U.S. 294 (1955).
[50] Yick Wo v. Hopkins, 118 U.S. 356 (1886).
[51] Takahashi v. Fish and Game Comm'n, 334 U.S. 410 (1948).

tions imposed on persons of Japanese descent during World War II.[52]
Hirabayashi v. United States and *Korematsu v. United States* were
justified by the Court as war measures taken by the Federal Government. But they were criticized by leading scholars immediately after
the decisions were published and the Court subsequently retreated
from its position.[53] Furthermore, they are no authority for racial
grouping by the States.[54]

The basis for the State courts' finding of constitutionality rests primarily upon two arguments:

A. The statutes are not discriminatory as they apply equally to all
races; and

B. The racial classifications made in the statutes are reasonable in
view of the legislative objective and, therefore, do not violate the due
process or equal protection clauses of the Fourteenth Amendment.[55]

EQUAL APPLICATION OF MISCEGENATION STATUTES

Pace v. Alabama[56] is often cited as holding that the miscegenation
statutes place an equal inhibition upon both white and non-white persons, and therefore are constitutional.[57] This is strained reasoning

---

[52] Korematsu v. United States, 323 U.S. 214 (1944); Hirabayashi v. United
States, 320 U.S. 81 (1943).

[53] Dembetz, "Racial Discrimination and the Military Judgment," 45 Colum. L.
Rev. 175 (1945); Rostow, "The Japanese American Cases—A Disaster," 54
Yale L. J. 489 (1945). See also Duncan v. Kahanamoku, 327 U.S. 304 (1946).

[54] However, this uniformity of protection has not been extended to aliens.
Clarke v. Deckebach, 274 U.S. 392 (1927); Truax v. Raich, 239 U.S. 33
(1915); Patsone v. Pennsylvania, 232 U.S. 138 (1914). See also, Konvitz, *The
Alien and the Asiatic in American Law.*

[55] A third argument sometimes advanced is that segregation promotes public
peace by preventing race conflicts which would arise upon desegregation. The
Supreme Court in Buchanan v. Warley, 245 U.S. 60, 81 (1917) stated that
"important as is the preservation of the public peace, this aim cannot be accomplished by laws or ordinances which deny rights created or protected by
the Federal Constitution." Judge Traynor is even more forceful in rejecting
this contention. "It is no answer to say that race tension can be eradicated
through the perpetuation by law of the prejudices which give rise to the tension." Perez v. Sharpe, 32 Cal. 2d 711, 725, 198 P.2d 17, 25 (1948).

[56] 106 U.S. 583 (1883).

[57] Thurgood Marshall, "The Supreme Court as Protector of Civil Rights:

since *Pace* was an appeal from a conviction for violation of an Alabama statute providing penalties for fornication and adultery where one party to the crime was white and the other Negro. In challenging the constitutionality of this statute, it was argued that a similar statute provided lesser penalties where both parties were white or both were Negro. The statute considered was tested by the Court, however, against the penalties in the statute itself, and those penalties were found to be equal for both the white and the Negro person involved.

> Indeed, the offense against which this latter section is aimed cannot be committed without involving the persons of both races in the same punishment. Whatever discrimination is made in the punishment prescribed in the two sections is directed against the offense designated and not against the person of any particular color or race. The punishment of each offending person, whether white or black, is the same.[58]

In considering the effect of this case, it should not be overlooked that penal prohibition of illicit intercourse can hardly be equated with a similar prohibition of a sanctified relationship. The *Pace* decision is far from a constitutional approval of a prohibition of interracial marriage.[59]

While there is apparent equal treatment of the different races and ethnic groups in the statutes on miscegenation, it is self-evident even if the doctrine of "separate but equal" were still valid, that it cannot apply in the marital relationship. How can it be said that when two persons are denied the right to marry because of race, they may find equal opportunity within their own groups? In *Perez*, decided before

---

Equal Protection of the Laws," *The Annals of the American Academy of Political and Social Science* 101 (May 1951):

> Pace v. Alabama . . . upheld the constitutionality of a legislative proscription of intermarriage between Negroes and white persons.

It should not be overlooked, however, that this was written in 1951 before *Brown v. Board of Education, supra* note 1.

[58] 106 U.S. at 585.

[59] In Moore v. Missouri, 159 U.S. 673, 678 (1895), the Court, citing the *Pace* case, said:

> The general doctrine is that [the Fourteenth Amendment] in respect of the administration of criminal justice, requires that no different degree or higher punishment shall be imposed on one than is imposed on all for like offenses. . . .

Brown and the 1956 decision in *Gayle v. Browder*,[60] the difference in the violation of constitutional rights in prohibitions of marriage and the denial of other less personal rights, was already indicated.

> A holding that . . . segregation does not impair the right of an individual to ride on trains or to enjoy a legal education is clearly inapplicable to the right of an individual to marry. Since the essence of the right to marry is freedom to join in marriage with the person of one's choice, a segregation statute for marriage necessarily impairs the right to marry.[61]

While the decision in the *Brown* case has changed the "holding" as to public education and *Gayle v. Browder* as to transportation, the latter part of the statement remains as true today as it was in 1948. The "separate but equal" theory, so recently completely rejected, has never logically had any place in the discussion of interracial marriage.

The choice of a spouse is a subjective act, the act of individuals and not races. It would therefore follow that a classification by statute of those prohibited from marrying each other must be made on an individual basis and not on a group basis.[62]

---

[60] 352 U.S. 903 (1956), affirming 142 F. Supp. 707 (D.C. Ala. 1956).

[61] Perez v. Sharpe, 32 Cal. 2d 711, 717, 198 P.2d 17, 21 (1948).

[62] "Here the petitioner's right was a personal one. It was as an individual that he was entitled to the equal protection of the laws. . . ." Missouri ex rel. Gaines v. Canada, 305 U.S. 337, 351 (1938); see also, Shelley v. Kraemer, 334 U.S. 1 (1948).

Even though discriminatory statutes generally affect the minority races more than whites, the anti-miscegenation statutes are more discriminating toward white persons. Thus the Virginia statute on miscegenation, *supra* note 1, reads in part:

> It shall hereafter be unlawful for any white person in this State to marry any save a white person, or a person with no other admixture of blood than white and [one-sixteenth or less] American Indian.

There is no other prohibition based on race in the Virginia statute. It follows that while a white person must seek a spouse only among whites (with or without one-sixteenth or less American Indian ancestry), the members of all other ethnic groups may freely marry anyone other than a white person within the borders of all the groups. See also State v. Pass, 59 Ariz. 16, 121 P.2d 882 (1942). In this case, the interesting proposition was raised that since the Arizona statute provided "the marriage of persons of Caucasian blood or their descendants, with Negroes, Mongolians, members of the Malay race, or Hindus or their descendants shall be null and void," persons of mixed ancestry could not marry anyone. The question was not resolved as the record did not indicate whether the parties were of mixed genes. The Arizona legislature subsequently removed the words "or their descendants" from the

SUPPOSED EFFECTS OF INTERRACIAL MARRIAGE UPON SOCIETY— A VALID LEGISLATIVE OBJECT?

Statutes prohibiting marriage on grounds other than racial ones have a place in society. Prohibition of marriages of feebleminded persons or of persons with communicable diseases is not uncommon. Each of these is supported by demonstrable scientific knowledge[63] that such marriages present a potential danger to society through physically or mentally ill offspring. In these statutes, the requirements of a reasonable legislative objective and a reasonable connection between the legislation and the ends sought have been met.[64]

In support of the statutes prohibiting interracial marriage, much the same argument is offered. Could it be demonstrated that biologically inferior children would be the result of such marriages, the necessity of a reasonable legislative objective would be met. While some courts have attempted a reasonable analysis, ordinarily they simply repeat outmoded and unscientific genetical conclusions. Thus a Georgia court said:

> The amalgamation of the races is not only unnatural, but it is always productive of deplorable results. Our daily observation shows us that the offspring of these unnatural connections are generally sickly and

---

statute. This same confusion is found in the Texas statute, and was pointed to in the Perez case, 32 Cal. 2d at 721, 198 P.2d at 23.

[63] In Jacobson v. Massachusetts, 187 U.S. 11 (1905), the Court had before it a statute providing for compulsory vaccination of all adults residing in a smallpox epidemic area. Jacobson refused to be vaccinated, contending that this was not a proper exercise of the police power. Holding that the police power extends to matters of health, the Court found that "for nearly a century most of the members of the medical profession have regarded vaccination, repeated after intervals, as a preventive of smallpox." (197 U.S. at 23). The Court concluded that there was a reasonable connection between the statute and the end sought.

In substantiating its conclusion as to the effect of vaccination, the Court in a copious footnote, beginning at page 32 of the opinion, set forth all of the available scientific evidence supporting the efficacy of vaccination.

For an excellent discussion of the use of social science at the trial level see, Greenberg, "Social Scientists Take the Stand," 54 Mich. L. Rev. 7 (1956).

[64] Quaker City Cab v. Pennsylvania, 277 U.S. 389, 400 (1928); Buck v. Bell, 274 U.S. 200 (1927); Purity Extract & Tonic Co. v. Lynch, 226 U.S. 192, 201 (1912).

effeminate, and that they are inferior in physical development and strength, to the full blood of either race.[65]

The Virginia Supreme Court in the *Naim* case found the legislative object to be "to preserve the racial integrity of . . . [the state's] citizens . . . [and] to regulate the marriage relation so that it will not have a mongrel breed of citizens."[66]

No authorities or sources whatever were cited for the opinions on race and heredity in that case. And the dissenting opinion in the California Supreme Court in 1948 in the *Perez* case is of the same school of thinking, that is, it completely disregards the twentieth-century developments in the science of human genetics. The rationale of the state courts is abhorrent to both science and jurisprudence. They adhere to and perpetuate three erroneous assumptions: (1) that "pure races" either exist in the present or have existed in the past; (2) that crossing between different racial groups results in biologically inferior offspring; (3) that cultural level is dependent upon racial attributes. Contemporary physical anthropology and human genetics disprove these three assumptions.

(1) *The Idea of "Pure Races"*

To speak of race "mixtures" or "mongrelization" is to imply that "pure races" either still exist or have existed in the past. Contemporary biological research and theory refute both of these implications. The idea of "pure" racial groups, either past or present, has long been abandoned by modern biological and social science. To the contrary:

Race mixture has been going on during the whole of recorded history. Incontrovertible evidence from studies on fossil human remains shows

---

[65] Scott v. Georgia, 39 Ga. 321, 323 (1869). That opinions such as this are not exclusively held by white people is evidenced by this quotation from Scarborough, *On the Trail of Negro Folk-Songs*, p. 20:

. . . I learned of a quarrel Uncle Israel had with one of the mulatto house servants about this question of color. She had disrespectfully called him a Nigger and he had retorted:

"What if I is a Nigger? I b'longs to a race of people. But you ain't. I didn't never read in de Bible about whar it speaks of mulattoes as a race of people. You is mules, dat's what you is."

. . . He said to me, "De mulattoes ain't live as long as white folks or colored either. Dey ain't healthy folks. I'll tell that to deir face."

[66] Naim v. Naim, 197 Va. 80, 89, 87 S.E.2d 749, 756 (1955).

that even in pre-history, at the very dawn of humanity, mixing of different stocks, at least occasionally, took place.[67]

The scientific position concerning the idea of "pure races" is contained in this statement by a distinguished American geneticist:

> The idea of a pure race is not even a legitimate abstraction; it is a subterfuge used to cloak one's ignorance of the phenomenon of racial variation.[68]

The idea of "pure races" is refuted by paleontological and genetical studies of human evolution. All mankind is a member of a single species, *Homo sapiens*. All known physical variations among men, therefore, continue to take place *within* species boundaries, not without. When considering human evolution and modern "races," we are not dealing with separate species. Interbreeding among human groups manifesting differences in physical attributes produces live, fertile offspring—the mark of membership in a single species. It has been established empirically that the offspring of mixed marriages are no less physically and psychologically sound than those where both parents are of the same race.[69]

---

[67] Dunn and Dobzhansky, *Heredity, Race and Society*, p. 115.

[68] Dobzhansky, "The Race Concept in Biology," *The Scientific Monthly*, LII (February, 1941), pp. 161–65. For additional corroborating evidence rejecting the idea of "pure races," see Boyd, *Genetics and the Races of Man: An Introduction to Modern Physical Anthropology*, pp. 184–209; Dobzhansky, "The Genetic Nature of Differences among Men," *Evolutionary Thought in America*, pp. 86–155; Kluckhohn, *Mirror for Man*, pp. 102–44; Ashley Montagu, "A Consideration of the Concept of Race; Origin and Evolution of Man," *Cold Spring Harbor Symposia on Quantitative Biology*, XV (1950), 315–36; this book, pp. 185–223.

[69] Reuter, *The Mulatto in the United States*, p. 117 et seq. That popular opinion is to the contrary is shown by an Associated Press dispatch from Bastrop, La., dated November 2, 1955, which read in part:

> The Morehouse Parish School Board has voted unanimously to discontinue use of a ninth-grade general science textbook which some persons say "contains un-American ideas on the origin of races."
> Superintendent of Schools Luckey told the board the book could be set aside if the school board objected to it. He said the title was "Science for Better Living."
> This passage was among those cited as objectionable:
> "Living things which belong to recognizable kinds, which are like in most physical traits, and which breed freely with each other, are said to

Under the sponsorship of the United Nations Educational, Scientific and Cultural Organization (UNESCO), thirteen scientists representing physical anthropology and human genetics met in June 1951 to consider the preparation of a statement which would effect a crystallization of scientific theory and opinion on matters of race and race differences. The *Statement on the Nature of Race and Race Differences* was released by UNESCO in September of 1952.[70]

The *Statement* at Article 7 said concerning "pure races":

> *There is no evidence for the existence of so-called "pure" races.* Skeletal remains provide the basis of our limited knowledge about earlier races. In regard to race mixture, the evidence points to the fact that human hybridization has been going on for an indefinite but considerable time. Indeed, one of the processes of race formation and race extinction or absorption is by means of hybridization between races. *As there is no reliable evidence that disadvantageous effects are produced thereby, no biological justification exists for prohibiting intermarriage between persons of different races.* [Emphasis added.]

(2) *The Assumption That Race Crossing Results in Biologically Inferior Offspring*

Ultimately, statutes prohibiting interracial marriage are a reflection of the popular but erroneous stereotype that such marriages give rise to biologically inferior offspring. The fact that the stereotype persists even when the weight of scientific evidence is against it testifies to its ideological rather than scientific character. Although there is no lack of research and literature assessing the biological consequences of race-crossing, "hardly any well-substantiated examples of disharmonious

---

belong to one species. All men on this earth belong to one species—homo sapiens."

Persons who object to the book said this was a plain insinuation that races "breed freely with each other" and is a dangerous Socialistic trend of thought to instill into the younger generation.

70 UNESCO has distributed the Statement in a variety of publications. It is one of several publications in the series The Race Question in Modern Science. For the names of those scientists who contributed to this Statement, see Appendix A, pp. 370–71. It was agreed that the Statement should be submitted to as many anthropologists and geneticists as possible; therefore, an additional sixty-nine renowned scientists contributed to its final form.

constitution resulting from miscegenation have been reported."[71] Independent evaluations of this literature tend to conclude that prohibitions against interracial marriage are primarily social and psychological and not biological.[72]

(3) The Assumption That Cultural Level Is Dependent Upon Racial Attributes

Statutes prohibiting interracial marriage commonly perpetuate another assumption that is totally inconsistent with valid knowledge pertaining to the relationship between race, progress, and cultural achievement.[73] There is no evidence to sustain the contention that cultural level is dependent upon racial or biological attributes.

Race, in its scientific dimension, refers only to the bio-genetic and physical attributes manifest by a specified population. It does not, under any circumstances, refer to culture (learned behavior), language, nationality, or religion. One of the fundamental axioms of both physical and cultural anthropology is that culture (behavior) is independent of race. Civilizations and cultural achievement are not based on genes or physical characteristics. There are no known racial or biological barriers to the acquisition or creation of any cultural tradition,[74] a fact amply demonstrated by the creation and dissemination of cul-

---

[71] Stern, *Principles of Human Genetics*, p. 570. See especially Chapter 26, "Genetic Aspects of Race Mixture," pp. 563–79.

[72] Boyd, *Genetics and the Races of Man*, pp. 364–65; Castle, "Biological and Social Consequences of Race Crossing," *American Journal of Physical Anthropology*, IX (1926), 145–56; Cook, "Racial Fusion Among California and Nevada Indians," *Human Biology*, 15 (1943), 153; Hankins, *The Racial Basis of Civilization*, pp. 328–51; Kroeber, *Anthropology*, pp. 198–201; this book, pp. 185–96.

[73] *Naim v. Naim, supra* note 17: "Both sacred and secular history teach that nations and races have better advanced in human progress when they cultivated their own distinctive characteristics and culture and developed their own particular genius." 197 Va. at 90, 87 S.E.2d at 756.

[74] The literature and research denying a direct association between racial membership and cultural achievement is voluminous. However, the following references are among those giving a cogent presentation of the position of contemporary biological and social science: Beals and Hoijer, *An Introduction to Anthropology*, pp. 195–98; Hankins, *The Racial Basis of Civilization*, pp. 367–71; Kroeber, *Anthropology*. pp. 190–92; Ashley Montagu, *An Introduction to Physical Anthropology*, pp. 352–81; this book, pp. 238–51.

tural innovations in the United States irrespective of the racial composition of that population.

The scientific material available at present does not justify the conclusion that inherited genetic or racial differences are a factor in producing the differences between cultures. Cultural and civilizational factors are transmitted by learning and education, not by the genes.[75] When the Selective Service System published its rate of rejections for mental deficiency, it showed that while Negro illiteracy exceeded white illiteracy in the South, white illiteracy in the Southeast exceeded Negro illiteracy in the Northwest and the far West.[76] Economic-sociopolitical factors and not race determine education and health. There are no racial monopolies on cultural achievement. Historical and comparative studies of human culture show that vast changes have taken place in the economic, political, and social institutions of a given society without any, or with little, change in the racial or genetic composition of the population concerned.

If the weight of the scientific evidence formerly available justified the fear of biologically inferior offspring through intermarriage, then a sound legislative objective was being sought. However, now that these theories have been proven false, the legislative object is also fallacious. Legislative determination cannot reverse empirical fact. Constitutional construction cannot remain unchanged when originally predicated upon a false premise.[77]

The statutes are self-contradictory, containing within themselves certain permissible areas of miscegenistic marriage. Apparently, "scientific" thought varies from State to State. As has been shown, some legislatures see no danger in white-Mongolian marriages, while others do. None, with the exception of North Carolina and Maryland, perceive any evidence of deterioration in the offspring of intermarriage among any of the races other than white.[78] Even as to Negroes, the

---

[75] UNESCO Statement on the Nature of Race and Race Differences. See Appendix A, pp. 361–71

[76] Ginzburg and Bray, *The Uneducated*, p. 43.

[77] The Court in *Brown v. Board of Education* recognized that a changing society might require a different constitutional construction when it said: "Public education is today a wholly different thing from what it was when the Fourteenth Amendment was adopted." 347 U.S. at 493.

[78] In North Carolina marriage between a Cherokee Indian of Robeson County

degree of Negro genes thought sufficient to cause contamination varies from State to State, and in the most absurd instance, Colorado prohibited (until March 14, 1957) in one part of the State interracial marriages which in another part of the State[79] were permitted.

It is not scientifically possible to determine whether a person is "one-eighth Negro," "one-half Malay," or is one of the many varieties of fractionated racial memberships. Such terms as "half-breeds," "octa-roons," "full-bloods," and the like, are misleading when used in anything but the fictional or social sense; for example, the popular expression that a person is "one-quarter Chinese" has no necessary biological or genetic meaning—it does mean, pragmatically, only that one of a set of grandparents of that person was *socially defined* as a person of Chinese ancestry. It carries no genetically meaningful import, for example, that one-quarter of the genes of that person are "Chinese." Genes are not known to be transmitted in any such predetermined or culturally labeled quantities—an observation that has prompted one scholar to remark:

> Laws prohibiting marriage between "whites and persons having one-eighth or more of Negro blood" are compounded of legal fiction and genetic nonsense.[80]

---

and a Negro or person of Negro descent to the third generation is prohibited. There is no similar restriction against Cherokees of counties other than Robe-son nor against Indians other than Cherokees regardless of their county. N.C. Gen. Stat. § 51–3 (1950). Maryland prohibits marriage between a Negro and "a member of the Malay race." Md. Ann. Code art. 27, § 398 (1957).

[79] Colo. Rev. Stat. c. 90 § 1–2 (1953).

> All marriages entered into between Negroes or mulattoes of either sex, and white persons are declared to be absolutely void. Nothing in this section shall be so construed as to prevent the people living in that portion of the state acquired from Mexico from marrying according to the customs of that country.

It would appear that the marital customs of Mexico would be a matter of judicial notice. Yet in one case it was held that since the customs of that country were not in the record, the court could not rule on whether the statute was complied with. Jackson v. Denver, 109 Colo. 196, 124 P.2d 240 (1942).

[80] Hager, "Some Observations on the Relationship Between Genetics and Social Science," *Psychiatry*, 13 (1950), 371, 375.

In actual fact, the miscegenist prohibition is based not upon ratiocination at all but rather upon deep-seated racial attitudes.[81] As was said by one court:

> ... the social relation and practices of the races have, in the interest of our civilization as well as in expression of the natural pride of the dominant Anglo-Saxon race and of its preservation from the degeneration social equality, between the races, would inevitably bring, imperatively necessitated and created immutable rules of social conduct and social restraint, that the just ends indicated might be attained and permanently maintained. ... Among these are: The inhibition against the authorization or legalization of marriage between any white person and a negro. ...[82]

CONCLUSION

When subjected to the test of the Fourteenth Amendment, such emotionalism must yield to rational thinking. Marriage is a civil right and as such subject to constitutional protection. Not only do the anti-miscegenation statutes have no scientific basis, but their philosophy is an affront to millions of our citizens.

Repugnant as is the rationale of "social practices,"[83] at least that statement has the virtue of honesty as distinguished from the biologic nonsense of "mongrel breed"[84] and "weak and effeminate offspring."[85] But the right of equal protection may not be denied even though a substantial segment of the population finds it distasteful. The Court required desegregation of the schools[86] and transportation[87] despite the violence of the opposition.

Classification by race based upon nonexistent racial traits does not serve any valid legislative purpose but merely continues a classification of Americans as superior and inferior in contradiction to the American concept of equality.

[81] Myrdal, *op. cit. supra* note 24.
[82] Story v. State, 178 Ala. 98, 103, 59, So. 480, 482 (1912).
[83] *Ibid.*
[84] Naim v. Naim, 197 Va. 80, 90, 87 S.E.2d. 749, 756 (1955).
[85] Scott v. Georgia, 39 Ga. 321, 324 (1869).
[86] Brown v. Board of Education, 347 U.S. 483 (1954); 349 U.S. 294 (1955).
[87] Gayle v. Browder, 352 U.S. 903 (1956), affirming 142 F. Supp. 707 (D. C. Ala. 1956).

State Legislation Against Mixed Marriages in the United States

PROHIBITED MARRIAGES [a]

State and Statutory Reference	Ethnic Groups Prohibited from Marrying Whites [b and c]	Penal Offense
ALABAMA Const. § 102; Code tit. 14, § 360	"negro or the descendant of any negro"	Felony (Code tit. 14, § 360)
ARKANSAS Stat. § 55–104	"any person who has in her or his veins any negro blood whatever"	Misdemeanor (Stat. § 55–105)
DELAWARE Code tit. 13, § 101	"a negro or mulatto"	Misdemeanor (Code tit. 13, § 102)
FLORIDA Const. art. XVI, § 24; Stat. § 741.11	"a negro . . . or a person of negro descent to the fourth generation, inclusive"	Felony (Stat. § 741.12)
GEORGIA Code § 53–106; chap. 53.3	"It shall be unlawful for a white person to marry anyone except a white person." "White persons are only persons of the white or Caucasian race who have no ascertainable trace of either negro, African, West Indian, Mongolian, Japanese or Chinese blood in their veins."	Felony (Code § 53–9903)

421

INDIANA Stat. § 44–104	A person "possessed of one-eighth or more of negro blood."	Felony (Stat. § 10–4222)
KENTUCKY Rev. Stat. § 402.020	"a negro or mulatto"	Felony (Stat. § 402–990)
LOUISIANA Civ. Code art. 94	"persons of color"	Felony (Crim. Code art. 740–79)
MARYLAND Code art. 27, § 398	"a negro . . . or a person of negro descent to the third generation inclusive . . . a person of the Malay race."[b]	"A white woman who shall suffer herself to be got with child by a negro or mulatto . . . shall be sentenced to the penitentiary for not less than eighteen months nor more than five years." (Code art. 27, § 513) (See note 36 and its text.)
MISSISSIPPI Const. art. 14, § 263; Code § 459	"a negro or mulatto or person who shall have one-eighth or more of negro blood or . . . a Mongolian or person who shall have one-eighth or more of Mongolian blood."	Felony (Code § 2339)
MISSOURI Rev. Stat. §§ 451.020 and 563.240	"negroes . . . and Mongolians." Negroes are defined as persons "having one-eighth part or more negro blood."	Felony (Rev. Stat. § 563.240)

NORTH CAROLINA Const. art. XIV, § 8; Gen. Stat. §§ 14–181 and 51–3	"a negro or Indian . . . or a person of negro or Indian descent to the third generation, inclusive." ᶜ	Misdemeanor, but sentence may be up to ten years. (Gen. Stat. § 14–181)
OKLAHOMA Stat. tit. 43, § 12	"any person of African descent."	Felony (Stat. tit. 43, § 13)
SOUTH CAROLINA Const. art. 3, § 34; Code § 20–7	"any mulatto, half-breed, Indian, negro or mestizo."	Misdemeanor (Code § 20–7)
TENNESSEE Const. art. 11, § 14, Code § 36–402	"negroes, mulattos, or persons of mixed blood descended from a negro to the third generation, inclusive."	Felony (Code §36–403)
TEXAS Rev. Civ. Stat. art. 4607	"Africans or the descendants of Africans."	Felony (Penal Code art. 492)
VIRGINIA Code § 20–54	"It shall be unlawful for any white person to marry any save a white person, or a person with no other admixture of blood than white and American Indian . . . the term 'white person' shall apply to such person who has no trace whatever of any blood other than Caucasian; but persons who have one-sixteenth or less of the blood of the American Indian and have no other non-Caucasic blood shall be deemed to be white persons."	Felony (Code § 20–59)

WEST VIRGINIA Code § 4701(1)	"a negro"	White persons may be fined not more than $100 and imprisoned for not more than one year. No penalties against Negro persons. (Code § 4697)
WYOMING Stats. § 20–18	"Negroes, Mulattoes, Mongolians and Malays"	Misdemeanor (Stats. § 20–19)

---

a In West Virginia, though the marriage is performed in violation of the prohibitory statute, it is valid until such time as a court declares it a nullity. In all the other states listed the marriage is void.

b In Maryland, a marriage between "a negro and a member of the Malay race, a person of negro descent, to the third generations, inclusive, and a member of the Malay race" is also prohibited.

c In North Carolina a marriage between "a Cherokee Indian of Robeson County and a negro, or between a Cherokee Indian of Robeson County and a person of negro descent to the third generation" is also prohibited.

The Terms "Abolition" and "Emancipation"

THE TERMS "abolition" and "emancipation" are frequently confused. They mean two different things. It may be of value once more to clarify their meaning. "Abolition" strictly refers to the abolition of the slave trade, and *not* to the abolition of the institution of slavery as such. While most abolitionists also desired to see the institution abolished, they strategically first concentrated their energies upon securing the abolition of the *trade* in slaves. "Emancipation," the second phase of their attack, was launched on a full scale only after the abolition of the slave trade was achieved. Thus, Thomas Clarkson, the leading abolitionist of the day, writes: "I know of no subject, where humanity and justice, as well as public and private interest, would be more intimately united than in that, which should recommend a mitigation of the slavery, with a view afterwards of the emancipation of the Negroes, wherever such may be held in bondage. This subject was taken up for consideration, so early as when the Abolition of the slave trade was first practically thought of, and by the very persons who first publicly embarked in that cause in England; but it was at length abandoned by them, not on the ground *that Slavery was less cruel, or wicked, or impolitic, than the slave trade*, but for other reasons. In the first place there were not at that time so many obstacles in the way of the Abolition, as of the Emancipation of the Negroes. In the second place Abolition could be effected immediately, and with but comparatively little loss, and no danger. Emancipation on the other hand, appeared to be rather a work of time. It was beset too with many difficulties, which required deep consideration, and which, if not treated with great caution and prudence, threatened the most alarming results. In the third place, it was supposed, that, by effecting the abolition of the slave trade, the axe would be laid to the root of the whole evil; so that by cutting off the more vital part of it, the other would gradually die away." [1]

---

[1] *Thoughts on the Necessity of Improving the Condition of the Slaves in the British Colonies, with a View to Their Ultimate Emancipation,* p. 1.

Freud on the Ego and Group Relations

L ET US KEEP before our eyes the nature of the emotional relations which hold between men in general. According to Schopenhauer's famous simile of the freezing porcupines no one can tolerate a too intimate approach to his neighbor.

"The evidence of psycho-analysis shows that almost every intimate emotional relation between two people which lasts for some time— marriage, friendship, the relations between parents and children— leaves a sediment of feelings of aversion and hostility, which have first to be eliminated by repression. This is less disguised in the common wrangles between business partners or in the grumbles of a subordinate at his superior. The same thing happens when men come together in larger units. Every time two families become connected by a marriage, each of them thinks itself superior to or of better birth than the other. Of two neighboring towns each is the other's most jealous rival; every little canton looks down upon the others with contempt. Closely related races keep one another at arm's length; the South German cannot endure the North German, the Englishman casts every kind of aspersion upon the Scotchman, the Spaniard despises the Portuguese. We are no longer astonished that greater difficulties should lead to an almost insuperable repugnance, such as the Gallic people feel for the German, the Aryan for the Semite, and the white races for the coloured.

"When this hostility is directed against people who are otherwise loved we describe it as ambivalence of feeling; and we explain the fact, in what is probably far too rational a manner, by means of the numerous occasions for conflicts of interest which arise precisely in such intimate relations. In the undisguised antipathies and aversions which people feel towards strangers with whom they have to do we may recognize the expression of self-love—or narcissism. This self-love works for the self-assertion of the individual, and behaves as though the occurrence of any divergence from his own particular lines of development involved a criticism of them and a demand for their alteration. We do not know why such sensitiveness should have been directed to just these details of differentiation; but it is unmistakable that in this whole connection men give evidence of a readiness of hatred, and aggressiveness, the source of which is unknown, and to which one is tempted to ascribe an elementary character.

"But the whole of this intolerance vanishes, temporarily or permanently, as the result of the formation of a group, and in a group. So long as a group formation persists or so far as it extends, individuals behave as though they were uniform, tolerate other people's peculiarities, put themselves on an equal level with them, and have no feeling of aversion towards them. Such a limitation of narcissism can, according to our theoretical views, only be produced by one factor, a libidinal tie with other people. Love for oneself knows only one barrier—love for others, love for objects. The question will at once be raised whether community of interest in itself, without any addition of libido, must not necessarily lead to the toleration of other people and to considerateness for them. This objection may be met by the reply that nevertheless no lasting limitation of narcissism is effected in this way, since this tolerance does not persist longer than the immediate advantage gained from other people's collaboration. But the practical importance of the discussion is less than might be supposed, for experience has shown that in cases of collaboration libidinal ties are regularly formed between the fellow-workers which prolong and solidify the relation between them to a point beyond what is merely profitable. The same thing occurs in men's social relations as has become familiar to psychoanalytic research in the course of the development of the individual libido. The libido props itself upon the satisfaction of the great vital needs, and chooses as its first objects the people who have a share in that process. And in the development of mankind as a whole, just as in individuals, love alone acts as the civilizing factor in the sense that it brings a change from egoism to altruism. And this is true both of the sexual life for women, with all the obligations it involves of sparing what women are formed for, and also of the desexualized, sublimated homosexual love for other men, which springs from work in common."[1]

---

[1] Freud, *Group Psychology and the Analysis of the Ego,* pp. 54–57.

Bibliography

Abbie, A. A. "A New Outlook on Physical Anthropology." *Proceedings of the New Zealand Association for the Advancement of Science*, XXVIII (1951), 52–63.

Abel, Wolfgang. "Über Europäer-Marokkaner und Europäer-Annamiten-Kreuzungen." *Zeitschrift für Morphologie und Anthropologie*, XXXVI (1937), 311–29.

Abercombie, M., C. J. Hickman, and M. L. Johnson. A Dictionary of Biology. London and New York, Penguin Books, 1951.

Abernethy, George L. (ed.). The Idea of Equality. Richmond, Va., John Knox Press, 1959.

Ackerknecht, Erwin H. "White Indians." *Bulletin of the History of Medicine*, XV (1944), 15–36.

Ackerman, Nathan W. "Anti-Semitic Motivation in a Psychopathic Personality." *Psychoanalytic Review*, XXXIV (1947), 76–101.

——— and Marie Jahoda. Anti-Semitism and Emotional Disorder. New York, Harper, 1950.

——— "The Dynamic Basis of Anti-Semitic Attitudes." *Psychoanalytic Quarterly*, XVII (1948), 240–60.

——— "Toward a Dynamic Interpretation of Anti-Semitic Attitudes." *American Journal of Orthopsychiatry*, XVIII (1948), 163–73.

Adachi, Buntaro. "Der Geruch der Europäer." *Globus*, LXXXIII (1903), 14–15.

Adamastor. White Man Boss. Boston, Beacon Press, 1951.

Adamic, Louis. A Nation of Nations. New York, Harper, 1945.

Adams, Romanzo C. Interracial Marriage in Hawaii. New York, Macmillan, 1937.

Adinaryan, S. P. "Before and After Independence: A Study of Racial and Communal Attitudes in India." *British Journal of Psychology*, XLIV (1953), 108–15.

Adorno, T. W., E. Frenkel-Brunswik, D. J. Levenson, and R. Nevitt Sanford. The Authoritarian Personality. New York, Harper, 1950.

Agronsky, Martin. "Racism in Italy." *Foreign Affairs*, XVII (1939), 391–401.

Alexander, Chester. "Antipathy and Social Behavior." *American Journal of Sociology*, LI (1946), 288–92.

Alexander, H. B. "A Comparison of the Ranks of American States in Army-Alpha and in Socio-economic Status." *School and Society*, XVI (1922), 388–92.

Allee, Warder C. Animal Aggregations. Chicago, University of Chicago Press, 1931.

——— "Biology and International Relations." *New Republic*, CXII (1945), 816–17.

——— Cooperation Among Animals. New York, Schuman, 1950.

——— The Social Life of Animals. New York, Norton, 1938.

——— "Where Angels Fear to Tread; a Contribution from General Sociology to Human Ethics." *Science*, XCVII (1943), 518–25.

——— *et al*. Principles of Animal Ecology. Philadelphia, Saunders, 1949.

Allen, B., *et al*. "Social Awareness in a City High School." *Intercultural Educational News*, VIII (1946), 1–7.

Allison, A. C. "Protection Afforded by the Sickle-Cell Trait Against Subtertian Malarial Infection." *British Medical Journal*, I (1954), 290–94.

Allport, Gordon W. "Human Nature and the Peace." *Psychological Bulletin*, XLII (1945), 376–78.

——— "Is Intergroup Education Possible?" *Harvard Educational Review*, XV (1945), 83–86.

——— The Nature of Prejudice. Cambridge, Mass., Addison-Wesley, 1953.

——— Personality and the Social Encounter. Boston, Beacon Press, 1960.

——— (ed.). ABC's of Scapegoating. Chicago, Central Y.M.C.A. College, 1943.

——— "Controlling Group Prejudice." *Annals of the American Academy of Political and Social Science*, CCXLIV (1946), 1–240.

Allport, Gordon W., and Bernard M. Kramer. "Some Roots of Prejudice." *Journal of Psychology*, XXII (1946), 9–39.

Anastasi, Anne. Differential Psychology. 3rd ed. New York, Macmillan, 1958.

Anderson, Robert T. "Lapp Racial Classifications as Scientific Myths." *Anthropological Papers of the University of Alaska*, XI (1962), 15–31.

Andrews, Charles F. "Racial Influences," in Arthur Porritt (ed.), The Causes of War, pp. 63–113. New York, Macmillan, 1932.

Angel, John L. "A Racial Analysis of the Ancient Greeks." *American Journal of Physical Anthropology*, N. S., II (1944), 329–76.

——— "Report on the Skeletons Excavated at Olynthus," in David M.

Robinson, Excavations at Olynthus, Pt. XI, Necrolynthia, a Study in Greek Burial Customs and Anthropology, pp. 211–40. Baltimore, Johns Hopkins Press, 1942.

——— "Skeletal Material from Attica." *Hesperia*, XIV (1945), 279–363.

——— "Social Biology of Greek Culture Growth." *American Anthropologist*, N. S., XLVIII (1946), 493–533.

Apthekar, Herbert. Essays in the History of the American Negro. New York, International Publishers, 1945.

Arendt, Hannah. The Origins of Totalitarianism. New York, Harcourt, Brace, 1951.

——— "Race-Thinking before Racism." *Review of Politics*, VI (1944), 36–73.

Argyris, Chris. Personality and Organization. New York, Harper, 1957.

Aristotle. De generatione animalium. I, 20.

——— Politics.

Asdell, S. A. "The Genetic Sex of Intersexual Goats and a Probable Linkage with the Gene for Hornlessness." *Science*, XCIX (1944), 124.

Ashmore, Harry S. An Epitaph for Dixie. New York, Norton, 1958.

——— The Negro and the Schools. Chapel Hill, University of North Carolina Press, 1954.

——— The Other Side of Jordan. New York, Norton, 1960.

Astrov, Margot. The Winged Serpent. New York, John Day, 1946.

Ausubel, David P. Theory and Problems of Child Development. New York, Grune and Stratton, 1958.

Babington, William D. Fallacies of Race Theories. London, Longmans, 1895.

Bachman, C. L. John Bachman. Charleston, Walker, Evans & Cogswell, 1888.

Baeumler, Alfred. "Race: A Basic Concept in Education"; trans. from the original article in the *Internationale Zeitschrift für Erziehung*, VIII, 1939. *World Education*, IV (1939), 506–09.

Bagehot, Walter. Physics and Politics. London, 1869; reprinted, New York, Knopf, 1948.

Bain, Read. "Man, the Myth-Maker." *Scientific Monthly*, LXV (1947), 61–69.

Baker, Emily V. "Do We Teach Racial Intolerance?" *Historical Outlook*, XXIV (1933), 86–89.

Baker, Herschel. The Dignity of Man. Cambridge, Harvard University Press, 1947.

Baldwin, James. The Fire Next Time. New York, Dial Press, 1963.

——— "Letter from a region in My Mind." *The New Yorker*, November 17, 1962, pp. 59–144.

Banton, Michael. "Beware of Strangers." *The Listener*, 3 April 1958, pp. 565–67.

—— The Coloured Quarter. London, Cape, 1955.

—— White and Coloured. London, Cape, 1959.

Barker, Ernest. National Character. 4th ed. London, Methuen, 1948.

Barnes, E. W. "The Mixing of Races and Social Decay." *Eugenics Review*, XLI (1949), 11–16.

Barnes, Harry E., and Negley K. Teeters. New Horizons in Criminology. New York, Prentice-Hall, 1943.

Barnes, I. "The Inheritance of Pigmentation in the Skin of the American Negro." *Human Biology*, I (1929), 321–28.

Barnett, Anthony. The Human Species. New York, Norton, 1950.

Barzun, Jacques. Race: a Study in Modern Superstition. New York, Harcourt, Brace, 1937.

Bastide, Roger, and Pierre van den Berghe. "Stereotypes, Norms and Interracial Behavior in São Paulo, Brazil." *American Sociological Review*, XXII (1957), 689–94.

Bates, Daisy. The Long Shadow of Little Rock. New York, McKay, 1962.

Bates, Daisy. The Passing of the Aborigines. London, Murray, 1938.

Battaglia, Raffaello. "La Genetica Umana e l'Incrocio Razziale," in Renato Biasutti (ed.), Le Razzi e i Popoli della Terra, I (1959), 323–54. (Torino, Unione-Tipografico.)

Beaglehole, Ernest. "Race, Caste and Class." *Journal of the Polynesian Society*, LXII (1943), 1–11.

—— and Pearl Beaglehole. Some Modern Maoris. Wellington, New Zealand Council for Educational Research, 1946.

Bean, R. Bennett. "Some Racial Peculiarities of the Negro Brain." *American Journal of Anatomy*, V (1906), 353–415.

Bellow, Barbara. "Prejudice in 'Seaside.'" *Human Relations*, I (1947), 98–120.

Bender, Lauretta. Aggression, Hostility, and Anxiety in Children. Springfield, Ill., Thomas, 1953.

—— "Genesis of Hostility in Children." *American Journal of Psychiatry*, CV (1948), 241–45.

Bendyshe, Thomas. "The History of Anthropology." *Memoirs Read before the Anthropological Society of London*, I (1863–64), 335–458.

Benedict, Ruth. Patterns of Culture. Boston, Houghton Mifflin, 1934.

—— Race: Science and Politics. New York, Viking, 1943.

—— and Gene Weltfish. The Races of Mankind. New York, Public Affairs Committee, 1943.

Benoist, Jean. L'Etude de la Structure Génétique d'une Population Mé-
tisée." *Anthropologica*, N. S., III (1961), 1–10.

Berg, Leo S. Nomogenesis, or Evolution Determined by Law. London,
Constable, 1926.

Berger, Morroe. Equality by Statute. New York, Columbia University
Press, 1952.

Bernard, Henry M. Some Neglected Factors in Evolution. New York,
Putnam, 1911.

Bernard, L. L. Instinct: A Study in Social Psychology. New York, Holt,
1924.

—— War and Its Causes. New York, Holt, 1944.

Berndt, Catherine H. "The Concept of the Primitive." *Sociologus*, X
(1960), 50–69.

Berndt, Ronald, and Catherine Berndt. The First Australians. Sydney,
Ure Smith, 1952.

—— From Black to White in South Australia. Chicago, University of
Chicago Press, 1952.

Bernhardi, Friedrich von. Germany and the Next War. New York,
Longmans, 1912.

[Bernier, François]. "Nouvelle division de la Terre, par les differentes
Especes ou races d'hommes qui l'habitent, envoyée par un fameux
Voyageur à Monsieur . . . à peu près en ces termes." *Journal des
Scavans*, April 24, 1684, pp. 85–89.

Berry, Brewton. "The Concept of Race in Sociology Textbooks." *Social
Forces*, XVIII (1940), 411–17.

—— Race Relations: the Interaction of Ethnic and Racial Groups.
Boston, Houghton Mifflin, 1951.

Bettelheim, Bruno, and Morris Janowitz. Dynamics of Prejudice. New
York, Harper, 1950.

—— "Prejudice." *Scientific American*, CLXXXIII (1950), 13.

Bibby, Cyril. Race, Prejudice, and Education. New York, Praeger, 1960.

Biddle, Francis. Democracy and Racial Minorities. New York, Institute
for Religious Studies, 1943.

Bidney, David. "The Concept of Myth and the Problem of Psychocultural Evolution." *American Anthropologist*, LXII (1950), 16–26.

Biesheuvel, S. African Intelligence. Johannesburg, South African Institute of Race Relations, 1943.

—— Race, Culture and Personality. Johannesburg, South African Institute of Race Relations, 1959.

Bigelow, Karl W. Cultural Groups and Human Relations. New York,
Columbia University Press, 1951.

Bilden, Ruediger. "Racial Mixture in Latin America—with Special Reference to Brazil," in Henry Laidler (ed.), The Role of the Races in Our Future Civilization. New York, League for Industrial Democracy, 1942.

Birch, Herbert G. "Psychological Differences as among Races." *Science*, CI (1945), 173–74.

Birdsell, Joseph B. "Some Implications of the Genetical Concept of Race in Terms of Spatial Analysis." *Cold Spring Harbor Symposia on Quantitative Biology*, XV (1950), 259–314.

——— "The Problem of the Early Peopling of the Americas as Viewed from Asia," in William S. Laughlin (ed.), Papers on the Physical Anthropology of the American Indian, pp. 1–68a. New York, The Viking Fund, 1951.

Bishop, L. K. "Democracy Demands Co-operative Living." *Education*, LXVIII (1946), 12–18.

Blalock, H. M., Jr. "A Power Analysis of Racial Discrimination." *Social Forces*, XXXIX (1961), 53–59.

Bloch, J. M. Miscegenation, Melaleukation, and Mr. Lincoln's Dog. New York, Schaum, 1958.

Bloom, Leonard, and Ruth Riemer. Removal and Return. Berkeley, University of California Press, 1949.

Blue, John T., Jr. "The Relationship of Juvenile Delinquency, Race, and Economic Status." *Journal of Negro Education*, XVII (1948), 469–77.

Blum, Harold F. "Does the Melanin Pigment of Human Skin Have Adaptive Value?" *Quarterly Review of Biology*, XXXVI (1961), 50–63.

——— "The Physiological Effects of Sunlight on Man." *Physiological Reviews*, XXV (1945), 483–530.

Blumenbach, Johann F. Anthropological Treatises; trans. by T. Bendyshe. London, Anthropological Society, 1865.

——— De generis humani varietate nativa. Göttingen, 1795. Trans. by T. Bendyshe, "On the Natural Variety of Mankind," in The Anthropological Treatises of Johann Friedrich Blumenbach. London, Anthropological Society, 1865.

Blumer, Herbert. "Race Prejudice as a Sense of Group Position," in Jitsuichi Masuoka and Preston Valien (eds.), Race Relations, pp. 217–27. Chapel Hill, University of North Carolina Press, 1961.

Boas, Franz. Anthropology and Modern Life. New York, Norton, 1928.

——— Changes in Bodily Form of Descendants of Immigrants. Final Report. (61st Congress, 2nd Session, Senate Document 208.) Washington, Government Printing Office, 1911. Reprinted, New York, Columbia University Press, 1912.

———— "Class Consciousness and Race Prejudice." *Christian Register*, CXXII (1943), 5–6.

———— "Heredity and Environment." *Jewish Social Studies*, I (1939), 5–14.

———— "History and Science in Anthropology: a Reply." *American Anthropologist*, XXXVIII (1936), 137–41.

———— The Mind of Primitive Man. New York, Macmillan, 1938.

———— "Race," in Encyclopedia of the Social Sciences, XIII, 25–26. New York, Macmillan, 1937.

———— Race and Democratic Society. New York, Augustin, 1945.

———— "Race and Progress." *Science*, LXXIV (1931), 1–8.

———— Race, Language and Culture. New York, Macmillan, 1940.

———— "Racial Purity." *Asia*, XL (1940), 231–34.

———— (ed.) General Anthropology. Boston, Heath, 1938.

Bogardus, Emory S. Immigration and Race Attitudes. Boston, Heath, 1938.

Bogart, Ernest L. Direct and Indirect Costs of the Great World War. New York, Oxford University Press, 1919.

Bolk-Fetlkamp, A. J. van. "Physical Anthropology in the Netherlands Indies since 1939." *Man*, XLIX (1949), 43–45.

Bonger, Willem A. Race and Crime; trans. by M. M. Hordyk. New York, Columbia University Press, 1943.

Bonifacy, A. "Les Métis Franco-Tonkinois." *Revue Anthropologique*, XXI (1911), 259–66.

Bonin, Gerhardt von. "On Racial Inequality." *The Interne* (1948).

———— "On the Size of Man's Brain, as Indicated by Skull Capacity." *Journal of Comparative Neurology*, LIX (1934), 1–28.

Boyd, William C. "Critique of Methods of Classifying Mankind." *American Journal of Physical Anthropology*, XXVII (1940), 333–64.

———— Genetics and the Races of Man. Boston, Little, Brown, 1950.

Bram, Joseph. "The Social Identity of the Jews." *Transactions of the New York Academy of Sciences*, Ser. 2, VI (1944), 1194–99.

Brameld, Theodore. Minority Problems in the Public Schools. New York, Harper, 1946.

Brandes, Georg. Hellas: Travels in Greece; trans. by Jacob W. Hartmann. New York, Adelphi, 1926.

Braunstein, Baruch. The Chuetas of Majorca. Columbia University Oriental Series, XXVIII/XXIX. New York, Columbia University Press, 1936.

Brenan, Gerald. The Spanish Labyrinth. New York, Macmillan, 1943.

Brend, William A. Foundations of Human Conflicts. London, Chapman & Hall, 1944.

Brenman, Margaret. "Urban Lower-Class Negro Girls." *Psychiatry,* VI (1943), 307–24.

Bridges, E. Lucas. Uttermost Part of the Earth. London, Hodder & Stoughton, 1948.

Briffault, Robert. "You Can't Change Human Nature." *Scribner's Magazine,* XCII (1932), 27–29.

Brown, Fred. "A Sociopsychological Analysis of Race Prejudice." *Journal of Abnormal and Social Psychology,* XXVII (1932–33), 364–74.

Brown, Ina C. National Survey of the Higher Education of Negroes. Publications of the U. S. Office of Education, Misc. 6. I. Washington, 1942.

—— Race Relations in a Democracy. New York, Harper, 1949.

Brown, Spencer. They See for Themselves. New York, Harper, 1944.

Brown, W. O. "Rationalization of Race Prejudice." *International Journal of Ethics,* LXIII (1933), 299–301.

Browne, Robert S. Race Relations in International Affairs. Washington, D. C., Public Affairs Press, 1961.

Browne, Thomas. Pseudodoxia Epidemica. London, Dod, 1646.

Brückner, G. H. "Untersuchungen zur Tiersoziologie, insbesondere zur Auflösung der Familie." *Zeitschrift für Psychologie,* CXXVIII (1933), 1–110.

Brutzkus, J. "Jewish Anthropology," in The Jewish People, I (1946), 10–26. New York.

Bryce, James, Viscount. Race Sentiment as a Factor in History. London, University of London Press, 1915.

Bryson, Gladys. Man and Society. Princeton, Princeton University Press, 1945.

Bryson, Lyman, Louis Finkelstein, and Robert M. MacIver (eds.). Approaches to Group Understanding. New York, Harper, 1947.

—— Aspects of Human Equality. New York, Harper, 1956.

Buffon, George L. L. Histoire naturelle, générale et particulière. Paris, 1749. Natural History, General and Particular; trans. by William Smellie, corrected by William Wood (London, 1812), III, 302 ff.

Bunak, V. V., et al. "Contemporary Raciology and Racism." *International Journal of American Linguistics,* XXVII (1961), 1–146.

Burger, John. The Black Man's Burden. London, Gollancz, 1943.

Burns, Alan. Colour Prejudice. London, Allen & Unwin, 1948.

Burrows, Edwin G. Hawaiian Americans. New Haven, Yale University Press, 1947.

Buss, Arnold H. The Psychology of Aggression. New York, Wiley, 1961.

Butcher, Margaret J. The Negro in American Culture. New York, Knopf, 1956.

Butler, Rohan D'O. The Roots of National Socialism. New York, Dutton, 1942.

Buxton, L. H. Dudley. "Cross Cousin Marriages, the Biological Significance," in R. S. Rattray, Religion and Art in Ashanti. Oxford, Oxford University Press, 1927.

Cabell, J. L. The Testimony of Modern Science to the Unity of Mankind. New York, R. Carter & Bros., 1859.

Calas, Nicholas. "Myth and Initiation." Chimera, IV (1946), 21–24.

Caldwell, W. E., and H. C. Moloy. "Anatomical Variations in the Female Pelvis and Their Effects in Labor, with a Suggested Classification." American Journal of Obstetrics and Gynecology, XXVI (1933), 479–514.

Calman, W. T. The Classification of Animals. New York, Wiley, 1949.

Cameron, V. K., and H. Smith. "The Physical Form of Mississippi Negroes." American Journal of Physical Anthropology, XVI (1931), 193–201.

Carey, A. T. Colonial Students. London, Secker & Warburg, 1956.

Carmichael, Emmet B. "Josiah Clark Nott." Bulletin of the History of Medicine, XXII (1948), 249–62.

Carpenter, Edmund. "Space Concepts of the Aivilik Eskimos." Explorations (Toronto), V (1955), 131–45.

Carson, Hampton L. Heredity and Human Life. New York, Columbia University Press, 1963.

Carter, G. S. Animal Evolution: a Study of Recent Views of Its Causes. London, Sidgwick & Jackson; New York, Macmillan, 1951.

Cassirer, Ernst. An Essay on Man. New Haven, Yale University Press, 1944.

—— The Myth of the State. New Haven, Yale University Press, 1946.

Castle, William E. "Biological and Social Consequences of Race Crossing." American Journal of Physical Anthropology, IX (1926), 145–56.

—— "Dog Crosses and Human Crosses." Journal of Heredity, XXIII (1942), 249–52.

—— "Race Mixture and Physical Disharmonies." Science, LXXI (1930), 603–06.

Catton, William R., Jr., and Sung Chick Hong. "The Relation of Apparent Minority Ethnocentrism to Majority Antipathy." American Sociological Review, XXVII (1962), 178–91.

Chamberlain, Houston S. The Foundations of the Nineteenth Century; trans. by John Lees, with an introduction by Lord Redesdale. 2 vols. London and New York, Lane, 1910.

Chandler, Albert R. Rosenberg's Nazi Myth. Ithaca, Cornell University Press, 1945.

Chappat, Janine S. A. "Race Prejudice and Preschool Education." MSS, Harvard School of Education, Cambridge, Mass.

Chase, Stuart. The Tyranny of Words. New York, Harcourt, Brace, 1938.

Chewings, Charles. Back in the Stone Age. Sydney, Angus & Robertson, 1936.

Childe, V. Gordon. The Dawn of European Civilization. 4th ed. New York, Knopf, 1947.

——— Man Makes Himself. New York, Oxford University Press, 1940.

——— "War in Prehistoric Societies." Sociological Review, XXXIII (1941), 126–38.

——— What Happened in History. New York, Mentor Books, 1948.

Cipriani, Lidio. Un assurdo etnico: L'Impero Etiopico. Florence, Bemporad & Fo., 1935.

Clark, Blake. "One World on an Island." '47, I (1947), 14–21.

Clark, Colin. "What's Wrong with Economics?" Encounter, X (1958), 14–23.

Clark, E., and R. H. Lhamon. "Observations on the Sweat Glands of Tropical and Northern Races." Anatomical Record, XII (1917), 139–47.

Clark, Kenneth. Prejudice and Your Child. Boston, Beacon Press, 1955.

Clark, W. W. Los Angeles Negro Children. Educational Research Bulletin, Los Angeles, 1923.

Clarkson, Jesse D., and Thomas C. Cochran (eds.). War as a Social Institution. New York, Columbia University Press, 1941.

Clarkson, Thomas. Thoughts on the Necessity of Improving the Condition of the Slaves in the British Colonies, with a View to Their Ultimate Emancipation. London, Richard Taylor, 1823.

Clift, Virgil A., A. W. Anderson, and C. G. Hullfish (eds.). Negro Education in America. New York, Harper, 1962.

Clinchy, Everett R. Intergroup Relations Centers. New York, Farrar, Straus, 1949.

Cobb, Thomas R. R. An Inquiry into the Law of Negro Slavery in the United States of America. Philadelphia, Johnson & Co., 1858.

Cobb, William M. "Physical Anthropology of the American Negro." American Journal of Physical Anthropology, XXIX (1942), 113–223.

——— "The Physical Constitution of the American Negro." Journal of Negro Education, III (1934), 340–88.

——— "Race and Runners." Journal of Health and Physical Education, VII (1936), 1–8.

——— "Your Nose Won't Tell." Crisis, XLV (1938), 332–36.

Cohen, Lester, "Letters to the Editor" [On the Jews]. Saturday Review of Literature, XXXI (1948), 19–21.

Cole, Stewart G., and Mildred Wise Cole. Minorities and the American Promise. New York, Harper, 1954.

Coleman, E. L. New England Captives Carried to Canada between 1677 and 1760. 2 vols. Portland, Maine, Southworth Press, 1925.

Coles, Kenneth. The Desegregation of Southern Schools: A Psychiatric Study. New York, Anti-Defamation League of B'nai B'rith, 1963.

Collias, Nicholas E. "Aggressive Behavior among Vertebrate Animals." Physiological Zoology, XVII (1944), 83–123.

Collier, John. "The Creative Value of Cultural Diversity." Trends & Tides, II (1946), 5–6.

Collins, Sydney. Coloured Minorities in Britain. London, Lutterworth Press, 1957.

—— "The Status of Coloured People in Britain." Phylon, XVIII (1957), 82–87.

Comas, Juan. " 'Scientific' Racism Again?" Current Anthropology, II (1961), 303–40.

Commission on Mixed Marriages in South Africa. Report. Pretoria, Government Printer, 1939.

Conant, Melvin (ed.). Race Issues on the World Scene. Honolulu, University of Hawaii Press, 1955.

Condliffe, J. B. New Zealand in the Making. London, Allen and Unwin, 1930.

Conklin, Edwin G. Heredity and Environment. Princeton, Princeton University Press, 1939.

—— Man: Real and Ideal. New York, Scribner, 1943.

—— What Is Man? Rice Institute Pamphlet, XXVIII (1941), 163. Houston, Texas.

Connolly, Cornelius J. External Morphology of the Primate Brain. Springfield, Ill., Thomas, 1950.

Cook, Cecil. Report of the 27th of June, 1933, by the Chief Protector of Aboriginals in the Northern Territory of Australia. Darwin, 1933. Reprinted in the Report of the Commission on Mixed Marriages in South Africa. Pretoria, Government Printer, 1939.

Cook, James G. The Segregationists. New York, Appleton-Century-Crofts, 1962.

Cooley, C. H., R. C. Angell, and L. J. Carr. Introductory Sociology. New York, Scribner, 1933.

Coomaraswamy, Ananda K. Am I My Brother's Keeper? New York, John Day, 1947.

Coon, Carleton S. "Have the Jews a Racial Identity?" in I. Graeber and Steuart H. Britt (eds.), Jews in a Gentile World. New York, Macmillan, 1942.

—— The Origin of Races. New York, Knopf, 1962.

—— The Races of Europe. New York, Macmillan, 1939.

—— and Stanley M. Garn and Joseph B. Birdsell. Races, a Study of the Problems of Race Formation in Man. Springfield, Ill., Thomas, 1950.

Corner, George W. Ourselves Unborn. New Haven, Yale University Press, 1944.

Corrigan, J. W. (ed.). Scientific Aspects of the Race Problem. New York, Longmans, 1941.

Coser, Lewis A. "Europe's Neurotic Nationalism." *Commentary*, I (1946), 59–63.

Cotton, W. A. The Race Problem in South Africa. London, Student Christian Movement, 1926.

Count, Earl (ed.). This Is Race. New York, Schuman, 1950.

Coupland, Reginald. Wilberforce: a Narrative. Oxford, Oxford University Press, 1923.

Cowdry, Edmund H. (ed.). Human Biology and Racial Welfare. New York, Hoeber, 1930.

Cox, Oliver C. "Race and Caste: a Distinction." *American Journal of Sociology*, L (1945), 360–68.

Crocker, William. "Botany of the Future." *Science*, LXXXVIII (1938), 391.

Crockett, Charis. The House in the Rain Forest. Boston, Houghton Mifflin, 1942.

Curriculum Office, Philadelphia Public Schools. Open-Mindedness Can Be Taught. Philadelphia, 1946.

Curtin, Philip D. "The Origin of the 'White Man's Burden.'" *The Listener*, LXVI (1961), 412–15.

Cuvier, Georges. Le Règne animal. Vol. I. Paris, Deterville, 1817.

Dabek-Szyszko, M. "The Great Bor Lie." *The Protestant*, VI (1946), 12–31.

Dahlberg, Gunnar. "An Analysis of the Conception of Race and a New Method of Distinguishing Races." *Human Biology*, XIV (1942), 372–85.

—— "Notes on the Conception of Type." *Acta Genetica et Statistica Medica*, I (1949), 174–78.

—— Race, Reason and Rubbish; a Primer of Race Biology. New York, Columbia University Press, 1942.

Danforth, C. H. "Distribution of Hair on the Digits in Man." *American Journal of Physical Anthropology*, IV (1921), 189–204.

Dark, Eleanor. The Timeless Land. New York, Macmillan, 1941.

Darlington, Cyril D. "The Genetic Understanding of Race in Man." *International Social Science Bulletin* (UNESCO), II (1950), 479–88.

Darwin, Charles. The Descent of Man. London, Murray, 1871.

—— The Origin of Species. London, Murray, 1859.

—— Variation of Animals and Plants under Domestication. London, Murray, 1867.

Davenport, Charles B. "Heredity of Hair Form in Man." *American Naturalist*, XLII (1908), 341.

—— Heredity of Skin Color in Negro-White Crosses. Publications of the Carnegie Institution of Washington, No. 188. Washington, D.C., 1913.

—— "The Mingling of Races," in E. V. Cowdry (ed.), Human Biology and Racial Welfare. New York, Hoeber, 1930.

—— "Some Criticisms of 'Race Crossing in Jamaica.'" *Science,* LXXII (1930), 501–02.

—— and A. G. Lowe. Army Anthropology: Based on Observations Made on Draft Recruits 1917–1918, and on Veterans at Demobilization, 1919. Medical Department of the U.S. Army in the World War. Vol. XV, Part 1. Washington, Government Printing Office, 1921.

Davenport, Charles B., and Morris Steggerda. Race Crossing in Jamaica. Washington, Carnegie Institution of Washington, 1929.

David, Paul R., and Laurence S. Snyder. "Genetic Variability and Human Behavior," in John H. Rohrer and Muzafer Sherif (eds.), Social Psychology at the Crossroads, pp. 53–82. New York, Harper, 1951.

Davidson, Helen H. Personality and Economic Background. New York, King's Crown Press, 1943.

Davidson, Henry A. "The Anatomy of Prejudice." *Common Ground,* I (1941), 3–12.

Davie, Maurice R. Negroes in American Society. New York, McGraw-Hill, 1950.

Davies, Horton. "Race Tensions in South Africa." *Hibbert Journal,* XLIX (1951), 118–27.

Davis, Allison. "The Distribution of the Blood Groups and the Concept of Race," in Lancelot Hogben (ed.), Political Arithmetic. New York, Macmillan, 1938.

—— "Racial Status and Personality Development." *Scientific Monthly,* LXII (1934), 354–62.

—— and Burleigh B. Gardner, and Mary R. Gardner. Deep South; A Social Anthropological Study of Caste and Class. Chicago, University of Chicago Press, 1941.

Davis, S. Race-Relations in Ancient Egypt. New York, Philosophical Library, 1952.

Day, Caroline B. A Study of Some Negro-White Families in the United States. Cambridge, Peabody Museum, Harvard University, 1932.

Dean, John P., and Alex Rosen. A Manual of Intergroup Relations. Chicago, University of Chicago Press, 1955.

Debra. "The Effect of the Existence of Segregation in the U.S. on the American Image in Africa." U. S. National Commission for UNESCO (Press Release, Nat. Conf. 8/18, October 25, 1961).

De Fleur, Melvin, and Frank R. Westie. "The Interpretation of Interracial Situations." Social Forces, XXXVIII (1959), 17–23.

Delage, Yves, and Marie Goldsmith. The Theories of Evolution. London, Palmer, 1912.

Detweiler, Frederick G. "The Rise of Modern Race Antagonisms." American Journal of Sociology, XXXVIII (1932), 738–47.

Deutsch, M., nd M. E. Collins. Interracial Housing. Minneapolis, University of Minnesota Press, 1952.

Dew, Thomas R. An Essay on Slavery. Richmond, Va., Randolph, 1849.

——— Review of the Debates in the Virginia Legislature of 1831 and 1832. Richmond, Randolph, 1832.

Dewey, John. "Does Human Nature Change?" in Problems of Men. New York, Philosophical Library, 1946.

Dickinson, A. "Race Mixture: a Social or a Biological Problem?" Eugenics Review, XLI (1949), 81–85.

Diller, Aubrey. Race Mixture among the Greeks before Alexander. Illinois Studies in Language and Literature, University of Illinois, Vol. XX. Urbana, 1937.

Dobzhansky, Theodosius. "The Genetic Nature of Differences among Men," in S. Persons (ed.), Evolutionary Thought in America, pp. 86–155. New Haven, Yale University Press, 1950.

——— "Comment." Current Anthropology, III (1962), 279–80.

——— "Genetics and Human Affairs." Teaching Biologist, XII (1943), 97–106.

——— Genetics and the Origin of Species. New York, Columbia University Press, 1st ed., 1937; 2d ed., 1941; 3rd ed., 1951.

——— Mankind Evolving. New Haven, Yale University Press, 1962.

——— "On Species and Races of Living and Fossil Man," American Journal of Physical Anthropology, N. S., II (1944), 251–65.

——— "The Race Concept in Biology." The Scientific Monthly, LII (1941), 161–65.

——— "Races and Methods of Their Study." Transactions of the New York Academy of Sciences, Ser. II, IV (1942), 115–23.

—— "Rules of Geographic Variation." A review of Darwinism and Geographic Regularities in Variation in Organisms, by E. I. Lukin (in Russian). Moscow-Leningrad Academy of Sciences of the U.S.S.R., 1943. *Science*, XCIX (1944), 127–28.

—— and Carl Epling. Contributions to the Genetics, Taxonomy, and Ecology of Drosophila Pseudoobscura and Its Relatives. Publication No. 554. Washington, Carnegie Institution of Washington, 1944.

Dobzhansky, Theodosius, and M. F. Ashley Montagu. "Natural Selection and the Mental Capacities of Mankind." *Science*, CV (1947), 587–90.

Dodd, William E. The Cotton Kingdom. New Haven, Yale University Press, 1919.

Dodge, Ernest S. "Early American Contacts in Polynesia and Fiji." *Proceedings of the American Philosophical Society*, CVII (1963), 102–06.

Dollard, John. Caste and Class in a Southern Town. New Haven, Yale University Press, 1937.

—— "Hostility and Fear in Social Life." *Social Forces*, XVII (1938), 15–26.

—— et al. Frustration and Aggression. New Haven, Yale University Press, 1939.

Donaldson, Henry H. "The Significance of Brain Weight." *Archives of Neurology and Psychiatry*, XIII (1925), 385–86.

Donnan, Elizabeth (ed.). Documents Illustrative of the History of the Slave Trade to America. 4 vols. Publication No. 409. Washington, Carnegie Institution of Washington, 1930.

Dornfeldt, Walter. "Studien über Schädelform und Schädelveränderung von Berliner Ostjuden und ihren Kindern." *Zeitschrift für Morphologie und Anthropologie*, XXXIX (1941), 290–372.

Dorsey, George A. "Race and Civilization," in Charles A. Beard (ed.), Whither Mankind, pp. 229–63. New York, Longmans, 1928.

Dostoevski, Feodor. The Brothers Karamazov.

Dover, Cedric. "Antar for the Anthropologist." *The Eastern Anthropologist*, V (1952), 165–69.

—— "The Classification of Man." *Current Science*, XXI (1952), 209–13.

—— Half-Caste. London, Secker and Warburg, 1937.

—— "Race." *Man*, art. 95 (1951), 1.

—— "The Racial Philosophy of Ibn Khaldun." *Phylon*, XIII (1952), 107–09.

—— "The Racial Philosophy of Johann Herder." *British Journal of Sociology*, III (1952), 124–33.

Doyle, Bertram W. The Etiquette of Race Relations in the South. Chicago, University of Chicago Press, 1937.

Dozier, E. P. "The Concepts of 'Primitive' and 'Native' in Anthropology," in Yearbook of Anthropology 1955, pp. 187–202. New York, Wenner-Gren Foundation, 1955.

Dumond, Dwight L. Antislavery. Ann Arbor, Mich., University of Michigan Press, 1961.

—— Antislavery Origins of the Civil War in the United States. Ann Arbor, University of Michigan Press, 1960.

Dunham, Barrows. Man against Myth. Boston, Little, Brown, 1947.

Dunn, Leslie C., and Theodosius Dobzhansky. Heredity, Race, and Society. New York, Mentor Books, 1946.

Dunn, Leslie C., and A. M. Tozzer. "An Anthropometric Study of Hawaiians of Pure and Mixed Blood." Papers of the Peabody Museum of American Archaeology and Ethnology, Harvard University, XI (1928), 90–211.

Dunn, R. "On the Physiological and Psychological Evidence in Support of the Unity of the Human Species." Transactions of the Ethnological Society of London, N. S., I (1861), 186–202.

Durbin, E. F. M., and John Bowlby. Personal Aggressiveness and War. New York, Columbia University Press, 1939.

Dvorin, E. P. Racial Separation in South Africa. Chicago, University of Chicago Press, 1952.

Dykeman, Wilma, and James Stokely. Seeds of Southern Change. Chicago, University of Chicago Press, 1962.

Dykes, Eva B. The Negro in English Romantic Thought. Washington, Associated Publishers, 1942.

East, E. M., and D. F. Jones. Inbreeding and Outbreeding. Philadelphia, Lippincott, 1919.

Edinger, Ludwig. Vorlesungen über den Bau der nervösen Zentralorgane des Menschen und der Tiere. Leipzig, Vogel, 1911.

Edwards, Edward A., and S. Quimby Duntley. "The Pigments and Color of Living Human Skin." American Journal of Anatomy, LXV (1939), 1–33.

Eells, Kenneth, et al. Intelligence and Cultural Differences. Chicago, University of Chicago Press, 1951.

Efron, David. Gesture and Environment. New York, King's Crown Press, 1941.

Eiseley, Loren. The Firmament of Time. New York, Atheneum, 1960.

Eisen, Nathaniel H. "Ethnic Differences." Perspectives in Biology and Medicine, V (1961), 139–41.

Eisler, Robert. "Metallurgical Anthropology in Hesiod and Plato and the Date of a 'Phoenician Lie.' " *Isis*, XL (1949), 108–12.

Elkin, A. P. The Australian Aborigines. 2d ed. Sydney, Angus & Robertson, 1954.

Elkins, Stanley M. "Culture Contacts and Negro Slavery." *Proceedings of the American Philosophical Society*, CVII (1963), 107–09.

—— "Science, Society and 'Everyman.' " *Journal of the Royal Society of New South Wales*, LXXV (1941), 11–20.

—— Slavery. Chicago, University of Chicago Press, 1959.

—— Society, the Individual and Change. Sydney, Camden College, 1940–45.

Ellinger, Tage U. H. "On the Breeding of Aryans." *Journal of Heredity*, XXXIII (1942), 141–43.

Ellis, Havelock. The Philosophy of Conflict. London, Constable, 1919.

Elton, Lord. Saint George or the Dragon. London, Collins, 1942.

Emerson, Alfred E. "Basic Comparisons of Human and Insect Societies." *Biological Symposia*, VIII (1942), 163–77.

—— "The Biological Basis of Social Cooperation." *Illinois Academy of Science Transactions*, XXXIX (1946), 9–18.

English, H. B., and A. C. English. A Comprehensive Dictionary of Psychological and Psychoanalytical Terms. New York, Longmans, 1958.

Epstein, Benjamin, and Arnold Forster. Some of My Best Friends . . . New York, Farrar, Straus & Cudahy, 1962.

—— The Troublemakers. New York, Doubleday, 1952.

Estel, L. "Race as an Evolutionary Concept." *American Journal of Physical Anthropology*, N. S., XIV (1956), 378.

Evans, Bergen. The Natural History of Nonsense. New York, Knopf, 1946.

Evans, Robley D. "Quantitative Inferences concerning the Genetic Effects of Radiation on Human Beings." *Science*, CIX (1949), 299–304.

Fairchild, Henry P. The Prodigal Century. New York. Philosophical Library, 1950.

Fairchild, Hoxie N. The Noble Savage. New York, Columbia University Press, 1928.

Faverty, Frederic E. Matthew Arnold the Ethnologist. Evanston, Ill., Northwestern University Press, 1951.

Fenichel, Otto. "A Psychological Approach to Anti-Semitism." *Commentary*, II (1946), 36–44.

Feuer, Lewis S. "Political Myths and Metaphysics." *Philosophy and Phenomenological Research*, XV (1955), 332–50.

"Filipino Group Seeks Ban on Nisei Evacuees," and "California Filipinos." *Pacific Citizen* (Salt Lake City), XIX (September 23, 1944), 3–4.

Finch, E. "The Effects of Racial Miscegenation," in *Papers on Inter-Racial Problems*, pp. 108–12. New York, 1911.

Finkelstein, Louis (ed.). The Jews: Their History, Culture, and Religion. 2 vols. New York, Harper, 1949.

Finney, D. J. "The Detection of Linkage." *Journal of Heredity*, XXXIII (1942), 156–60.

Finot, Jean. Race Prejudice. New York, Dutton, 1907; Los Angeles, Zeitlin & ver Brugge, 1944.

Fischer, Eugen. "Rasse und Rassenentstehung beim Menschen." *Wege zum Wissen*, LXII (1927), 1–137. Berlin, Ulstein.

—— Die Rehobother Bastards und das Bastardierungsproblem beim Menschen. Jena, 1913.

—— "Variable Characters in Human Beings," in Edwin Baur, Eugen Fischer, and Fritz Lenz, Human Heredity, pp. 114–66. New York, Macmillan, 1931.

Fishberg, Maurice. The Jews. New York, Scribner, 1911.

Fisher, R. A. The Genetical Theory of Natural Selection. Oxford, Clarendon Press, 1930.

Fitzpatrick, Thomas B., M. Seiji, and A. David McGugan. "Melanin Pigmentation." *New England Journal of Medicine*, CCLXV (1961), 328–32, 374–78, 430–34.

Fleming, R. M. "Physical Heredity in Human Hybrids." *Annals of Eugenics*, IX (1939), 55–81.

Fleure, Herbert J. "The Distribution of Types of Skin Colour." *Geographical Review*, XXXV (1945), 580–95.

—— "Some Biological Considerations in Social Evolution." *Eugenics Review*, XLI (1949), 134–40.

Flower, William H. "On the Classification of the Varieties of the Human Species," in Essays on Museums. London, Macmillan, 1898.

—— "The Study of Race," in Essays on Museums. London, Macmillan, 1898.

Forster, Arnold, and Benjamin Epstein. Cross Currents. New York, Doubleday, 1956.

Fortuyn, A. B. D. "The Origin of Human Races." *Science*, XC (1939), 352–53.

Foster, T. S. Travels and Settlements of Early Man. London, Benn, 1929.

Francis, E. K. "Minority Groups—A Revision of Concepts." *British Journal of Sociology*, II (1951), 219–30.

—— "The Nature of the Ethnic Group." *American Journal of Sociology*, LII (1947), 393–400.

Frank, Lawrence K. Nature and Human Nature. New Brunswick, Rutgers University Press, 1951.

Franklin, Benjamin. Autobiography. The Writings of Benjamin Franklin, I (1907), 376.

Franklin, John H. The Militant South. Cambridge, Harvard University Press, 1956.

Franzblau, R. N. "Race Differences in Mental and Physical Traits." Archives of Psychology, No. 177 (1935).

Frazier, E. Franklin. "A Comparison of Negro-White Relations in Brazil and in the United States." Transactions of the New York Academy of Sciences, Series II, VI (1944), 251–69.

—— The Negro in the United States. New York, Macmillan, 1949.

—— Race and Culture Contacts in the Modern World. New York, Knopf, 1957.

Freedman, Maurice (ed.). A Minority in Britain. London, Valentine, Mitchell, 1955.

Fremont-Smith, Frank. "The Influence of Emotional Factors upon Physiological and Pathological Processes." Bulletin of the New York Academy of Medicine, XV (1939), 560–69.

—— "The Physiological Basis of Aggression." Child Study, XV (1938), 1–8.

Frenchman, D. "Mixing of Races." Eugenics Review, XLI (1949), 98.

Frenkel-Brunswik, Else. "Patterns of Social and Cognitive Outlook in Children and Parents." American Journal of Orthopsychiatry, XXI (1951), 543–58.

—— and R. Nevitt Sanford. "Some Personality Factors in Anti-Semitism." Journal of Psychology, XX (1945), 271–91.

Freud, Sigmund. The Future of an Illusion. London, Hogarth Press, 1928.

—— Group Psychology and the Analysis of the Ego. London, Hogarth Press, 1922.

—— Introductory Lectures on Psycho-Analysis. London, Allen and Unwin, 1922.

Freyre, Gilberto. The "Mansions" and the "Shanties." New York, Knopf, 1963.

—— The Masters and the Slaves (Casa-Grande & Senzala). New York, Knopf, 1946.

Friedenthal, H. "Die Sonderstellung des Menschen in der Natur." Wege zum Wissen, VIII (1925). Berlin, Ulstein.

Fromm, Erich. Escape from Freedom. New York, Farrar and Rinehart, 1942.

—— "Sex and Character." Psychiatry, VI (1943), 21–31.

Fry, H. K. "Aboriginal Mentality." *Medical Journal of Australia,* I (1935), 353–60.

Fuller, J. L. Nature and Nurture: A Modern Synthesis. New York, Doubleday, 1954.

Fuller, L. The Crusade Against Slavery. New York, Harper, 1960.

Furnas, J. C. Goodbye to Uncle Tom. New York, William Sloane, 1956.

—— The Road to Harpers Ferry. New York, William Sloane, 1959.

Fyfe, William Hamilton. "Colonial University Colleges." *The Listener,* XLV (1951), 531–32.

—— The Illusion of National Character. London, Watts, 1946.

Gallagher, Buell G. Color and Conscience. New York, Harper, 1946.

Galton, Francis. Inquiries into the Human Faculty and Its Development. London, Macmillan, 1883.

Garlick, J. P. Review. *Annals of Human Genetics,* XXV (1961), 169–70.

Garn, Stanley M. Human Races. Springfield, Ill., Thomas, 1961.

Garrett, Henry E. "The Equalitarian Dogma." *Perspectives in Biology and Medicine,* IV (1961), 480–84.

—— "The Scientific Racism of Juan Comas." *The Mankind Quarterly,* II (1961), 100–06.

—— and W. C. George. "Findings on Race Cited." *New York Times,* October 10, 1962, p. 46.

Garth, Thomas R. Race Psychology. New York, Whittlesey House, 1931.

Gates, R. Ruggles. "Disadvantages of Race Mixture." *Nature,* CLXX (1952), 896.

—— "The Genetics of the Australian Aborigines." *Acta Geneticae Medicae et Gemellologiae,* IX (1960), 7–50.

—— Human Ancestry. Cambridge, Harvard University Press, 1948.

—— "A Pedigree Study of Amerindian Crosses in Canada." *Journal of the Royal Anthropological Institute,* LVIII (1928), 511–32.

—— "Phylogeny and Classification of Hominids and Anthropoids." *American Journal of Physical Anthropology,* N. S., II (1944), 279–92.

—— "Studies in Race Crossing." *Zeitschrift für Morphologie und Anthropologie,* XLVII (1956), 233–315.

—— "Studies in Race Crossing: The Japanese War Children." *Zeitschrift für Morphologie und Anthropologie,* XLIX (1958), 129–47.

Geddes, Patrick, and J. Arthur Thomson. Evolution. New York, Holt, 1911.

—— Sex. London, William & Norgate, 1911.

Genovese, Eugene D. "The Slave South: An Interpretation." *Science & Society,* XXV (1962), 320–37.

George, Katherine. "The Civilized West Looks at Primitive Africa: 1400–1800. A Study in Ethnocentrism." *Isis,* XLIX (1958), 62–72.

Gerard, R. "Higher Levels of Integration." *Biological Symposia*, VIII (1942), 67–87.

Gibbs, Henry. Twilight in South Africa. New York Philosophical Library, 1950.

Gibson, R. W. The Morality of Nature. New York, Putnam, 1923.

Gillin, John (ed.). For a Science of Social Man. New York, Macmillan, 1954.

—— "'Race' Relations without Conflict: A Guatemalan Town." *American Journal of Sociology*, LIII (1948), 337–43.

Ginsberg, Morris. "Anti-Semitism." *Sociological Review*, XXXV (1943), 1–11.

—— "National Character." *British Journal of Psychology*, XXXII (1942), 196–204.

—— Sociology. London, Butterworth, 1932.

Girant, Marcel. Le Métis canadien. Paris, Institut d'Ethnologie, 1950.

Gittler, Joseph B. (ed.). Understanding Minority Groups. New York, Wiley, 1956.

Glaser, S. "Sweat Glands in the Negro and the European." *American Journal of Physical Anthropology*, XVIII (1934), 371–76.

Glass, Bentley. Genes and the Man. New York, Teachers College, Columbia University, 1943.

—— and C. C. Li. "The Dynamics of Racial Intermixture—An Analysis Based on the American Negro." *American Journal of Human Genetics*, V (1953), 1–20.

Glazer, N. "Ethnic Groups in America," in M. Berger, *et al.* (eds.), Freedom and Control in Modern Society, pp. 156–73. New York, Van Nostrand, 1944.

Glazer, Nathan, and Daniel P. Moynihan. Beyond the Melting Pot. Cambridge, M.I.T. Press and Harvard University Press, 1963.

Glicksberg, Charles I. "Intercultural Education." *Common Ground*, VI (1946), 61–68.

Gobineau, Joseph A. de, Count. Essai sur l'inégalité des races humaines; trans. by H. Hotz, The Moral and Intellectual Diversity of Races. Philadelphia, Lippincott, 1856; Paris, 1853–55.

—— The Renaissance, with an introductory essay by Oscar Levy; trans. by Paul V. Cohn. London, Allen & Unwin, 1927.

Godsell, Philip H. "Is There Time To Save the Eskimo?" *Natural History*, LXI (1952), 56–62.

Goldschmidt, Richard. "Anthropological Determination of 'Aryanism.'" *Journal of Heredity*, XXXIII (1942), 215–16.

Goldsmith, Oliver. On National Prejudices. The Miscellaneous Works. New York, Putnam, 1850.

Goldstein, Marcus S. Demographic and Bodily Changes in Descendants of Mexican Immigrants. Austin, Institute of Latin-American Studies, 1943.

Goldstein, Nathaniel L. "New York Proves It: Laws CAN Cut Discrimination." *Christian Century*, CXXVII (1948), 30–32.

Golin, Milton. "How Deadly the Thought." *Journal of the American Medical Association*, CLXXI (1959), 148–54.

Goodman, Mary E. Race Awareness in Young Children. Cambridge, Mass., Addison-Wesley Press, 1952.

Gordon, Charles. "Ineligible Aliens." *New Republic*, CXII (1945), 502–03.

Gordon, M. M. "Social Structure and Goals in Group Relations," in M. Berger *et al.* (eds.), Freedom and Control in Modern Society, pp. 141–57. New York, Van Nostrand, 1944.

—— and J. P. Roche. "Segregation—Two-Edged Sword." *New York Times Magazine*, April 25, 1954.

Gorer, Geoffrey. "Some Notes on the British Character." *Horizon*, XX (1949–50), 369–79.

Gossett, Thomas F. Race: The History of an Idea. Dallas, Texas, Southern Methodist University Press, 1963.

Graeber, Isacque, and Steuart H. Britt (eds.). Jews in a Gentile World. New York, Macmillan, 1942.

Grant, Madison. The Passing of the Great Race. New York, Scribner, 1st ed., 1916; 2d ed., 1918; 3rd ed., 1919; 4th ed., 1921.

Graubard, Mark. Man, the Slave and Master. New York, Covici, Friede, 1938.

Greenberg, Jack. Race Relations and American Law. New York, Columbia University Press, 1959.

Greene, John C. "The American Debate on the Negro's Place in Nature." *Journal of the History of Ideas*, XV (1954), 384–96.

—— "Some Early Speculations on the Origin of Human Races." *American Anthropologist*, XLVI (1954), 31–41.

Griffin, John H. Black Like Me. Boston, Houghton Mifflin Co., 1961.

Grodzins, Milton M. Americans Betrayed. Chicago, University of Chicago Press, 1949.

Guillaume-Louis, P., and Dubreil-Chambardel. "Le Cerveau d'Anatole France," *Bulletin de l'Academie de Médecine (Paris)*, XCVIII (1927), 328–36.

Haarhoff, T. J. The Stranger at the Gate. New York, Macmillan, 1948.

Haddon, Alfred C. History of Anthropology. London, Watts, 1934.

Hahn, Eduard. Die Haustiere. Leipzig, Duncker und Humbolt, 1896.

Haldane, J. B. S. "The Argument from Animals to Men," in Ashley

Montagu (ed.), Culture and the Evolution of Man, pp. 65–83. New York, Oxford University Press, 1962.

—— The Causes of Evolution. New York, Longmans, 1932.

—— Heredity and Politics. New York, Norton, 1938.

—— "The Interaction of Nature and Nurture." *Annals of Eugenics*, XIII (1946), 196–205.

—— New Paths in Genetics. New York, Harper, 1942.

Hall, E. Raymond. "Zoological Subspecies of Man at the Peace Table." *Journal of Mammalogy*, XXVII (1946), 358–64.

Haller, Mark H. Eugenics: Hereditarian Attitudes in American Thought. New Brunswick, N. J., Rutgers University Press, 1963.

Halligan, Alice L. "A Community's Total War against Prejudice." *Journal of Educational Sociology*, XVI (1943), 374–80.

Hallowell, A. Irving. "Some Psychological Characteristics of the Northeastern Indians," in Man in Northeastern North America, *Papers of the R. S. Peabody Foundation for Archaeology*, III (1946), 195–225.

Hambly, Wilfrid D. "Primitive Warfare." *Chicago Natural History Museum Bulletin*, XVII (1946), 4–5.

Handlin, Oscar. Race and Nationality in American Life. Boston, Little, Brown, 1957.

Hanhart, Ernst. "Infectious Diseases," in Arnold Sorsby (ed.), Clinical Genetics. St. Louis, Mo., Mosby, 1953.

Hanke, Lewis. Aristotle and the American Indians. London, Hollis & Carter, 1958.

—— "The Dawn of Conscience in America: Spanish Experiments and Experiences with Indians in the New World." *Proceedings of the American Philosophical Society*, CVII (1963), 83–92.

Hankins, Frank H. The Racial Basis of Civilization. New York, Knopf, 1931.

Harper, Ida H. The Life and Works of Susan B. Anthony. Indianapolis, Bowen-Merrill Co., 1898; Indianapolis, The Hollenbeck Press, 1908.

Harper, William. A Memoir on Slavery. Charleston, Burges, 1838.

Harris, D. B., H. G. Gough, and W. E. Martin. "Children's Ethnic Attitudes: II, Relationships to Parental Beliefs Concerning Child Training." *Child Development*, XXI (1950), 169–81.

Harris, Marvin. "Caste, Class, and Minority." *Social Forces*, XXXVII (1958), 246–54.

Hart, C. W. M. "The Race Myth." *University of Toronto Quarterly*, XI (1942), 180–88.

Hartman, Walter. "Ethnic Differences." *Perspectives in Biology and Medicine*, V (1961), 136–38.

Hartmann, H., E. Kris, and M. Lowenstein. "Notes on the Theory of

Aggression." *The Psychoanalytic Study of the Child*, III/IV (1949), 9–36.

Hay, Malcolm. Europe and the Jews. Boston, Beacon Press, 1960.

Hayakawa, S. I. Language in Action. New York, Harcourt, Brace, 1941.

—— "Race and Words." *Common Sense*, XII (1943), 231–35.

Hechst, Bela. "Über einen Fall von Mikroencephalie ohne Geistigen Defekt." *Archiv für Psychiatrie und Nervenkrankheiten*, XCVII (1932), 64–76.

Heiser, Victor. An American Doctor's Odyssey. New York, Norton, 1936.

Hellman, Ellen, and Leah Abrahams. Handbook on Race Relations in South Africa. London, Oxford University Press, 1949.

Helm, J. D., and M. H. Jacobs. "Some Apparent Differences between the Erythrocytes of White and Negro Subjects." *Journal of Cellular and Comparative Physiology*, XXII (1943), 43–50.

Herbert, Xavier. Capricornia. New York, Appleton-Century, 1943.

Herder, Johann G. von. Outlines of a Philosophy of the History of Man; trans. by T. Churchill from Ideen zur Philosophie der Geschichte der Menschheit. Riga, 1784; London, J. Johnson, 1803.

Herrick, C. Judson. "A Neurologist Makes up His Mind." *Scientific Monthly*, L (1939), 99–110.

Herskovits, Melville J. The American Negro. New York, Knopf, 1928.

—— The Anthropometry of the American Negro. New York, Columbia University Press, 1930.

—— The Myth of the Negro Past. New York, Harper, 1941.

—— "Rear-Guard Action." *Perspectives in Biology and Medicine*, V (1961), 122–28.

—— "Social Selection and the Formation of Human Types." *Human Biology*, I (1929), 250–62.

—— "Who Are the Jews?" in Louis Finkelstein (ed.), The Jews: Their History, Culture, and Religion, II, pp. 1151–71. New York, Harper, 1949.

Hertz, Friedrich. Nationalism. London, Routledge, 1944.

—— Race and Civilization. London, Kegan Paul, 1928.

Highet, Gilbert. Man's Unconquerable Mind. New York, Columbia University Press, 1954.

Hill, J. Eric. "A Zoologist Looks at Raciology: a Reply to Dr. E. Raymond Hall's 'Zoological Subspecies at the Peace Table.'" *Journal of Mammalogy*, XXVIII (1947), 87–89.

Hippocrates. Airs, Waters, and Places; trans. by W. H. S. Jones. Vol. I. Cambridge, Harvard University Press, 1923.

Hirschfeld, Magnus. Men and Women. New York, Putnam, 1935.

—— Racism. London, Gollancz, 1938.

Hoffman, Frederick L. "Miscegenation in Hawaii." *Journal of Heredity,* VIII (1917), 12.

Hofstadter, Richard. Social Darwinism in American Thought, 1860–1915. Philadelphia, University of Pennsylvania Press, 1944.

Hogben, Lancelot. Dangerous Thoughts. New York, Norton, 1940.

—— Genetic Principles in Medicine and Social Science. New York, Knopf, 1932.

—— (ed.) Political Arithmetic. New York, Macmillan, 1938.

Hokanson, Jack E. "The Effects of Guilt Arousal and Severity of Discipline on Adult Aggressive Behavior." *Journal of Clinical Psychology,* XVII (1961), 29–32.

Holbé, T. V. "Métis de Cochinchine." *Revue Anthropologique,* XXIV (1914), 281–93; XXVI (1916), 449–66.

Holleman, J. F. African Interlude. Johannesburg, National Bockhandel, 1959.

Holmes, S. J. Life and Morals. New York, Macmillan, 1948.

—— The Negro's Struggle for Survival. Berkeley, University of California Press, 1937.

Holsti, Rudolf. The Relation of War to the Origin of the State. Helsingfors, New Printing Co., 1913.

Holt, Anne. Walking Together. London, Allen & Unwin, 1938.

Home, Henry. (See Kames, Lord.)

Homma, H. "On Apocrine Sweat Glands in White and Negro Men and Women." *Johns Hopkins Hospital Bulletin,* XXXVIII (1926), 367–71.

Honigsheim, Paul. "Voltaire as Anthropologist." *American Anthropologist,* XLVII (1945), 104–08.

Hook, Sidney. "Naturalism and Democracy," in Y. V. Krikorian (ed.), Naturalism and the Human Spirit, pp. 40–64. New York, Columbia University Press, 1944.

—— Reason, Social Myths, and Democracy. New York, John Day, 1941.

Horowitz, E. "The Development of Attitudes toward the Negro." *Archives of Psychology,* No. 194 (1936).

Horrell, Muriel. A Survey of Race Relations in South Africa. Johannesburg, South African Institute of Race Relations, 1962.

Housman, A. E. The Name and Nature of Poetry. New York, Cambridge University Press, 1933.

Howe, Irving, and B. J. Widick. "The U.A.W. Fights Race Prejudice." *Commentary,* VIII (1949), 261–68.

Howells, W. W. (ed.). Ideas on Human Evolution. Cambridge, Harvard University Press, 1962.

Hoyle, Fred. The Nature of the Universe. New York, Harper, 1951.

Hrdlička, Aleš. The Old Americans. Baltimore, Williams and Wilkins, 1925.

Huard, P., and A. Bigot. "Recherches sur Quelques Groupes Ethniques Observés en Indochine." *Travaux de l'Institut Anatomique de l'École Superieure de Médicine de l'Indochine* (Hanoi), VI (1939).

Huddleston, Trevor. Naught for Your Comfort. New York, Doubleday, 1956.

Hughes, Everett C., and H. M. Hughes. Where Peoples Meet: Ethnic and Racial Frontiers. Glencoe, Ill., Free Press, 1952.

Hulse, Frederick S. "Race as an Evolutionary Episode." *American Anthropologist*, LXIV (1962), 929–45.

Humboldt, Alexander von. Cosmos: A Sketch of a Physical Description of the Universe; trans. from the German by E. C. Otté. Vol. I. London, Bohn, 1849.

Humboldt, Wilhelm von. Über die Kawi-Sprache auf der Insel Java. Vol. III. Berlin, Königlichen Akademie der Wissenschaften, 1836.

Humphrey, Norman D. "American Race and Caste." *Psychiatry*, IV (1941), 159–60.

—— "American Race Relations and the Caste System." *Psychiatry*, VIII (1945), 379–81.

Hunt, J. McV. Intelligence and Experience. New York, Ronald Press, 1961.

Hunt, James. "The Negro's Place in Nature." *Memoirs of the Anthropological Society* (London), I (1863), 1–64.

Hutton, J. H. Caste in India. New York, Cambridge University Press, 1946.

Huxley, Julian S. Evolution in Action. New York, Harper, 1953.

—— Evolution: The Modern Synthesis. New York, Harper, 1942.

—— Heredity East and West. New York, Schuman, 1949.

—— Man Stands Alone. New York, Harper, 1941.

—— (ed.) The New Systematics. New York, Oxford University Press, 1940.

Huxley, Julian S., and Alfred S. Haddon. We Europeans. New York, Harper, 1936.

Huxley, Thomas H. "Emancipation—Black and White," in Science and Education, pp. 64–71. New York, Collier, 1901.

—— "On the Methods and Results of Ethnology," in Man's Place in Nature. London, Williams & Norgate. New York, Appleton, 1865.

—— and Julian S. Huxley. Touchstone for Ethics. New York, Harper, 1948.

Idriess, Ion L. Over the Range. Sydney, Angus & Robertson, 1937.

Imamura, Yutaka. "What is Race?" *Hiroshima Journal of Medical Sciences,* I (1951), 1–10.

Isaacs, Harold R. "American Race Relations and the United States Image in World Affairs." *Human Relations,* X (1962), 266–80.

—— "Back to Africa." *The New Yorker,* May 13, 1961.

—— The New World of Negro Americans. New York, John Day, 1963.

—— "World Affairs and U.S. Relations: A Note on Little Rock." *The Public Opinion Quarterly,* XXII (1958), 364–70.

Isocrates. Panegyricus, 4, 50; trans. by George Norlin. Loeb Classical Library, I, pp. xxiv, 149. Cambridge, Harvard University Press, 1928.

Jacks, L. P. The Confessions of an Octogenarian. London, Allen & Unwin, 1942.

Jackson, Lydia. Aggression and Its Interpretation. London, Methuen, 1954.

Jacobs, Melville, and Bernhard J. Stern. Outline of Anthropology. New York, Barnes & Noble, 1947.

James, H. E. O., and Cora Tenen. "Grievances and Their Displacement." *Occupational Psychology* (1946), 1–7.

Janowsky, Oscar I. Nationalities and National Minorities. New York, Macmillan, 1945.

Jastrow, Joseph. The Story of Human Error. New York, Appleton-Century, 1936.

Javits, Jacob J. Discrimination—U.S.A. New York, Harcourt, Brace, 1960.

Jefferson, Thomas. Notes on the State of Virginia, 1781–1785, in Saul K. Padover (ed.), The Complete Jefferson. New York, Tudor Publishing Co., 1943, pp. 567–697.

Jenkins, William S. Pro-Slavery Thought in the Old South. Chapel Hill, University of North Carolina Press, 1935.

Jenks, Albert E. Indian-White Amalgamation: an Anthropometric Study. University of Minnesota Studies in the Social Sciences, No. 6. Minneapolis, 1916.

Jennings, Herbert S. The Biological Basis of Human Nature. New York, Norton, 1930.

—— Genetics. New York, Norton, 1935.

—— "The Laws of Heredity and Our Present Knowledge of Human Genetics on the Material Side," in J. W. Corrigan (ed.), Scientific Aspects of the Race Problem. New York, Longmans, 1941.

—— Prometheus. New York, Dutton, 1925.

Johnson, Alvin. "Race in the World to Come." *Yale Review,* XXXIII (1943), 193–200.

Johnson, Charles S. Patterns of Negro Segregation. New York, Harper, 1943.

——— "Race Relations and Social Change," in Edgar T. Thompson (ed.), Race Relations and the Race Problem, pp. 271–303. Durham, Duke University Press, 1939.

Johnson, F. Ernest (ed.). Foundations of Democracy. New York, Harper, 1947.

Johnston, Harry H. The Story of My Life. Indianapolis, Bobbs-Merrill, 1943.

Jost, Hudson. "Some Physiological Changes during Frustration." Child Development, XII (1941), 9–15.

Kahler, Erich. Man the Measure. New York, Braziller, 1943.

Kalmus, H. Genetics. London, Pelican Books, 1948.

——— Variation and Heredity. London, Routledge, 1957.

Kames, Lord. Sketches of the History of Man. Edinburgh, Tourneiseu, 1774; 2d ed., 1796.

Kardiner, Abram, and Lionel Ovesey. The Mark of Oppression. New York, Norton, 1951.

Kartman, Leo. "Sociological Excursions of Biologists." Scientific Monthly, LXII (1943), 337–46.

Kautsky, Karl. Are the Jews a Race? New York, International Publishers, 1926.

Keesing, Felix M. The Changing Maori. New Plymouth, N.Z., Avery & Sons, 1928.

Keith, Arthur. "An Anthropologist in Retirement," I–XV. Literary Guide and Rationalist Review, Vol. LVII (1943), and Vol. LIX (1944).

——— An Autobiography. New York, Philosophical Library, 1950.

——— "Darwinian Exhibition in Moscow." Nature, CXL (1942), 393.

——— Essays on Human Evolution. New York, Putnam, 1947.

——— "Must a Rationalist Be a Pacifist?" Truth Seeker, LXVI (1939), 33–34.

——— "Nationalism." Sunday Express (London), August 27, 1939.

——— Nationality and Race. London, Oxford University Press, 1919.

——— A New Theory of Human Evolution. New York, Philosophical Library, 1948.

——— The Place of Prejudice in Modern Civilization. New York, John Day, 1931.

Kellogg, Vernon L. Military Selection and Race Deterioration. New York, Oxford University Press, 1916.

Kelly, Caroline. "The Reaction of White Groups in Country Towns of New South Wales to Aborigines." Social Horizons, I (1943), 34–40.

Kennard, Margaret A., and John F. Fulton. "Age and Reorganization of the Central Nervous System." *Journal of the Mount Sinai Hospital*, IX (1942), 594–606.

King, James C. "Inbreeding, Heterosis and Information Theory." *American Naturalist*, XCV (1962), 345–64.

Klatt, B. "Mendelismus, Domestikation und Kraniologie." *Archiv für Anthropologie*, N. S., XVIII (1921), 225–50.

Klineberg, Otto. "Mental Testing of Racial and National Groups," in J. W. Corrigan (ed.), Scientific Aspects of the Race Problem, pp. 251–94. New York, Longmans, 1941.

—— Negro Intelligence and Selective Migration. New York, Columbia University Press, 1935.

—— Race Differences. New York, Harper, 1935.

—— "Race Differences: the Present Position of the Problem." *International Social Science Bulletin* (UNESCO), II (1950), 460–66.

—— Social Psychology. New York, Holt, 1940.

—— (ed.) Characteristics of the American Negro. New York, Harper, 1944.

Klingberg, Frank J. The Anti-Slavery Movement in England. New Haven, Yale University Press, 1926.

Kloepfer, H. W. "An Investigation of 171 Possible Linkage Relationships in Man." *Annals of Eugenics*, XIII (1946), 35–71.

Kluckhohn, Clyde. "Anthropological Research and World Peace," in World Peace: a Symposium, pp. 143–66. 4th Congress on Philosophy, Science and Religion. New York, Harper, 1944.

—— Mirror for Man. New York, Whittlesey House, 1949.

—— "The Myth of Race," in Willard R. Sperry (ed.), Religion and Our Racial Tensions, pp. 3–27. Cambridge, Harvard University Press, 1945.

—— and William H. Kelly. "The Concept of Culture," in Ralph Linton (ed.), The Science of Man in the World Crisis, pp. 78–106. New York, Columbia University Press, 1945.

Knobloch, Hilda, and Benjamin Pasamanick. "A Developmental Questionnaire for Infants Forty Weeks of Age: An Evaluation. *Monographs of the Society for Research in Child Growth and Development*, XX (1956), No. 2.

Koenig, Frederick W., and Morton B. King, Jr. "Cognitive Simplicity and Prejudice." *Social Forces*, XL (1962), 220–22.

Koestler, Arthur. Thieves in the Night. New York, Macmillan, 1946.

Kohl, Johann G. England, Wales, and Scotland. London, Chapman & Hall, 1844.

Kohn, Hans. "Race Conflict," in *Encyclopaedia of the Social Sciences*, XIII, 40. New York, Macmillan, 1937.

Korzybski, Alfred. Science and Sanity. 2d ed. Lancaster, Science Press, 1941.

Koumaris, John. "On the Morphological Variety of Modern Greeks." *Man*, XLVIII (1948), 126–27.

Krauss, William W. "Race Crossing in Hawaii." *Journal of Heredity*, XXXII (1941), 371–78.

Kretschmer, Ernst. The Psychology of Men of Genius. New York, Harcourt, Brace, 1931.

Kroeber, Alfred L. "The Superorganic." *American Anthropologist*, XIX (1917), 163–213.

Krogman, Wilton M. "The Concept of Race," in Linton (ed.), The Science of Man in the World Crisis, pp. 38–62. New York, Columbia University Press, 1944.

—— The Physical Anthropology of the Seminole Indians. Comitato Italiano per lo studio dei problemi della popolazione, Roma, 1935, serie 3, II, ix–199.

Kropotkin, Petr. Mutual Aid, a Factor in Evolution. Rev. ed. New York, McClure, 1904.

Kuno, Yas. Human Perspiration. Springfield, Ill., Thomas, 1956.

Kuper, Leo, Hilstan Watts, and Ronald Davies. Durban: A Study in Racial Ecology. New York, Columbia University Press, 1958.

La Barre, Weston. "The Cultural Basis of Emotions and Gestures." *Journal of Personality*, XVI (1947), 49–68.

Lader, Lawrence. The Bold Brahmins. New York, Dutton, 1961.

Laidler, Harry W. (ed.). The Role of the Races in Our Future Civilization. New York, League for Industrial Democracy, 1942.

Lamont, Corliss. "National and Racial Minorities," in Ernest J. Simmons (ed.), USSR: a Concise Handbook. Ithaca, N. Y., Cornell University Press, 1947.

Landes, R. "A Preliminary Statement of a Survey of Negro-White Relationships in Britain." *Man*, LII (1952), 133.

Landry, Stuart O. The Cult of Equality. New Orleans, Pelican Publishing Co., 1945.

Langmuir, Irving. "Science, Common Sense and Decency." *Science*, XCVII (1943), 1–7.

Lapiere, R. T. "Race Prejudice: France and England." *Social Forces*, VII (1928), 102–11.

Lasker, Bruno. Race Attitudes in Children. New York, Holt, 1929.

Lasker, Gabriel W. "Migration and Physical Differentiation." *American Journal of Physical Anthropology*, N. S., IV (1946), 273–300.

Laslett, Peter (ed.). The Physical Basis of Mind. New York, Macmillan, 1950.

Lassek, A. M. The Human Brain. Springfield, Ill., Thomas, 1957.

Laufer, Berthold. "Methods in the Study of Domestications." *Scientific Monthly*, XXV (1927), 251–55.

Laughlin, William S. (ed.). Papers on the Physical Anthropology of the American Indian. New York, The Viking Fund, 1951.

—— "Races of Mankind." *Anthropological Papers of the University of Alaska*, VIII (1960), 89–99.

League of Coloured Peoples. Race Relations and the Schools. London, 1944.

Leake, Chauncey D. "Ethicogenesis." *Proceedings of the Philosophical Society of Texas*, X (1944), 7–34.

Lee, Alfred L. Fraternities Without Brotherhood. Boston, Beacon Press, 1955.

Lee, Alfred M., and Norman D. Humphrey. Race Riot. New York, Dryden Press, 1943.

Lefroy, C. E. C. "Australian Aborigines: a Noble-Hearted Race." *Contemporary Review*, CXXXV (1929), 22.

Le Gros Clark, W. E. Fitting Man to His Environment. Newcastle upon Tyne, King's College, 1949.

Leibnitz, Gottfried W. von. Otium Hanoveriana; sive, Miscellanea . . . Leipzig, 1718.

Leighton, Alexander. The Governing of Men. Princeton, Princeton University Press, 1945.

Le Jeune, Paul. Quebec and Hurons: 1640. Jesuit Relations, Vol. XIX. Cleveland, Burrows Bros., 1898.

Leschi, Jeanne. Races Mélanodermes et Leucodermes: Pigmentation et Fonctionnement Cortico-Surrénalien. Paris, Masson, 1952.

Lestchinsky, Jacob." The Jew in Ruined Europe." *Chicago Jewish Forum*, IV (1945), 10–16.

Levin, G. "Racial and 'Inferiority' Characters in the Human Brain." *American Journal of Physical Anthropology*, XXII (1937), 345–80.

Levin, Meyer (ed). "Journal of Kibbutz Buchenwald." *Commentary*, I (1946), 31–39.

Lewin, Kurt. Resolving Social Conflicts. New York, Harper, 1948.

Lewis, Julian H. The Biology of the Negro. Chicago, University of Chicago Press, 1942.

Lewis, Wyndham. The Lion and the Fox. London, Grant Richards, 1927.

Lieberson, Stanley. Ethnic Patterns in American Cities. New York, Free Press, 1963.

Lillie, Ralph S. "The Psychic Factor in Living Organisms." *Philosophy of Science*, X (1943), 262–70.

Limson, Marciano. "Observations on the Bones of the Skull in White and Negro Fetuses and Infants." *Contributions to Embryology*, No. 136 (1932), 204–22.

Lincoln, C. Eric. The Black Muslims in America. Boston, Beacon Press, 1961.

Lind, Andrew W. Hawaii's Japanese: an Experiment in Democracy. Princeton, Princeton University Press, 1946.

———— (ed.) Race Relations in World Perspective. Honolulu, University of Hawaii Press, 1955.

Lindsay, Lord. The Good and the Clever. New York, Cambridge University Press, 1945.

Linnaeus, Carolus. Systema naturae. Leyden, 1735, and 1753.

Linton, Ralph. "Error in Anthropology," in Joseph Jastrow (ed.), The Story of Human Error, pp. 292–321. New York, Appleton-Century, 1935.

———— (ed.) Most of the World. New York, Columbia University Press, 1949.

———— The Science of Man in the World Crisis. New York, Columbia University Press, 1944.

———— The Study of Man. New York, Appleton-Century, 1936.

Lippitt, R., and M. Radke. "New Trends in the Investigation of Prejudice." *Annals of the American Academy of Political and Social Science*, CCXLIV (1946), 167–76.

Lippmann, Walter. Public Opinion. New York, Signet Books, 1946.

Lipschütz, Alejandro. El Indoamericanismo y el problema racial en las Américas. Segundo edición. Santiago, Chile, Editorial Nascimento, 1944.

Littel, S. Harrington. "All Races Necessary." *New York Times*, September 3, 1944.

Little, Kenneth L. "Loudon Square." *Sociological Review*, XXXIV (1942), 119–46.

———— Negroes in Britain. London, Kegan Paul, 1948.

———— "A Note on Colour Prejudice amongst the English 'Middle Class.'" *Man*, XLII (1943), 104–07.

———— "The Psychological Background of White-Coloured Contacts in Britain." *Sociological Review*, XXXV (1943), 12–28.

———— Race and Society. UNESCO. New York, Columbia University Press, 1952.

———— "Race Relations in English Society." *Man*, XLII (1942), 90–91.

———— "Some Anthropological Characteristics of Anglo-Negro Children." *Journal of the Royal Anthropological Institute*, LXXIII (1943), 57–73.

—— "The Study of Racial Mixture in the British Commonwealth." *Eugenics Review*, XXXII (1941), 114–20.

Liu, William T. "The Community Reference System, Religiosity, and Race Attitudes." *Social Forces*, XXXIX (1961), 324–28.

Livingston, Sigmund. Must Men Hate? New York, Harper, 1944.

Livingstone, Frank R. "On the Non-Existence of Human Races." *Current Anthropology*, III (1962), 279–81.

Lloyd, Arthur Y. The Slavery Controversy 1831–1860. Chapel Hill, University of North Carolina Press, 1939.

Lloyd, F., and D. A. Pidgeon. "An Investigation into the Effects of Coaching on Nonverbal Test Material With European, Indian, and African Children." *British Journal of Educational Psychology*, XXI (1961), 145–51.

Locke, Alain, and Bernhard J. Stern. When Peoples Meet. New York, Progressive Education Association, 1942.

Logan, Spencer. A Negro's Faith in America. New York, Macmillan, 1946.

Lomax, Louis E. The Negro Revolt. New York, Harper, 1962.

—— The Reluctant African. New York, Harper, 1960.

[Long, Edward]. The History of Jamaica. London, 1774.

—— "Observations on the Gradation in the Scale of Being Between the Human and the Brute Creation. Including Some Curious Particulars Respecting Negroes." *The Columbian Magazine or Monthly Miscellany*, II (1788), 15.

Long, Herman H. "Race Prejudice and Social Change." *American Journal of Sociology*, LVII (1951), 15–19.

Loram, T. C., and T. F. McIlwraith (eds.). The North American Indian. Toronto, University of Toronto Press, 1943.

Lorimer, Frank, and Frederick Osborn. Dynamics of Population. New York, Macmillan, 1934.

Lotsy, J. P., and W. A. Goddijn. "Voyages of Exploration to Judge of the Bearing of Hybridization upon Evolution. I. South Africa." *Genetica*, X (1928), viii–315.

Loumala, K. "California Takes Back Its Japanese Evacuees." *Applied Anthropology*, III (1946), 25–39.

Love, J. R. B. Stone Age Bushmen of To-Day. London, Blackie, 1936.

Lowenstein, Alfred K. Brutal Mandate. New York, Macmillan, 1962.

Lowenthal, Leo, and Norbert Guterman. Prophets of Deceit. New York, Harper, 1949.

Lowie, Robert H. "Intellectual and Cultural Achievements of Human

Races," in J. W. Corrigan (ed.), Scientific Aspects of the Race Problem, pp. 189–249.

Lowy, Samuel. Co-operation, Tolerance, and Prejudice. London, Routledge, 1948.

Lubell, Samuel. "Racist Dress Rehearsal for November." *Commentary*, XIII (1952), 307–15.

Lucaks, John. See Tocqueville, Alexis de.

Ludwig, Emil. Talks with Mussolini. Boston, Little, Brown, 1933.

Lurie, Edward. "Louis Agassiz and the Races of Man." *Isis*, XLV (1954), 227–42.

Luthuli, Albert. Let My People Go. New York, McGraw-Hill, 1962.

McCarthy, Frederick D. Australia's Aborigines. Melbourne, Colorgravure Publications, 1959.

MacCaughey, V. "Race Mixture in Hawaii." *Journal of Heredity*, X (1919), 41–47, 90–95.

McClure, Matthew T. "Greek Genius and Race Mixture," in Studies in the History of Ideas, III, pp. 25–33. New York, Columbia University Press, 1935.

McCord, William, Jane McCord, and Alan Howard. "Early Familial Experiences and Bigotry." *American Sociological Review*, XXV (1960), 717–22.

McCown, Theodore D., and Arthur Keith. The Stone Age of Mount Carmel. Vol. II. Oxford, Clarendon Press, 1939. (See the review of this work by M. F. Ashley Montagu, *American Anthropologist*, XLII [1940], 518–22.)

MacCrone, I. D. Group Conflicts and Race Prejudice. Johannesburg, South African Institute of Race Relations, 1947.

——— Race Attitudes in South Africa. London, Oxford University Press, 1937.

——— "Reaction to Domination in a Colour-Caste Society: a Preliminary Study of the Race Attitudes of a Dominated Group." *Journal of Social Psychology*, XXVI (1947), 69–98.

McDill, Edward. "Anomie, Authoritarianism, Prejudice, and Socio-Economic Status: An Attempt at Clarification." *Social Forces*, XXXIX (1961), 239–45.

McDonagh, Edward C. "Status Levels of American Jews." *Sociology and Social Research*, XXXII (1948), 944–53.

Mace, C. A. "National Stereotypes—Their Nature and Function." *Sociological Review*, XXXV (1943), 29–36.

McElroy, W. A. "Aesthetic Appreciation in Aborigines of Arnhemland. A Comparative Experimental Study." *Oceania*, XXIII (1952), 81–94.

Macfarlane, John M. The Causes and Course of Organic Evolution. New York, Macmillan, 1918.

McFie, J. "The Effect of Education on African Performance on a Group of Intellectual Tests." *British Journal of Educational Psychology*, XXX (1961), 232–40.

McInnes, Colin. City of Spades. New York, Macmillan, 1958.

MacIver, Robert M. The More Perfect Union. New York, Macmillan, 1948.

—— (ed.) Discrimination and National Welfare. New York, Harper, 1949.

—— Unity and Difference in American Life. New York, Harper, 1947.

McKay, Vernon. Africa in World Politics. New York, Harper & Row, 1963.

McKitrick, Eric L. (ed.). Slavery Defended: The Views of the Old South. Englewood Cliffs, N. J., Prentice-Hall, 1963.

McLaren, Jack. My Crowded Solitude. London, Newnes, 1926.

Maclean, Joan C. (ed.). Africa: The Racial Issue. New York, Wilson, 1954.

Macleod, James C. The American Indian Frontier. New York, Knopf, 1928.

MacMunn, G. F. Slavery through the Ages. Philadelphia, Saunders, 1938.

McQueen, Robert, and Churn Browning. "The Intelligence and Educational Achievement of a Matched Sample of Negro and White Students." *School and Society*, LXXXVIII (1960), 327–29.

McWilliams, Carey. Brothers under the Skin. 2d ed. Boston, Little, Brown, 1951.

—— A Mask for Privilege. Boston, Little, Brown, 1948.

—— Prejudice—the Japanese-Americans: Symbol of Racial Intolerance. Boston, Little, Brown, 1944.

—— "Race Discrimination and the Law." *Science and Society*, IX (1945), 1–22.

Mahalanobis, Prasanta A. "Analysis of Race Mixture in Bengal." *Journal of the Asiatic Society of Bengal*, XXIII (1927), 301–33.

—— "Anthropological Observations on the Anglo-Indians of Calcutta." *Records of the Indian Museum*, XXIII (1922–40), 1–187.

Maier, Norman R. F. Frustration. Ann Arbor, University of Michigan Press, 1961.

—— Principles of Human Relations. New York, Wiley, 1952.

—— and Theodore C. Schneirla. Principles of Animal Psychology. New York, McGraw-Hill, 1935.

Mair, L. P. Australia in New Guinea. London, Christophers, 1948.

Malafa, R. On the Bodily Differences between Sprinters and Non-Sportsmen. Brno, Publications de la Faculté des Sciences de la Université Masaryk, 1933.

Malinowski, Bronislaw. A Scientific Theory of Culture and Other Essays. Chapel Hill, University of North Carolina Press, 1944; New York, Oxford University Press, 1960.

——— "War—Past, Present, and Future," in J. D. Clarkson and T. C. Cochran (eds.), War as a Social Institution. New York, Columbia University Press, 1941.

Mall, Franklin P. "On Several Anatomical Characters of the Human Brain, Said to Vary according to Race and Sex." American Journal of Anatomy, IX (1909), 1–32.

Mandelbaum, David G. Soldier Groups and Negro Groups. Berkeley, University of California Press, 1953.

Mannix, Daniel P., and Malcolm Cowley. Black Cargoes. New York, Viking Press, 1962.

Mannoni, O. Prospero and Caliban. New York, Praeger, 1956.

Manuel, Frank E. "From Equality to Organicism." Journal of the History of Ideas, XIII (1956), 54–69.

Marcuse, F. L., and M. E. Bitterman. "Notes on the Results of Army Intelligence Testing in World War I." Science, CIV (1946), 231–32.

Marden, Charles F. Minorities in American Society. New York, American Book Company, 1952.

Marquand, Leo. Peoples and Policies of South Africa. New York, Oxford University Press, 1952.

Marrow, Alfred J. Changing Patterns of Prejudice. New York, Chilton, 1962.

——— Living Without Hate. New York, Harper, 1951.

Martin, James G. "Intergroup Tolerance—Prejudice." Journal of Human Relations, X (1961), 197–204.

——— "Tolerant and Prejudiced Personality Syndromes." Journal of Intergroup Relations, II (1961), 171–75.

——— and Frank R. Westie. "The Tolerant Personality." American Sociological Review, XXIV (1959), 521–28.

Marvin, Francis S. (ed.). Western Races and the World. London, Oxford University Press, 1922.

Maslow, Will. "Civil Rights Legislation and the Fight for Equality, 1862–1952." University of Chicago Law Review, XX (1952), 363–413.

——— "The Law and Race Relations," in Gordon Allport (ed.), "Controlling Group Prejudice." Annals of the American Academy of Political and Social Science, CCXLIV (1946), 75–81.

Mason, Philip. Christianity and Race. London, Lutterworth Press, 1956.
—— Common Sense About Race. New York, Macmillan, 1961.
—— An Essay on Racial Tension. London, Royal Institute of National Affairs, 1954.
Massing, Paul W. Rehearsal for Destruction. New York, Harper, 1949.
Masuoka, Jitsuichi, and Preston Valien (eds.). Race Relations. Chapel Hill, University of North Carolina Press, 1961.
Masuoka, J., and R. L. Yokley. "Essential Structural Requisites in Race Relations." Social Forces, XXXIII (1954), 30–35.
Mather, Kirtley. The Measurement of Linkage in Heredity. 2d ed. London, Methuen, 1951.
Mathew, J. Eaglehawk and Crow. London, Nutt, 1899.
Matthews, Z. K. "The Black Man's Outlook." Saturday Review, XXXVI (May 2, 1953), 13–14, 51–52.
Mayr, Ernst. Animal Species and Evolution. Cambridge, Harvard University Press, 1963.
—— "Speciation Phenomena in Birds." Biological Symposia, II (1941), (1941), 59–88.
—— Systematics and the Origin of Species. New York, Columbia University Press, 1942.
Mead, Margaret. Peoples and Places. Cleveland & New York, World Publishing Co., 1959.
—— "Warfare Is Only an Invention—Not a Biological Necessity." Asia, XL (1940), 402–05.
Meggers, Betty J. "Environmental Limitation on the Development of Culture." American Anthropologist, LVI (1954), 801–24.
Mekeel, Scudder. "Cultural Aids to Constructive Race Relations." Mental Hygiene, XXIX (1945), 177–89.
Mendelson, Wallace. Discrimination. Englewood Cliffs, N. J., Prentice-Hall, 1962.
Merton, Robert K. "Discrimination and the American Creed," in Robert MacIver (ed.), Discrimination and National Welfare, pp. 99–126. New York, Harper, 1959.
—— "Social Structure and Anomie." American Sociological Review, III (1938), 680.
—— and M. F. Ashley Montagu. "Crime and the Anthropologist." American Anthropologist, XLII (1940), 384–408.
Mielche, Hakon. Journey to the World's End. New York, Doubleday, 1941.
Miller, Clyde R. "Community Wages Total War on Prejudice." The Nation's Schools, XXXIII (1944), 16–18.
Miller, Hugh. The Community of Man. New York, Macmillan, 1949.

———— Progress and Decline. Los Angeles, Ward Ritchie Press, 1963.

Miller, Kelley. "Is Race Prejudice Innate or Acquired?" *Journal of Applied Sociology*, XI (1927), 516–24.

Miller, Mary D., and Florence Rutter. Child Artists of the Australian Bush. London, Harrap, 1952.

Miller, Michael. "Outlawing Anti-Semitism." *Ideas for Action*, June, 1946.

Miller, Sarah. The People of South Africa. New York, Knopf, 1954.

Milner, Lucille B. "Jim Crow in the Army." *New Republic*, CX (1944), 339–42.

———— "Miscegenation in South Africa." *Nature*, VII (1940), p. 357.

Miner, Horace. Timbuctoo. Princeton, Princeton University Press, 1953.

Mintzer, George J., and Newman Levy. The International Anti-Semitic Conspiracy. New York, the American Jewish Committee, 1946.

Moloney, James C. "Authoritarianism and Intolerance." *International Journal of Psychoanalysis*, XXIX (1948), 2–4.

Money-Kyrle, R. E. Psychoanalysis and Politics. London, Duckworth, 1951; New York, Norton, 1952.

Monro, D. H. "The Concept of Myth." *Sociological Review*, XLII (1950), 115–32.

Montagu, M. F. Ashley. "Answer by an Anthropologist to a Geneticist about the Understanding of Race in Man." *International Social Science Bulletin* (UNESCO), III (1951), 1007–10.

———— "Anti-feminism and Race Prejudice." *Psychiatry*, IX (1946), 69–71.

———— "The Biologist Looks at Crime." *Annals of the Academy of Political and Social Science*, CCXVII (1941), 46–57.

———— The Biosocial Nature of Man. New York, Grove Press, 1956.

———— Coming into Being among the Australian Aborigines. New York, Dutton, 1938.

———— "Comments on Comparative Studies in Human Biology." *Science*, C (1944), 383–84.

———— "The Concept of Race." *American Anthropologist*, LXIV (1962), 919–28.

———— "A Consideration of the Concept of Race." *Cold Spring Harbor Symposia on Quantitative Biology*, XV (1950), 315–36.

———— "Constitutional and Prenatal Factors in Infant and Child Health," in M. J. E. Senn (ed.), The Healthy Personality, pp. 148–210. New York, Josiah Macy, Jr., Foundation, 1950.

———— "A Cursory Examination of the Relations between Physical and Social Anthropology." *American Journal of Physical Anthropology*, XXVI (1940), 41–61.

—— Darwin, Competition and Cooperation. New York, Schuman, 1952.

—— The Direction of Human Development. New York, Harper, 1955.

—— Education and Human Relations. New York, Grove Press, 1958.

—— Edward Tyson, M.D., F.R.S. (1650–1708), and the Rise of Human and Comparative Anatomy in England. Philadelphia. *Memoirs of the American Philosophical Society*, XX (1943), xxxix–488.

—— "Escape from Freedom." *Psychiatry*, V (1942), 122–29.

—— "The Future of the Australian Aborigines." *Oceania*, VIII (1938), 343–50.

—— "Genetics and the Origin of Man in the Americas." *Man*, XLIII (1943), 131–35.

—— Human Heredity. Cleveland & New York, World Publishing Co., 1959. 3rd ed., New York, New American Library, 1963.

—— The Humanization of Man. Cleveland & New York, World Publishing Co., 1962.

—— "A Hybrid Gibbon." *Journal of Mammalogy*, XXXI (1950), 150–53.

—— "The Intelligence of Northern Negroes and Southern Whites in the First World War." *American Journal of Psychology*, LXVIII (1945), 161–88.

—— "The Intelligence of Southern Whites and Northern Negroes." *Psychiatry*, VII (1944), 184–89.

—— "Intelligence Tests and the Negro in America." *Wasu* (West African Students' Union, London), I (1926), 5–7.

—— An Introduction to Physical Anthropology. 3rd ed. Springfield, Ill., Thomas, 1960.

—— Life Before Birth. New York, New American Library, 1964.

—— Man: His First Million Years. Cleveland & New York, World Publishing Co., 1957.

—— Man in Process. Cleveland & New York, World Publishing Co., 1961.

—— The Natural Superiority of Women. New York, Macmillan, 1953.

—— "The Nature of Race Relations." *Social Forces*, XXV (1947), 336–42.

—— "The Negro's Problem: the White Man." *Bulletin of Negro History*, VIII (1945), 177–79.

—— On Being Human. New York, Schuman, 1950.

—— On Being Intelligent. New York, Schuman, 1951.

—— "On the Breeding of 'Aryans.'" *Psychiatry*, VI (1943), 254–55.

—— "On the Phrase 'Ethnic Group' in Anthropology." *Psychiatry*, VIII (1945), 27–33.

—— "On the Primate Thumb." *American Journal of Physical Anthropology*, XV (1931), 291–314.

—— "On the Relation between Body Size, Waking Activity, and the Origin of Social Life in the Primates." *American Anthropologist*, LXVI (1944), 141–45.

—— "The Origin and Nature of Social Life and the Biological Basis of Coöperation." *Journal of Social Psychology*, XXIX (1949), 267–83.

—— "Physical Anthropology," in Otto Glasser (ed.), *Medical Physics*. Chicago, Year Book Publishers, Vol. I, 1944; Vol. II, 1950.

—— "Physical Anthropology and Anatomy." *American Journal of Physical Anthropology*, XXVIII (1941), 261–71.

—— "Prehistoric Hybridization." *Man*, LXII (1962), 25.

—— "The Premaxilla in Man." *Journal of the American Dental Association*, XXIII (1936), 2043–57.

—— "The Premaxilla in the Primates." *Quarterly Review of Biology*, X (1935), 182–84.

—— Prenatal Influences. Springfield, Ill., Thomas, 1962.

—— "Race, Caste and Scientific Method." *Psychiatry*, IV (1941), 337–38.

—— The Science of Man. New York, Odyssey Press, 1964.

—— "Science Versus Value Commitments." *Perspectives in Biology and Medicine*, V (1961), 131–35.

—— "The Significance of the Variability of the Upper Lateral Incisor Teeth in Man." *Human Biology*, XII (1940), 323–58.

—— " 'Social Instincts.' " *Scientific American*, CLXXXII (1950), 54–56.

—— "Social Time: a Methodological and Functional Analysis." *American Journal of Sociology*, XLIV (1938), 282–84.

—— "The Socio-Biology of Man." *Scientific Monthly*, L (1940), 483–90.

—— "Some Anthropological Terms: A Study in the Systematics of Confusion." *American Anthropologist*, XLVII (1945), 119–33.

—— Statement on Race. 2d ed. New York, Schuman, 1952.

—— (ed.) Culture and the Evolution of Man. New York, Oxford University Press, 1962.

—— Studies and Essays in the History of Science and Learning. New York, Schuman, 1946.

Montagu, M. F. Ashley, and Theodosius Dobzhansky. "Natural Selection and the Mental Capacities of Mankind." *Science*, CV (1947), 587–90.

Montesquieu, Charles de Secondat. The Spirit of the Laws. Book XV, Chapter V. Trans. by Thomas Nugent. New York, Hafner, 1949.

Moore, Doris L. The Vulgar Heart. London, Cassell, 1945.

Moore, George H. Notes on the History of Slavery in Massachusetts. New York, Appleton, 1866.

Morant, Geoffrey M. "The Future of Physical Anthropology." Man, XLIV (1944), 16–18.

——— The Races of Central Europe. New York, Norton, 1939.

——— "Racial Theories and International Relations." Journal of the Royal Anthropological Institute of Great Britain and Ireland, LXIX (1939), 151–62.

Morgan, Thomas H. Evolution and Genetics. Princeton, Princeton University Press, 1925.

Morlan, G. K. "An Experiment on the Identification of Body Odor." Journal of Genetic Psychology, LXXVII (1950), 257–65.

Morland, J. Kenneth. "Racial Recognition by Nursery School Children in Lynchburg, Va." Social Forces, XXXVII (1958), 132–37.

Morton, Newton E. "Genetics of Interracial Crosses in Hawaii." Eugenics Quarterly, IX (1962), 23–24.

Mountford, Charles P. Brown Men and Red Sand. London, Phoenix House, 1950.

Mourant, A. E. The Distribution of the Human Blood Groups. Springfield, Ill., Thomas, 1954.

Mudgett, Helen P. Democracy for All. Minneapolis, General Extension Division, University of Minnesota, 1945.

Muller, Hermann J. "Genetics in the Scheme of Things." Proceedings of the Eighth International Congress of Genetics. Hereditas, supplementary vol., 1949, pp. 96–127.

——— "On the Variability of Mixed Races." American Naturalist, LXX (1936), 409–42.

——— Out of the Night. New York, Vanguard Press, 1935.

Murdock, K., and Louis R. Sullivan. "A Contribution to the Study of Mental and Physical Measurements in Normal Children." American Physical Educational Review, XXVIII (1923), 209–15, 278–88, 328.

Murphy, Douglas. Congenital Malformations. 2d ed. Philadelphia, Lippincott, 1947.

Murphy, Gardner. Personality. New York, Harper, 1947.

Murphy, John. Lamps of Anthropology. Manchester, Manchester University Press, 1943.

Murphy, T. D. Ambassadors in Arms. Honolulu, University of Hawaii Press, 1954.

Murray, Pauli. States' Laws on Race and Color. Cincinnati, Methodist Woman's Division of Christian Service, 1950.

Myers, Gustavius. History of Bigotry in the United States. New York, Random House, 1943.

Myers, Henry A. Are Men Equal? New York, Putnam, 1945.

Myrdal, Gunnar. An American Dilemma: the Negro Problem and Modern Democracy. 2 vols. New York, Harper, 1944.

Myres, John L. Who Were the Greeks? Berkeley, University of California Press, 1930.

Nabours, R. K. "Emergent Evolution and Hybridism." Science, LXXI (1930), 371–75.

Nash, E., H. Nash, B. Pasamanick, and H. Knobloch. "Further Observations on the Development of Negro Children: Status at Seven Years." Unpublished material.

Nash, Manning. "Race and the Ideology of Race." Current Anthropology, III (1962), 285–88.

Nash, Philleo. "An Introduction to the Problem of Race Tension," in C. T. Loram and T. F. McIlwraith (eds.), The North American Indian Today, pp. 331–35. Toronto, University of Toronto Press, 1943.

Nash, Walter. "Democracy's Goal in Race Relationships—with Special Reference to New Zealand," in Harry W. Laidler (ed.), The Role of the Races in Our Future Civilization, pp. 12–16. New York, League for Industrial Democracy, 1942.

Nasmyth, George. Social Progress and the Darwinian Theory. New York, Putnam, 1916.

Ndem, Eyo B. "The Status of Coloured People in Britain." Phylon, XVIII (1957), 82–87.

Nef, John U. War and Human Progress. Cambridge, Harvard University Press, 1950.

Neumann, Franz L. Behemoth: the Structure and Practice of National Socialism. New York, Oxford University Press, 1942.

Neuville, Henri. L'Espèce, la race et le mètissage en anthropologie. Mémoire II, Archives de L'Institut de Paléontologie Humaine. Paris, 1933.

——— "Les Métissages de l'Îsle Pitcairn." L'Anthropologie, XLIII (1933), 267, 485.

Neville, A. O. Australia's Coloured Minority. Sydney, Currawong Press, 1947.

Newhall, Richard A. The Columbus Letter. Williamstown, Mass., Chapin Library, Williams College, 1953.

Newman, M. T. "The Application of Ecological Rules to the Racial Anthropology of the Aboriginal New World." American Anthropologist, LV (1955), 309–27.

Nichols, Charles H. Many Thousand Gone. Leiden, Brill, 1963.

Nichols, Lee. Breakthrough on the Color Front. New York, Random House, 1954.

Nilsson, Martin P. "The Race Problem of the Roman Empire." *Hereditas*, II (1921), 370–90.

Norlin, George. The Quest of American Life. University of Colorado Studies, Series B. Studies in the Humanities, Vol II. Boulder, 1945.

—— Things in the Saddle. Cambridge, Harvard University Press, 1940.

Nott, Josiah C. Types of Mankind. Philadelphia, Lippincott, 1854.

—— and George R. Gliddon. Indigenous Races of the Earth. Philadelphia, Lippincott, 1857.

Numelin, Ragnar. The Beginnings of Diplomacy. New York, Philosophical Library, 1950.

Nye, Russel B. "Civil Liberties and the Anti-Slavery Controversy." *Science & Society*, IX (1945), 125–46.

—— Fettered Freedom. East Lansing, Mich., Michigan State College Press, 1949.

Oakesmith, John. Race and Nationality. London, Heinemann, 1919.

Odum, Howard. Race and Rumors of Race. Chapel Hill, University of North Carolina Press, 1943.

Ogden, C. K., and I. A. Richards. The Meaning of Meaning. New York, Harcourt, Brace, 1923.

Okubo, Mine. Citizen 13660. New York, Columbia University Press, 1946.

Oldham, Joseph H. Christianity and the Race Problem. London, Student Christian Movement Press, 1925.

Oliver, Douglas. The Pacific Islands. Cambridge, Harvard University Press, 1951.

Olivier, Sidney. "Colour Prejudice." *Contemporary Review*, CXXIV (1923), 448–57.

—— Jamaica the Blessed Island. London, Faber & Faber, 1936.

Olson, Bernard E. Faith and Prejudice. New Haven, Yale University Press, 1963.

Opler, Morris E. "Cultural and Organic Conceptions in World History." *American Anthropologist*, XLVI (1944), 448–60.

—— "The Use and Abuse of the Word 'Aryan,'" *El Palacio*, LIII (1946), 9–12.

Osborn, Frederick. A Preface to Eugenics. New York, Harper, 1940.

Padover, Saul K. "Who Are the Germans?" *Foreign Affairs*, XIII (1935), 509–18.

Paine, Thomas. African Slavery.

Park, Robert E. "The Bases of Race Prejudice." *Annals of the American Academy of Political and Social Science*, CXL (1928), 11–20.

Parkes, James. An Enemy of the People: Antisemitism. New York, Pelican Books, 1946.

—— The Jewish Problem in the Modern World. New York, Oxford University Press, 1946.

Parsons, Talcott, "Certain Primary Sources and Patterns of Aggression in the Social Structure of the Western World." *Psychiatry*, X (1947), 167–81.

Pasamanick, Benjamin. "A Comparative Study of the Behavioral Development of Negro Infants." *Journal of Genetic Psychology*, LXIX (1946), 3–44.

—— "Some Misconceptions Concerning Differences in the Racial Prevalence of Mental Disease." *American Journal of Orthopsychiatry*, XXXIII (1963), 72–86.

Pastore, Nicholas. The Nature-Nurture Controversy. New York, King's Crown Press, 1949.

Paterson, Donald G. Physique and Intellect. New York, Century, 1930.

Paton, D. M. (ed.). Church and Race in South Africa. London, Student Christian Movement Press, 1958.

Patten, William. The Grand Strategy of Evolution. Boston, Badger, 1920.

Patterson, Sheila. Colour and Culture in South Africa. London, Routledge, 1953.

—— Dark Strangers. London, Tavistock, 1963.

Peacock, George. Life of Thomas Young. London, Murray, 1855.

Pearce, Roy H. The Savages of America. Baltimore, Johns Hopkins Press, 1953.

Pearl, Raymond. "The Biology of Superiority." *American Mercury*, XII (1927), 257–66.

—— "On the Correlation between Intelligence and the Size of the Head." *Journal of Comparative Neurology and Psychology*, XVI (1906), 189–99.

—— "Some Biological Considerations about War." *American Journal of Sociology*, LXVI (1941), 487–503.

Pearson, Karl. "Relationship of Intelligence to Size and Shape of the Head and Other Mental and Physical Characters." *Biometrika*, V (1906), 105–46.

—— and A. G. Davin. "On the Biometric Constants of the Human Skull." *Biometrika*, XVI (1924), 328–64.

Pearson, Karl, and T. L. Woo. "Further Investigation of the Morphometric Characters of the Individual Bones of the Human Skull." *Biometrika*, XXVII (1935), 424–66.

Peckham, Howard H. Captured by Indians. New Brunswick, N. J., Rutgers University Press, 1954.

Penfield, Wilder. "Letter to the Editor." *Perspectives in Biology and Medicine*, VI (1963), 540–41.

Penrose, Lionel S. "Evidence of Heterosis in Man." *Proceedings of the Royal Society*, B, CXLIV (1955), 203–13.

—— "Review of Dunn and Dobzhansky's Heredity, Race and Society." *Annals of Eugenics*, XVII (1952), 252–53.

Perry, W. J. "Man the Primeval Pacifist." *Vincula* (University of London Student Journal), 14 Dec. 1925, p. 64.

Persons, Stow (ed.). Evolutionary Thought in America. New Haven, Yale University Press, 1950.

Petersen, William. "Prejudice in American Society." *Commentary*, XXVI (1958), 342–48.

Phillips, Norman. The Tragedy of Apartheid. New York, McKay, 1960.

Pickering, S. P. "Correlation of Brain and Head Measurements and Relation of Brain Shape and Size to Shape and Size of the Head." *American Journal of Physical Anthropology*, XV (1931), 1–52.

Pierson, Donald. Negroes in Brazil. Chicago, University of Chicago Press, 1942.

Plato. The Republic, 547 *a*.

Plimpton, Ruth T. Operation Crossroads. New York, Viking Press, 1962.

Pliny. Natural History. Bk. VII, 1.5.

Polanyi, Karl. The Great Transformation. New York, Rinehart, 1944.

Poliakov, Leon. Harvest of Hate. London, Elek Books, 1956.

Pollard, Albert F. "The War of Nature and a Peace of Mind." *Vincula* (University of London Student Journal), 14 Dec. 1925, pp. 60–61.

Pope, Liston. The Kingdom Beyond Caste. New York, Friendship Press, 1957.

—— Millhands and Preachers. New Haven, Yale University Press, 1942.

Popper, Karl R. The Open Society and Its Enemies. Princeton, Princeton University Press, 1950.

Porteous, S. D. The Psychology of a Primitive People. New York, Longmans, 1931.

Pourchet, Maria J. "Brazilian Mestizo Types," in Julian H. Steward (ed.), Handbook of South American Indians, V, 111–20. Washington, Smithsonian Institution, 1950.

Powdermaker, Hortense. Probing Our Prejudices. New York, Harper, 1944.

Poynter, C. W. M., and J. J. Keegan. "A Study of the American Negro Brain." *Journal of Comparative Neurology*, XXV (1915), 183–202.

Price, Gwilym A. "Racial Integration in Industry." *New York Herald Tribune*, November 1, 1955, p. 16.

Price, Willard. "Race Barriers Broken." *The Spectator,* 5 September 1952, pp. 291–92.

Putnam, Carleton. Race and Reason. Washington, D.C., Public Affairs Press, 1961.

Raab, Earl (ed.). American Race Relations Today. New York, Anchor Books, 1962.

Race, R. R., and Ruth Sanger. Blood Groups in Man. 3rd ed. Springfield, Ill., Thomas, 1958.

Radin, Paul. The Racial Myth. New York, Whittlesey House, 1934.

Radke, Marian, and Helen Trager. "Children's Perceptions of the Social Roles of Negroes and Whites." *Journal of Psychology*, XXIX (1950), 3–33.

Radke-Yarrow, M., H. Trager, and Jean Miller. "The Role of Parents in the Development of Children's Ethnic Attitudes." *Child Development*, XXIII (1952), 13–53.

Ramos, Arthur. Introdução à antropologia Brasileira. Rio de Janeiro.

———— The Negro in Brazil. (Translation of O Negro Brasileiro, Rio de Janeiro, 1934, made by Richard Pattee.) Manuscript. Washington, D.C., 1939.

Ramsey, Paul. Christian Ethics and the Sit-In. New York, Association Press, 1961.

Ranson, Stephen W. The Anatomy of the Nervous System. 7th ed. Philadelphia, Saunders, 1939.

Rauschning, Hermann. The Voice of Destruction. New York, Putnam, 1940.

Read, Herbert, and Charles P. Mountford (eds.). Australia: Aboriginal Painting from Arnhemland. UNESCO World Art Series. New York, Columbia University Press, 1955.

Redding, J. Saunders. They Came in Chains. Philadelphia, Lippincott, 1950.

Redfield, Robert. "Culture Contact without Conflict." *American Anthropologist*, XLI (1939), 514–17.

———— "Race and Class in Yucatan," in Cooperation in Research, pp. 511–32. Publication No. 501. Washington, Carnegie Institution of Washington, 1938.

Reece, E. J. "Race Mingling in Hawaii." *American Journal of Science*, XX (1914), 104–16.

Reel, Frank A. The Case of General Yamashita. Chicago, University of Chicago Press, 1949.

Reid, Ira De A. (ed.). "Racial Desegregation and Integration." *Annals* of the Academy of Political and Social Science, CCCIV (March 1956), 1–211.

Reid, R. R., and J. H. Mulligan. "Relation of Cranial Capacity to Intelligence." Journal of the Royal Anthropological Institute of Great Britain and Ireland, LIII (1923), 322–32.

Reinemann, J. O. "The Mulatto Children in Germany." Mental Hygiene, XXVII (1953), 365–76.

Reinheimer, Hermann. Evolution by Coöperation: a Study in Bio-economics. London, Kegan Paul, 1913.

—— Symbiosis; a Socio-physiological Study of Evolution. London, Headley, 1920.

Renan, Ernest. The Future of Science; trans. by Albert D. Vandam and C. B. Pitman. London, Chapman & Hall, 1891.

—— "Judaism: Race or Religion" [1883]. Contemporary Jewish Record, VI (1943), 436–48.

Renard, G. Life and Work in Prehistoric Times. New York, Knopf, 1929.

Report of the Commission on Mixed Marriages in South Africa. Pretoria, Government Printer, 1939.

Reuter, Edward B. The American Race Problem. New York, Crowell, 1938.

—— "Competition and the Racial Division of Labor," in Edgar T. Thompson (ed.), Race Relations and the Race Problem, pp. 47–60. Durham, Duke University Press, 1939.

Ribeiro, Rene. "Situação Etnica do Nordeste." Sociologia, XV (1953), 210–59.

Richmond, Anthony H. "Racial Relations in England." Midwest Journal, III (1951), 1–13.

Richmond, Arthur. Colour Prejudice in Britain. London, Routledge, 1954.

—— The Colour Problem. New York, Penguin Books, 1955.

—— Economic Insecurity and Stereotypes as Factors in Colour Prejudice." Sociological Review, XLII (1950), 147–70.

—— "Memories of South Africa." The Listener, LX (1958), 736–39.

Ride, L. T. "The Problem of Depopulation with Special Reference to British North Borneo." The Caduceus (University of Hongkong), XIII (1934), 182–83.

Risdon, D. L. "A Study of the Cranial and Other Human Remains from Palestine Excavated at Tell Duweir (Lachish)." Biometrika, XXXI (1939), 99–166.

Ritner, Peter. The Death of Africa. New York, Macmillan, 1960.

Roback, A. A. A Dictionary of International Slurs. Cambridge, Sci-Art Publishers, 1944.

Robb, James H. Working-Class Anti-Semite. London, Tavistock Publications, 1955.

Robertson, J. M. The Germans. London, Williams and Norgate, 1916.

Robertson, T. C. "Racism Comes to Power in South Africa." *Commentary*, VI (1948), 423–29.

Robeson, Eslanda G. African Journey. New York, John Day, 1945.

Robinson, David M. Excavations at Olynthus, Pt. XI, Necrolynthia, a Study in Greek Burial Customs and Anthropology. Baltimore, Johns Hopkins Press, 1942.

Rodenwaldt, Ernst. Die Mestizen auf Kisar. 2 vols. The Hague, Martinus Nijhoff, 1927.

Roe, Anne, and George G. Simpson (eds.). Behavior and Evolution. New Haven, Yale University Press, 1958.

Roen, S. R. "Personality and Negro-White Intelligence." *Journal of Abnormal and Social Psychology*, LXI (1960), 148–50.

Roquette-Pinto, Edgardo. "Contribuição à antropologia do Brasil." *Revista de Imigração e Colonização*, Ano I, III, No. 3, 1940, Rio de Janeiro.

Rose, Arnold, and Caroline Rose. America Divided. New York, Knopf, 1948.

Rose, Arnold (ed.). Race Prejudice and Discrimination. New York, Knopf, 1951.

Rosen, Bernard C. "Race, Ethnicity, and the Achievement Syndrome." *American Sociological Review*, XXIV (1959), 47–60.

Rosenberg, Alfred. Der Mythus des 20. Jahrhunderts. Munich, Hoeneichen-Verlag, 1930.

——— Memoirs of Alfred Rosenberg. New York, Ziff-Davis, 1949.

Ross, E. Dennison. Both Ends of the Candle. London, Faber & Faber, 1943.

Rousseau, Jean J. The Social Contract; trans. by G. D. H. Cole. New York, Dutton, 1932.

Rowse, A. L. Appeasement: A Study in Political Decline, 1933–39. New York, Norton, 1961.

Ruchames, Louis. The Abolitionists. New York, Putnam, 1963.

——— Race, Jobs, and Politics. New York, Columbia University Press, 1953.

Rumney, Jay, and Joseph Maier. The Science of Society. London, Duckworth, 1953.

Russell, A. G. Colour, Race and Empire. London, Gollancz, 1944.

Russell, Richard J., and Fred B. Kniffen. Culture Worlds. New York, Macmillan, 1951.

Ryle, Gilbert. The Concept of Mind. New York, Barnes & Noble, 1949.

Sachar, Abram L. Sufferance Is the Badge: the Jew in the Contemporary World. New York, Knopf, 1939.

Sachs, Bernard. "South Africa: Life on a Volcano." Commentary, IX (1950), 530–37.

Sachs, Wulf. Black Anger. Boston, Little, Brown, 1947.

Saenger, Gerhart. The Social Psychology of Prejudice. New York, Harper, 1953.

Saffin, John. A Brief and Candid Answer to a Late Printed Sheet, Entitled, The Selling of Joseph. Boston, 1701.

Sahlins, Marshall D., and Elman R. Service (eds.). Evolution and Culture. Ann Arbor, Michigan, University of Michigan Press, 1960.

Saldanha, P. H. "The Genetic Effects of Immigration in a Rural Community of São Paulo, Brazil." Acta Geneticae Medicae et Gemellologiae, XI (1962), 158–224.

Samuel, Maurice. The Great Hatred. New York, Knopf, 1948.

Sanchez, G. "The American of Mexican Descent." Chicago Jewish Forum, XX (1961/62), 120–24.

Sancton, Thomas. "Trouble in Dixie." New Republic, CVIII (1943), 51.

Sanders, Barkev S. Environment and Growth. Baltimore, Warwick & York, 1934.

Sargent, C. W., C. H. Westfall, and F. M. Adams. "The Obstetric Risk of the Japanese Woman with a Caucasoid Husband." American Journal of Obstetrics and Gynecology, LXXVI (1958), 137–40.

Sartre, Jean P. "Portrait of the Anti-Semite." Partisan Review, XIII (1946), 163–78.

Savitz, L. D., and R. F. Tomasson. "The Identifiability of Jews." American Journal of Sociology, LXIV (1959), 468–75.

Schaer, K. Fritz. Charakter, Blutgruppe und Konstitution, Grundriss einer Gruppentypologie auf philosophischer Grundlage. Zurich and Leipzig, Rascher, 1941.

Scheinfeld, Amram. The New You and Heredity. Philadelphia, Lippincott, 1950.

Schemann, Ludwig. Die Rassenfrage im Schrifttum der Neuzeit. Munich, Lehmann's Verlag, 1931.

———— Die Rasse in den Geistwissenschaften. 3 vols. München, 1928–37.

———— (ed.) Correspondence entre Alexis de Tocqueville et Arthur de Gobineau, 1843–1859. 2d ed., Paris, 1908.

Schiff, Fritz, and William C. Boyd. Blood Grouping Technic. New York, Interscience Publishers, 1942.

Schlaifer, Robert. "Greek Theories of Slavery from Homer to Aristotle." *Harvard Studies in Classical Philology*, XLVII (1936), 165–204.

Schmidt, Royal J. "Cultural Nationalism in Herder." *Journal of the History of Ideas*, XVII (1956), 407–17.

Schneirla, Theodore C. " 'Cruel' Ants—and Occam's Razor." *Journal of Comparative Psychology*, XXXIV (1942), 79–83.

—— "Problems in the Biopsychology of Social Organization." *Journal of Abnormal and Social Psychology*, XLI (1946), 385–402.

Schrödinger, Erwin. What Is Life? New York, Macmillan, 1945.

Schultz, Adolph H. "Fetal Growth in Man." *American Journal of Physical Anthropology*, VI (1923), 389–400.

—— "Fetal Growth of Man and Other Primates." *Quarterly Review of Biology*, I (1926), 465–521.

—— "The Skeleton of the Trunk and Limbs of Higher Primates." *Human Biology*, II (1930), 381–83.

Schwartz, Solomon. "The New Anti-Semitism of the Soviet Union." *Commentary*, VII (1949), 535–45.

Schwesinger, Gladys C. Heredity and Environment. New York, Macmillan, 1933.

Scott, J. P. Aggression. Chicago, University of Chicago Press, 1958.

—— "The Magnification of Differences by a Threshold." *Science*, C (1944), 569–70.

—— "Minutes of the Conference on Genetics and Social Behavior." Bar Harbor, Roscoe B. Jackson Memorial Laboratory, 1947.

Seligmann, Herbert J. Race against Man. New York, Putnam, 1939.

Sen, Mihir. "The Calamity of Colour." *Mankind* (Hyderabad), VI (1961), 48–55.

Shafer, Boyd C. Nationalism: Myth and Reality. New York, Harcourt, Brace, 1955.

Shannon, A. H. The Negro in Washington. New York, Webb, 1930.

Shapiro, Harry L. Descendants of the Mutineers of the Bounty. *Memoirs of the Bernice P. Bishop Museum* (Honolulu), XI (1929), 1–106.

—— The Heritage of the Bounty. New York, Simon and Schuster, 1936.

—— Migration and Environment. New York, Oxford University Press, 1939.

—— Race Mixture. Paris, UNESCO, 1953.

Sherif, Muzafer, and Carolyn W. Sherif. Groups in Harmony and Tension. New York, Harper, 1953.

—— and M. O. Wilson. Group Relations at the Crossroads. New York, Harper, 1953.

Sherrington, Charles. Man On His Nature. New York, Macmillan, 1941.

Sherwin, Oscar. "The Founding Fathers." *Negro History Bulletin,* VIII (1945), 173–76, 189–91.

Shoemaker, Don (ed.). With All Deliberate Speed. New York, Harper, 1957.

Shufeldt, R. W. The Negro a Menace to American Civilization. Boston, Badger, 1907.

Siegal, Saul M. "The Relationship of Hostility to Authoritarianism." *Journal of Abnormal and Social Psychology,* LII (1956), 368–72.

Siemens, G. J. "Anthropometric Effects of Recorded Cases of Miscegenation among Certain Caucasian Sub-Groups." *Ohio Journal of Science,* L (1950), 45–52.

Sigerist, Henry E. A History of Medicine, I. New York, Oxford University Press, 1951, p. 101.

Sikes, E. E. The Anthropology of the Greeks. London, Nutt, 1914.

Silberman, C. E. "The City and the Negro." *Fortune,* LXV (1962), 88ff.

Silberman, Leo, and Betty Spice. Colour and Class in Six Liverpool Schools. Liverpool, University of Liverpool Press, 1951.

Silone, Ignazio. Bread and Wine. New York, Penguin Books. 1946.

Simar, Théophile. Etude critique sur la fondation de la doctrine des races au 18e et son expansion au 19e siècle. Brussels. Lamertin, 1922.

Simmel, Ernst (ed.). Anti-Semitism: A Social Disease. New York, International Universities Press, 1946.

Simmons, Katherine. "Cranial Capacities by Both Plastic and Water Techniques with Cranial Linear Measurements of the Reserve Collection, White and Negro." *Human Biology,* XIV (1942), 473–98.

Simon, Yves R. Community of the Free. New York, Holt, 1947.

—— "Secret Sources of the Success of the Racist Ideology." *Review of Politics,* VII (1945), 74–105.

Simons, H. J. "Mental Disease in Africans: Racial Determinism." *Journal of Mental Science,* CIV (1958), 377–88.

Simons, R. D. G. The Colour of the Skin in Human Relations. New York, Elsevier, 1961.

Simpson, George E. and Milton J. Yinger. Racial and Cultural Minorities. 2d ed. New York, Harper, 1958.

Simpson, George G. The Major Features of Evolution. New York, Columbia University Press, 1953.

Sinnott, Edmund W. "The Biological Basis of Democracy." *Yale Review,* XXXV (1945), 61–73.

Smith, G. Elliot. "The Influence of Racial Admixture in Egypt." *Eugenics Review,* VII (1915), 163–83.

Smith, Lillian. Now Is the Time. New York, Viking, 1955.

Smith, Samuel S. An Essay on the Causes of the Variety of Complexion and Figure in the Human Species. Philadelphia, 1787; 2d ed., New Brunswick, N. J., Simpson, 1810.

Smyth, Albert H. (ed.). The Writings of Benjamin Franklin, 10 vols. New York, Macmillan, 1905–07.

Snell, George D. "Hybrids and History. The Role of Race and Ethnic Crossing in Individual and National Achievement." *Quarterly Review of Biology*, XXVI (1951), 331–47.

Snitow, Virginia L. "I Teach Negro Girls." *New Republic*, CVII (1942), 603–05.

Snowden, F. M., Jr. "The Negro in Ancient Greece." *American Anthropologist*, L (1948), 31–44.

—— "The Negro in Classical Italy." *American Journal of Philology*, LXVIII (1947), 266–92.

Snyder, Laurence H. "The Genetic Approach to Human Individuality." *Science*, CVIII (1948), 586.

—— "The Principles of Gene Distribution in Human Populations." *Yale Journal of Biology and Medicine*, XIX (1947), 817–33.

—— "The Study of Human Heredity." *Scientific Monthly*, LI (1940), 536–41.

Snyder, Louis, L. The Idea of Racialism. Princeton, N. J., Van Nostrand, 1962.

—— Race: A History of Modern Ethnic Theories. New York, Longmans, 1939.

Sorokin, Pitirim A. "The Roles of Similarity and Dissimilarity in Social Solidarity and Antagonism." *Journal of Legal and Political Sociology*, III (1944), 34–55.

—— Sociocultural Casuality, Space, Time. Durham, Duke University Press, 1943.

—— "What Is a Social Class?" *Journal of Legal and Political Sociology*, IV (1946), 15–28.

—— and Robert K. Merton. "Social Time: a Methodological and Functional Analysis." *American Journal of Sociology*, XLII (1937), 615–29.

Sowden, Lewis. The Union of South Africa. New York, Doubleday, Doran, 1943.

Spicer, Edward H. (ed.). Human Problems in Technological Change. New York, Russell Sage Foundation, 1952.

Spitz, David. Patterns of Anti-Democratic Thought. New York, Macmillan, 1949.

Spuhler, James N. "An Estimate of the Number of Genes in Man." *Science*, CVIII (1948), 279.

———— (ed.) The Evolution of Man's Capacity for Culture. Detroit, Mich., Wayne State University Press, 1959.

Stampp, Kenneth. The Peculiar Institution. New York, Knopf, 1956.

Stanton, William. The Leopard's Spots: Scientific Attitudes Toward Race in America, 1815–59. Chicago, University of Chicago Press, 1960.

Stapleton, Laurence. Justice and World Society. Chapel Hill, University of North Carolina Press, 1944.

Statement on Race (UNESCO) 1950 and 1952. See Montagu.

Steggerda, Morris. "The McAdory Art Test Applied to Navaho Indian Children." Journal of Comparative Psychology, XXII (1936), 283–86.

Stegner, Wallace. One Nation. Boston, Houghton Mifflin, 1945.

Stein, Leon. The Racial Thinking of Richard Wagner. New York, Philosophical Library, 1950.

Steinberg, Milton. A Partisan Guide to the Jewish Problem. New York, Bobbs-Merrill, 1945.

Stern, Curt. "The Biology of the Negro." Scientific American, CXCI (1954), 80–85.

———— Principles of Human Genetics. San Francisco, Freeman, 1949.

Stockard, Charles R. The Genetic and Endocrine Basis for Differences in Form and Behavior. Philadelphia, Wistar Institute of Anatomy and Biology, 1941.

Stonequist, Everett V. The Marginal Man: A Study in Personality and Culture Conflict. New York, Scribner, 1937.

Strandskov, Herluf H. "The Distribution of Human Genes." Scientific Monthly, LII (1942), 203–15.

———— "Further Comments on Comparative Studies in Human Biology." Science, C (1944), 146–47.

———— "The Genetics of Human Populations." American Naturalist, LXXVI (1942), 156–64.

Stuart, Donald. Yandy. Melbourne, Australia, Georgian House, 1959.

Stuckert, Robert P. "African Ancestry of the White American Population." Ohio Journal of Science, LVIII (1959), 155–60.

Sullivan, Louis R. "Anthropometry of Siouan Tribes." Proceedings of the National Academy of Sciences, VI (1920), 131–34.

Sullivan, Louis R., and K. Murdock. "A Contribution to the Study of Mental and Physical Measurements in Normal Children." American Physical Education Review, XXVIII (1923), 209–15, 278–88, 328.

"Survey of the National Opinion Research Center of the University of Denver," Pacific Citizen, XXI (August 31, 1946), 3.

Symonds, Percival M. The Dynamics of Human Adjustment. New York, Appleton-Century, 1946.

────── "How Teachers Solve Personal Problems." *Journal of Educational Research*, II (1941), 80–93.

Tachibana, K. "A Study of Racial Preference." *Proceedings of the VIIIth Annual Meeting of the Japanese Psychological Association* (1941), pp. 64–65. Abstracted from the Japanese in *Far Eastern Science Bulletin*, III, No. 3 (Sept. 1943), 35.

Taft, Donald R. Cultural Opportunities through Race Contacts." *Journal of Negro History*, XIV (1929), 12–20.

Tant, François. Thrésor de la langue française. Jean Nicot (ed.). Paris, P. Doucer, 1600.

Tao, Yun-Juei. "Chinesen-Europäerinnen-Kreuzung." *Zeitschrift für Morphologie und Anthropologie*, XXXIII (1935), 349–408.

Tawney, R. H. Equality. New York, Harcourt, Brace, 1952.

Taylor, Joe G. Negro Slavery in Louisiana. Baton Rouge, La., Louisiana Historical Association, 1963.

Teller, Judd L. Scapegoat of Revolution. New York, Scribner, 1954.

Tenenbaum, Joseph. Race and Reich: The Story of an Epoch. New York, Twayne, 1957.

Tenenbaum, Samuel. Why Men Hate. New York, Jewish Book Guild of America, 1947.

Terry, Michael. Hidden Wealth and Hiding People. New York, Putnam, 1934.

Thomas, Dorothy S., and Richard S. Nishimoto. The Spoilage. Berkeley, University of California Press, 1946.

Thomas, William I. "The Relative Mental Endowment of Races," in Primitive Behavior, pp. 770–800. New York, McGraw-Hill, 1937.

Thompson, Charles H. (ed.). The Physical and Mental Abilities of the American Negro. *Journal of Negro Education*, III (1934), 317–564.

────── Racial Minorities and the Present International Crisis. *Journal of Negro Education*, X (1941), 305–622.

Thompson, David. Equality. London & New York, Cambridge University Press, 1949.

Thompson, Edgar T. (ed.). Race Relations and the Race Problem. Durham, Duke University Press, 1939.

Thomson, Arthur, and L. H. Dudley Buxton. "Man's Nasal Index in Relation to Certain Climatic Conditions." *Journal of the Royal Anthropological Institute of Great Britain and Ireland*, LIII (1923), 92–122.

Thomson, David. England in the Nineteenth Century. New York, Penguin Books, 1950.

Thomson, M. L. "Relative Efficiency of Pigment and Horny Layer Thickness in Protecting Skin of Europeans and Africans Against Solar

Ultraviolet Radiation." *Journal of Physiology*, CXXVII (1955), 236–46.

Thorne, Frederick E. "The Attitudinal Pathoses." *Journal of Clinical Psychology*, V (1949), 1–21.

—— "The Frustration-Anger-Hostility States: A New Diagnostic Classification." *Journal of Clinical Psychology*, IX (1953), 334–39.

Thorpe, W. H. "Biological Races in *Hyponemeuta padella* L." *Journal of the Linnaean Society* (Zoölogy), XXXVI (1928), 621.

—— "Biological Races in Insects and Allied Groups." *Biological Reviews*, V (1930), 177.

—— "Ecology and the Future of Systematics," in Julian Huxley (ed.), The New Systematics, pp. 340–64. Oxford, Clarendon Press, 1940.

Tindale, Norman B. "Survey of the Half-Caste Problem in South Australia." *Proceedings of the Royal Geographical Society, South Australian Branch*, session 1940–41, pp. 66–161.

Tirala, Lothar G. Rasse, Geist und Seele. Munich, Lehmann's Verlag, 1935.

Tobias, Phillip V. "On a Bushman-European Hybrid Family." *Man*, LIV (1955), 179–82.

Tocqueville, Alexis de. The European Revolution and Correspondence with Gobineau. John Lukacs (ed.). New York, Anchor Books, 1959.

Todd, T. Wingate. "Cranial Capacity and Linear Dimensions." *American Journal of Physical Anthropology*, VI (1923), 97–194.

—— "Entrenched Negro Physical Features." *Human Biology*, I (1929), 57–69.

—— "The Skeleton," in Growth and Development of the Child, Part II (White House Conference on Child Health and Protection), 26–130. New York, Century, 1933.

—— and Anna Lindala. "Dimensions of the Body, Whites and American Negroes of Both Sexes." *American Journal of Physical Anthropology*, XII (1928), 35–119.

Todd, T. Wingate, and D. W. Lyon. "Cranial Suture Closure; Its Progress and Age Relationship. Part IV. Ectocranial Closure in Adult Males of Negro Stock." *American Journal of Physical Anthropology*, VIII (1925), 149–68.

Todd, T. Wingate, and L. van Gorder. "The Quantitative Determination of Black Pigmentation in the Skin of the American Negro." *American Journal of Physical Anthropology*, IV (1921), 239–60.

Tolles, Frederick B. "Nonviolent Contact: The Quakers and the Indians." *Proceedings of the American Philosophical Society*, CVII (1963), 93–101.

Tolman, Edward C. "A Stimulus-Expectancy Need-Cathexis Psychology." *Science*, CI (1945), 160–66.

Topinard, Paul. "La Notion de race en anthropologie." *Revue d'Anthropologie*, 2d ser., II (1879), 589–660.

To Secure These Rights: the Report of the President's Committee on Civil Rights. Washington, Government Printing Office, 1947.

Toynbee, Arnold J. A Study of History, I, 207–49. New York, Oxford University Press, 1934.

Trachtenberg, Joshua. The Devil and the Jews. New York, Meridian Books, 1961.

Trager, H. G., and M. R. Yarrow. They Learn What They Live: Prejudice in Young Children. New York, Harper, 1952.

Trembley, Francis J. "Evolution and Human Affairs." *Proceedings of the Pennsylvania Academy of Science*, XXIII (1949), 181–95.

Trevor, Jack C. "Race Crossing in Man." *Eugenics Laboratory Memoirs*, XXXVI (1953), iv–45.

——— "Some Anthropological Characteristics of Hybrid Populations." *Eugenics Review*, XXX (1938), 21–31.

Trotter, Mildred. "A Study of Facial Hair in White and Negro Races." *Washington University Studies* (Scientific Studies), IX (1922), 273–89.

Trudeau, Arthur G. "Army Experience and Problems of Negro Education," in Education for Victory, III, 13–16. Washington, U. S. Office of Education, 1945.

Tumin, Melvin M. (ed.). Race and Intelligence. New York, Anti-Defamation League of B'nai B'rith, 1963.

Turgot, Robert J. Tableaux Philosophique des Progrès Successifs de L'Esprit Humain, in Gustave Schelle (ed.), Œuvres de Turgot. Paris, Alcan, 1913, p. 214.

Ulich, Robert. The Human Career. New York, Harper, 1955.

UNESCO. Human Rights: Comments and Interpretations. New York, Columbia University Press, 1949.

——— Race and Science. New York, Columbia University Press, 1961.

——— The Race Concept. New York, UNESCO, 1958.

"Unwanted Heroes." *New Republic*, CVI (1942), 655.

Van Den Berghe, Pierre L. "The Dynamics of Racial Prejudice: An Ideal-Type Dichotomy." *Social Forces*, XXXVII (1958), 138–41.

Van Rensburg, Patrick. Guilty Land: The History of Apartheid. New York, Praeger, 1962.

Van Til, William, John J. DeBoer, R. Will Burnett, and Kathleen C. Ogden. Democracy Demands It. New York, Harper, 1947.

Vernier, Chester G. American Family Laws. Stanford, Stanford University Press, 1931. I, Section 44, 204–09; 1938 Supplement, Stanford University Press, 1938, pp. 24–25.

Vickery, William. "A Redefinition of Prejudice for Purposes of Social Science Research." *Human Relations*, I (1948), 419–28.

Vickery, William E., and Stewart G. Cole. Intercultural Education in American Schools. New York, Harper, 1943.

Virchow, Rudolf. "Gesammtbericht über die von der deutschen anthropologischen Gesellschaft veranlassten Erhebungen über die Farbe der Haut, der Haare und der Augen der Schulkinder in Deutschland," *Archiv für Anthropologie*, XVI (1886), 275–475.

Vogelin, Eric. "The Growth of the Race Idea." *Review of Politics*, II (1940), 283–317.

Waddington, C. H. The Ethical Animal. New York, Atheneum, 1960.

—— "Human Ideals and Human Progress." *World Review*, August (1946), 29–36.

Wagley, Charles (ed.). Race and Class in Rural Brazil. UNESCO. New York, Columbia University Press, 1952.

—— and Marvin Harris. Minorities in the New World. New York, Columbia University Press, 1958.

Wallace, Bruce. "Heterotic Mutation," in Lytt I. Gardner (ed.), Molecular Genetics and Human Disease, pp. 212–30. Springfield, Ill., Thomas, 1960.

—— "Race and Reason." *Eugenics Quarterly*, IX (1962), 161–65.

Wallace, Henry A. The Genetic Basis for Democracy. New York, American Committee for Democracy and Intellectual Freedom, 1939.

—— "Racial Theories and the Genetic Basis for Democracy." *Science*, LXXXIX (1939), 140–43.

Wallas, Graham. Human Nature in Politics. 3rd ed. London, Constable, 1920.

Wallis, Wilson D. "Some Phases of the Psychology of Prejudice." *Journal of Abnormal and Social Psychology*, XXIV (1930), 418–29.

—— "Variability in Race Hybrids." *American Anthropologist*, XL (1938), 680–97.

Walpole, Hugh R. Semantics: The Nature of Words and Their Meanings. New York, Norton, 1941.

Walter, W. Grey. The Living Brain. New York, Norton, 1953.

Warner, W. Lloyd, and Allison Davis. "A Comparative Study of American Caste," in Edgar T. Thompson (ed.), Race Relations and the Race Problem, pp. 219–45. Durham, Duke University Press, 1939.

Warner, W. Lloyd, and Leo Srole. The Social Systems of American Ethnic Groups. New Haven, Yale University Press, 1945.

Warner, W. Lloyd, et al. Democracy in Jonesville. New York, Harper, 1949.

Warsaw Correspondent. "Jews and the Catholic Church in Poland." Jewish Chronicle (London), 25 June 1948, p. 11.

Washburn, Sherwood L. (ed.). Social Life of Early Man. Chicago, Quadrangle Books, 1961.

—— "The Study of Race." American Anthropologist, LXV (1963), 521–31.

Watson, Goodwin. Action for Unity. New York, Harper, 1947.

Waxman, Julia. Race Relations: a Selected List of Readings on Racial and Cultural Minorities in the United States with Special Emphasis on Negroes. Chicago, Julius Rosenwald Fund, 1945.

Webb, Beatrice, and Sidney Webb. Soviet Communism: a New Civilization. 2 vols. New York, Longmans, 1935.

Weidenreich, Franz. Apes, Giants, and Man. Chicago, University of Chicago Press, 1946.

—— "The Brachycephalization of Recent Mankind." Southwestern Journal of Anthropology, I (1945), 1–54.

—— Rasse und Körperbau. Berlin, Springer, 1927.

Weinberg, Robert L. "Group Libel and the Law." Chicago Jewish Forum, VI (1948), 85–90.

Weinert, Hans. Der Geistige Aufstieg der Menschheit vom Ursprung bis zur Gegenwart. Stuttgart, Ferdinand Enke, 1951.

Weinreich, Max. Hitler's Professors: the Part of Scholarship in Germany's Crimes against the Jewish People. New York, Yiddish Scientific Institute, 1946.

Weizsäcker, C. F. von. The History of Nature. Chicago, University of Chicago Press, 1950.

Went, F. W. "The Ecology of Desert Plants." Scientific American, CXCII (1955), 68–75.

Weslager, Clinton A. Delaware's Forgotten Folk. Philadelphia, University of Pennsylvania Press, 1943.

Westerman, George W. A Study of Socio-Economic Conflicts on the Panama Canal Zone. Panamá, Liga Cívica Nacional, 1949.

Westermann, W. L. "The Slave Systems of Greek and Roman Antiquity." Memoirs of the American Philosophical Society, XL (1955), xi–180.

—— "Slavery and the Elements of Freedom in Ancient Greece." Quarterly Bulletin of the Polish Institute of Arts and Sciences in America, I (1943), 332–47.

Westie, Frank R. "Negro-White Status Differentials and Social Distance." American Sociological Review, XVII (1952), 550–58.

Wheeler, William M. "Social Evolution," in E. V. Cowdry (ed), Human Biology and Racial Welfare. New York, Hoeber, 1930.
—— Social Life among Insects. New York, Harcourt, Brace, 1923.
White, Charles. An Account of the Regular Gradation in Man. London, Dilly, 1799.
White, Garvin. "Canadian Apartheid." *Canadian Forum*, XXXI (1951), 102–03.
White, Leslie A. The Science of Culture. New York, Farrar, Straus, 1949.
White, Walter. A Rising Wind. New York, Doubleday, 1945.
—— "Why I Remain a Negro." *Saturday Review of Literature*, XXX (1947), 13–49, 50–52.
Widney, Joseph P. Mankind: Racial Values and Racial Prospects, I, p. 167. Los Angeles, Pacific Publishing Co., 1917.
Wilde, Oscar. "The True Function and Value of Criticism." *Nineteenth Century*, XXVIII (1890), 123–47.
Wilder, Burt G. The Brain of the American Negro. New York, First National Negro Conference, 1909.
Wilkins, George H. Undiscovered Australia, pp. 242–62. London, Benn, 1928.
Williams, Eric. Capitalism and Slavery. Chapel Hill, University of North Carolina Press, 1944.
Williams, G. D. "Maya-Spanish Crosses in Yucatan." *Papers of the Peabody Museum of American Archaeology and Ethnology, Harvard University*, XIII (1931), 1–256.
Williams, J., and R. Scott. "Growth and Development of Negro Infants. IV. Motor Development and its Relationship to Child Rearing Practices in Two Groups of Negro Infants." *Child Development*, XXIV (1953), 103–21.
Williams, Robin M., Jr. The Reduction of Intergroup Tensions: a Survey of Research on Problems of Ethnic, Racial, and Religious Group Relations. New York, Social Science Research Council, 1947.
Williams, Watkins. "Heterosis and the Genetics of Complex Characters." *Nature*, CLXXXIV (1959), 527–30.
Wilson, Janet. "The Early Anti-Slavery Propaganda." *More Books* (the bulletin of the Boston Public Library), Nov., Dec. 1944, p. 3; Feb. 1945, pp. 51–56.
Wissler, Clark. "Growth of Children in Hawaii; Based on Observations by Louis R. Sullivan." *Bernice P. Bishop Museum Memoirs* (Honolulu, 1930), 105–257.
Wittenberg, Philip. "Miscegenation," in Encyclopaedia of the Social Sciences, V, 531–34. New York, Macmillan, 1938.

Witty, Paul A. "New Evidence on the Learning Ability of the Negro." *Journal of Abnormal and Social Psychology*, XL (1945), 401–04.

—— and Harvey C. Lehman. "Racial Differences: the Dogma of Superiority." *Journal of Social Psychology*, I (1930), 394–418.

Woods, Frances J. Cultural Values of American Ethnic Groups. New York, Harper, 1956.

Woodward, C. Van. The Strange Case of Jim Crow. New York, Oxford University Press, 1955.

Wootton, Barbara. Testament for Social Science. New York, Norton, 1951.

Wright, Quincy. A Study of War. 2 vols. Chicago, University of Chicago Press, 1942.

Wright, Richard. The Color Curtain. Cleveland & New York, World Publishing Co., 1956.

Wright, Sewall. Principles of Live Stock Breeding. U.S. Department of Agriculture Bulletin 905. Washington Government Printing Office, 1920.

—— "The Roles of Mutation, Inbreeding, Crossbreeding, and Selection in Evolution," in *Proceedings of the Sixth International Congress of Genetics*, I (1932), 356–66. Ithaca, N. Y.

Wundt, Wilhelm. Philosophische Studien. Vol. III. Leipzig, Engelmann, 1883.

Wynes, Charles E. Race Relations in Virginia 1870–1902. Charlottesville, University of Virginia Press, 1961.

Yerkes, Robert M. (ed.). "Psychological Examining in the United States Army." *Memoirs of the National Academy of Sciences*, XV (1921), 690, 691.

Young, Donald. American Minority Peoples. New York, Harper, 1932.

—— "Techniques of Race Relations." *Proceedings of the American Philosophical Society*, XCI (1947), 150–61.

Young, Kimball. "Prejudices: an Outgrowth of Subjective Environment," in Source Book for Social Psychology. New York, Knopf, 1927.

Zanden, J. W. Vander. "The Ideology of White Supremacy." *Journal of the History of Ideas*, XX (1959), 355–402.

Zirkle, Conway. "Father Adam and the Races of Man." *Journal of Heredity*, XLV (1954), 29–34.

Zollschan, I. Racialism against Civilization. London, New Empire Publishing Co., 1942.

About the Author

Ashley Montagu was born in London, England, in 1905, and studied anthropology at the Universities of London and Florence, and Columbia University, where he was awarded the degree of Doctor of Philosophy for a thesis on the Australian aborigines. Professor Ashley Montagu has been scientific worker at the British Museum (Natural History), Curator of Physical Anthropology at the Wellcome Historical Medical Museum, London, Assistant Professor of Anatomy at New York University, Anthropologist to the Division of Child Research at the same university, Associate Professor of Anatomy at the Hahnemann Medical College and Hospital, Philadelphia, and Chairman and Professor of Anthropology, Rutgers University. He has also been a visiting lecturer and professor at Harvard and the University of Delaware, Regents Professor at the University of California at Santa Barbara, Senior Lecturer in Anthropology on the Veterans Administration Postgraduate Training Program in Psychiatry and Neurology, and was Rapporteur of the UNESCO Committee of Experts on Race which drafted the famous UNESCO Statement on Race. He has been Family Affairs and Anthropological Adviser to NBC, and has appeared on many radio and television programs in his capacity as an anthropologist. He is Chairman of the Anisfield-Wolf Award Committee which awards annual prizes for meritorious works in the field of race relations, Advisory Consultant to the Peace Research Institute, Washington, D.C., Advisory Consultant to the International Childbirth Education Association, and he is an associate and advisory editor of *Acta Geneticae Medicae et Gemellologiae*. Professor Ashley Montagu is a member of many scientific and learned societies, and is the author of twenty-seven books, mostly in the field of anthropology. He has also contributed several hundred articles to the scientific and general periodicals of this and other countries. His hobbies are gardening and book collecting.